National Center for Construction Education and Research

Sheet Metal Level One

Prentice
Hall

Upper Saddle River, New Jersey
Columbus, Ohio

This information is general in nature and intended for training purposes only. Actual performance of activities described in this manual requires compliance with all applicable operating, service, maintenance, and safety procedures under the direction of qualified personnel. References in this manual to patented or proprietary devices do not constitute a recommendation of their use.

Copyright © 2001 by the National Center for Construction Education and Research (NCCER), Gainesville, FL 32614-1104 and published by Pearson Education, Inc., Upper Saddle River, New Jersey 07458. All rights reserved. Printed in the United States of America. This publication is protected by Copyright and permission should be obtained from the NCCER prior to any prohibited reproduction, storage in a retrieval system, or transmission in any form or by any means, electronic, mechanical, photocopying, recording, or likewise. For information regarding permission(s), write to: NCCER, Curriculum Revision and Development Department, P.O. Box 141104, Gainesville, FL 32614-1104.

10 9 8 7 6
ISBN 0-13-061613-3

Preface

This volume was developed by the National Center for Construction Education and Research (NCCER) in response to the training needs of the construction and maintenance industries. It is one of many in the NCCER's standardized craft training program. The program, covering more than 30 craft areas and including all major construction skills, was developed over a period of years by industry and education specialists. Sixteen of the largest construction and maintenance firms in the United States committed financial and human resources to the teams that wrote the curricula and planned the nationally accredited training process. These materials are industry-proven and consist of competency-based textbooks and instructor's guides.

The NCCER is a non-profit educational entity affiliated with the University of Florida and supported by the following industry and craft associations:

PARTNERING ASSOCIATIONS

- American Fire Sprinkler Association
- American Society for Training and Development
- American Welding Society
- Associated Builders and Contractors, Inc.
- Associated General Contractors of America
- Association for Career and Technical Education
- Carolinas AGC, Inc.
- Carolinas Electrical Contractors Association
- Citizens Democracy Corps
- Construction Industry Institute
- Construction Users Roundtable
- Design-Build Institute of America
- Merit Contractors Association of Canada
- Metal Building Manufacturers Association

- National Association of Minority Contractors
- National Association of State Supervisors for Trade and Industrial Education
- National Association of Women in Construction
- National Insulation Association
- National Ready Mixed Concrete Association
- National Utility Contractors Association
- National Vocational Technical Honor Society
- North American Crane Bureau
- Painting and Decorating Contractors of America
- Portland Cement Association
- SkillsUSA-VICA
- Steel Erectors Association of America
- Texas Gulf Coast Chapter ABC
- U.S. Army Corps of Engineers
- University of Florida
- Women Construction Owners and Executives, USA

Some of the features of the NCCER's standardized craft training program include:

- A proven record of success over many years of use by industry companies.
- National standardization providing portability of learned job skills and educational credits that will be of tremendous value to trainees.
- Recognition: upon successful completion of training with an accredited sponsor, trainees receive an industry-recognized certificate and transcript from the NCCER.
- Compliance with Apprenticeship, Training, Employer, and Labor Services (ATELS) requirements (formerly BAT) for related classroom training (CFR 29:29).
- Well-illustrated, up-to-date, and practical information.

FEATURES OF THIS BOOK

Capitalizing on a well-received campaign to redesign our textbooks, NCCER is publishing select textbooks in a two-column format. *Sheet Metal Level One* incorporates the design and layout of our full-color books along with special pedagogical features. The features augment the technical material to maintain the trainees' interest and foster a deeper appreciation of the trade.

Did You Know? explains fun facts and interesting tidbits about the sheet metal trade from historical to modern times.

Riveting Ideas provides helpful hints for those entering the field by presenting tricks of the trade from experts in the sheet metal trade.

We're excited to be able to offer you these improvements and hope they lead to a more rewarding learning experience.

As always, your feedback is welcome! Please let us know how we are doing by visiting NCCER at www.nccer.org or e-mail us at info@nccer.org.

Acknowledgments

This curriculum was revised as a result of the farsightedness and leadership of the following sponsors:

Action Air Inc.
Air Handling Services Inc.
Air Systems Engineering
Cobb Mechanical
Encompass Services Corp.
    SE Region
Encompass Mechanical Services
Gulfside Mechanical/
    Comfort Systems USA

Interstate Mechanical Corporation
Mike Van Zeeland
    Heating and Cooling, Inc.
New Mexico State University
Sheet Metal Duct Inc.
Washington CITC
Washington ABC

This curriculum would not exist were it not for the dedication and unselfish energy of those volunteers who served on the Authoring Team. A sincere thanks is extended to:

Mike Bergen
Steve Boyd
James David Duckett
Maynard Kettner
Larry Marye
Curtis McMullen
Robert Monastra

Nick Phillips
Dave Price
Glenn Schwenneker
Ricky Sonnier
Jackie Wilkie
Mike Van Zeeland

A final note: This book is the result of a collaborative effort involving the production, editorial, and development staff at Prentice-Hall, Inc., and the National Center for Construction Education and Research. Thanks to all of the dedicated people involved in the many stages of this project.

Contents

Contents

Introduction to the Sheet Metal Trade

COURSE MAP

This course map shows all of the modules in the first level of the Sheet Metal curriculum. The suggested training order begins at the bottom and proceeds up. Skill levels increase as you advance on the course map. The local Training Program Sponsor may adjust the training order.

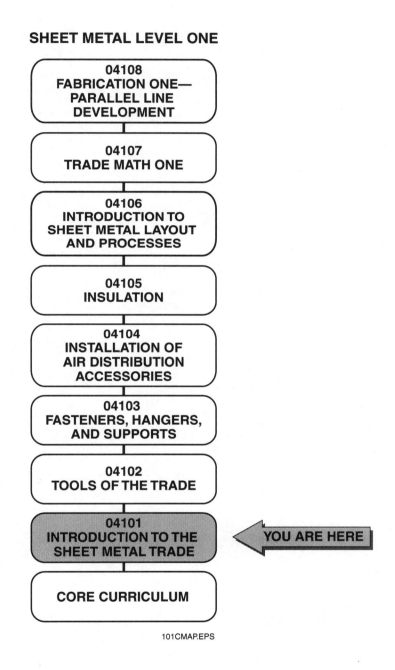

SHEET METAL LEVEL ONE

04108
FABRICATION ONE—
PARALLEL LINE
DEVELOPMENT

04107
TRADE MATH ONE

04106
INTRODUCTION TO
SHEET METAL LAYOUT
AND PROCESSES

04105
INSULATION

04104
INSTALLATION OF
AIR DISTRIBUTION
ACCESSORIES

04103
FASTENERS, HANGERS,
AND SUPPORTS

04102
TOOLS OF THE TRADE

04101
INTRODUCTION TO THE
SHEET METAL TRADE

YOU ARE HERE

CORE CURRICULUM

101CMAP.EPS

Copyright © 2001 National Center for Construction Education and Research, Gainesville, FL 32614-1104. All rights reserved. No part of this work may be reproduced in any form or by any means, including photocopying, without written permission of the publisher.

MODULE 04101 CONTENTS

Figures

Tables

Introduction to
the Sheet Metal Trade

Objectives

When you finish this module, you will be able to do the following:

1. Describe what is meant by pride of craftsmanship in the sheet metal trade.
2. Name the general applications of sheet metal construction.
3. List the basic tools and equipment used in the sheet metal trade.
4. Summarize the history and development of the sheet metal trade.
5. Describe what is involved in being part of a sheet metal training program.
6. Describe how to use a sheet metal gauge.

Prerequisites

Before you begin this module, it is recommended that you successfully complete the following: Core Curriculum.

Required Trainee Materials

1. Pencil and paper
2. Appropriate personal protective equipment

1.0.0 ◆ INTRODUCTION

The sheet metal trade is an important part of the construction industry—residential, commercial, industrial, and architectural. Fiberglass and sheet metal are used to make ducts for **HVAC** (heating, ventilating, and air conditioning) systems as well as for **HVAC/R** (heating, ventilating, air conditioning, and refrigeration) systems. Sheet metal is also used for vents, hoods, food service equipment, gutters and downspouts, siding, ceilings, skylights, and partitions. It has applications in transportation, manufacturing, and countless product designs and repairs.

If you enjoy working with your hands to make things, and working with your head to solve problems, you will enjoy working in the sheet metal trade. Besides having an interest in this challenging career, you'll also need to be able to do the following:

- Perform basic math and geometry calculations.
- Read and understand **blueprints, cut sheets,** layout and fabrications instructions, and safety instructions.
- Communicate clearly both orally and in writing with your supervisor, your co-workers, and, most important, your customers.

Something to Think About

The following banner appears on the Web site of a full-service sheet metal contractor.
"A person who works with his or her hands is a laborer.
A person who works with his or her hands and mind is a craftsperson.
A person who works with his or her hands, mind, and heart is an artist."
—James R. Sanders, Sanders Brothers, Inc.

DID YOU KNOW?

ASHRAE

ASHRAE, the American Society of Heating, Refrigerating and Air Conditioning Engineers, is an international organization of 50,000 persons with chapters throughout the world. The society is organized for the sole purpose of advancing the arts and sciences of heating, ventilating, air conditioning, and refrigeration for the public's benefit through research, standards writing, continuing education, and publications.

- Adapt to using new technologies, new techniques, and new materials through continuous, lifelong learning.

2.0.0 ◆ PRIDE OF CRAFTSMANSHIP

There is one more quality you must develop to be successful in this or any trade. This quality is called **pride of craftsmanship.** Following is just a partial list of the kinds of things you do when you take pride in your work:

- Set goals toward which you will work to improve your skills.
- Pursue continuing lifelong education and training.
- Have a positive attitude about your work.
- See yourself as part of a team that does important work.
- Be at work on time or let your supervisor know in advance when you can't report.
- Do tasks carefully and on schedule. Follow all safety guidelines and procedures.
- Keep your work area safe and clean.
- Treat safety seriously. Wear the **appropriate personal protective equipment** to ensure your safety while on the job. This equipment includes a hard hat, gloves, safety goggles, hearing and respiratory protection, and appropriate workboots.
- Always aim for excellence in every task you perform.
- Take personal responsibility. This means that you do your own quality assurance checks to ensure that your work is done properly and safely.

Think about pride of craftsmanship this way. Imagine that you are the **general contractor** of an 80-story office building. You can't go around to every part of the job and check every person to be sure that all of the **trades** are doing every one of their tasks properly. Yet it is your responsibility to ensure that the completed building is properly constructed, is safe, and meets the required specifications. The same thing is true when you build a new home. You can't be on site every day to make sure that all the systems have been installed correctly. Yet you want to ensure that the home will be safe. In both cases, you must rely on the workers' pride of craftsmanship. If they take pride in what they do, you can trust that the work will be done competently, properly, and safely. Taking pride in your work makes you trustworthy, too.

There's another reason for having pride of craftsmanship. Your income depends on your skills and reliability. That's because your company's income and reputation depend on the skills of its workers. A company with reliable workers and a good reputation will always be busy, and that means you'll be busy too. The sheet metal trade can provide satisfying work and a good income for you and your family.

3.0.0 ◆ THE HISTORY OF SHEET METAL

The metalwork trade has developed significantly over the years. From basic tools and weaponry to ornate artwork, the craft of metalwork has been a part of civilization for over six thousand years. Today, metalwork continues to improve and change at a rapid pace. It is a key part of the craft industry, and therefore an important component of society as a whole.

3.1.0 Sheet Metal in Ancient Times

No one knows for certain when metals were first used. That's because the history of metalwork is not, in most cases, written down. Instead, we have learned about metalworking from studying the objects made by ancient metalworkers.

Historians believe that copper was one of the earliest metals discovered and that its first use dates from at least 4000 B.C.E. (before the common era). The discovery of how to extract copper from the rocks containing it may have happened accidentally. Pottery makers who used copper oxides (an **alloy**) to color their pots may have found traces of copper in the kiln after a firing. They probably experimented until they found the right conditions that would release copper cleanly from ore. Eventually, the more efficient hot-air furnace replaced the pottery kiln for smelting ore. The basic design used a goatskin bellows to force air into an insulated furnace; the furnace had outlets to let the waste, or slag, run off. The basic operating principle is not that different today.

DID YOU KNOW?

An Oriental Recipe for Copper Alloys

An ancient Chinese book called *K'ao Kung Chi* mentions copper as the best metal for a variety of uses. It includes the following recipes for making weapons and everyday objects:

Axes	4 parts copper to 1 part tin
Spears	3 parts copper to 1 part tin
Swords and knives	2 parts copper to 1 part tin
Mirrors	1 part copper to 1 part tin

Early metalworkers also found that adding other metals made copper easier to work with, improved its melting rate, and made it stronger. These additions to the copper, called alloys, enabled early peoples to make bronze (tin plus copper) and brass (zinc plus copper).

The first recorded use of iron was by the Assyrians in about 3000 B.C.E. They used iron to make cooking utensils and artwork, but its biggest impact was in weaponry. Consider the advantage of having a weapon with a sharpened metal edge compared to having one made of rock. When the Assyrians began making and using iron weapons, they became the most powerful nation of their time. The Assyrian Empire covered a large part of the Middle East, including what is now known as Iraq, Iran, and Turkey.

Iron came into more general use in about 500 B.C.E. By that time, other metals such as silver, gold, and pewter had joined copper, tin, brass, and bronze, but none were used as widely as they are now. Only the wealthy could afford metal objects. Metal was made into tools and ornaments, but we also have evidence that it was used to decorate palaces and temples. This may have been the first development of a trade in metal-related construction.

Most historians agree that the sheet metal trade originated with the ancient workers who worked with lead. The Babylonians were expert at using this material. Some historians believe that lead was used to line the Hanging Gardens of Babylon so that the plant containers could hold water. In Greece, the Parthenon was built with a lead roof. The Romans developed soldering for lead pipes used to carry drinking and bath water. An interesting theory suggests that lead poisoning led to the demise of the ancient Roman civilization.

3.2.0 Sheet Metal in the Middle Ages

During the Middle Ages in Europe, skilled sheet metal workers, called **metalsmiths**, forged and hammered metal into armor. By the fifteenth cen-

DID YOU KNOW?

Ancient Sheet Metal Workers

Ancient buildings did not have ventilation systems as we know them, but sheet metal workers still had work. These artisans created beautiful decorations for temples and palaces.

The Sumerians, for example, beat copper into thin sheets and shaped them on a wooden background to create wall decorations, which they attached to buildings with copper clamps, nails, or wires. One of the most famous of these decorations shows a lion-headed eagle holding two stags by their tails. The stags' antlers were made of wrought copper and then **soldered** into their sockets with lead. The piece is 7 feet 9½ inches long and 3 feet 6 inches high.

tury (the 1400s), they had perfected their trade into a high art. If you have the chance to visit a museum that has an armor collection, take a close look at the engraving on some of the suits of armor. All of it was crafted by hand.

Advances in metalwork also occurred as a result of the great churches and cathedrals built during this period, which featured lead or copper roofs and gutters. Many of these buildings still have their original metal roofs today. How many shingle or tarpaper roofs do you think will last for centuries?

Metalwork was also found in everyday life. In medieval England, tradesmen known as **tinkers** traveled from village to village repairing kitchen utensils made of pewter. Unlike today, it was not possible to just go to a store to buy new forks, spoons, or knives. So the tinkers made their living repairing these everyday items. To survive slow periods of pewter repair, tinkers were willing to tackle almost any kind of metalworking job. They often had to experiment or *tinker* to get the desired result. Eventually, **tin plate** replaced pewter. Tin workers, known as **tinners,** set up shops and gradually replaced the traveling tinkers.

3.3.0 Sheet Metal in Modern Times

Forged iron on a large scale was the next great development in sheet metal. Iron had been produced for centuries in Europe, and in England a factory for coating iron with tin plate was established in 1728.

Many of the tools used in the sheet metal trade were developed from tinwork done at this time. These tools include stakes, which were used to make such things as candle molds and powder horns, and milling rolls, which allowed sheet copper to be made.

At about the same time that Paul Revere was establishing his copper rolling mill, Edward Converse invented the **bar folder**, which some have called the first true American sheet metal fabricating machine (see *Figure 1*). However, Edward's

Figure 1 ◆ Adjustable bar folder.

101F01.EPS

? **DID YOU KNOW?**

Paul Revere & Sons, Copper Rolling Mill

Paul Revere was the first American to successfully roll copper into sheets for commercial use. In 1800, at age 65, he turned a gunpowder mill into a copper rolling mill. To succeed, this one-time silversmith had to learn new technology. He also had to locate hard-to-find raw materials. And he had to learn how to work with the cumbersome new federal government. His work included ships for the country's new navy, a dome for the Massachusetts State House, and boilers for Robert Fulton's steamships.

brother-in-law Seth Peck obtained the patent. Peck, along with his partners Stowe and Wilcox, developed the Pexto Company, a sheet metal equipment manufacturing company that today is called Roper Whitney.

Around this same time, the iron industry expanded, and rolling mills in Pennsylvania and Delaware produced the first black iron sheets. Manufacturers wanted to come up with practical ways to coat these sheets to make them more durable. They first coated the iron sheets with lead to produce **terneplate**. By the 1850s, however, American mills adopted the European method for coating iron, which produced **galvanized** sheet metal.

The Industrial Revolution of the 1800s in the United States advanced ironworking tremendously. By 1890, more iron was produced here than in England, which had been the world leader in iron production.

Meanwhile, copper sheet production grew rapidly as well, and metalsmithing expanded beyond the tinner's shop to become a fully developed trade of the construction industry. Although

? **DID YOU KNOW?**

Making Terneplate

How is terneplate made? Metal sheets are dipped into a series of heated baths. The first is zinc chloride, the second is molten terne metal, and the third is palm oil. Terneplate resists corrosion; it is strong, is easily formed, and can be soldered. Although it is still used for roofing, gutters, and downspouts, more durable steel products that are easier to manufacture have largely replaced terneplate.

this expansion was helped by the production of galvanized sheets, it was also pushed along by the development of warm-air furnaces and the **cornice brake**, which revolutionized metalworking.

An interesting story is associated with the invention of the cornice brake. The name really has nothing to do with cornices as we know them now. At one time, the word *cornice* was also used to mean *gutter*. An unknown inventor saw a heavy stone cornice (or gutter) fall and kill two workmen. The inventor reasoned that if the cornice were made of metal, it wouldn't be as heavy or as dangerous. So he created a machine that would form all the depressions (or bends) in sheet metal that the stone cornice had. The result was the metal-forming machine that we usually refer to now as a **hand brake**. The hand brake is used to make **ductwork**, ventilators, chimney caps, and most other kinds of **fabrications**. The brake is now one of the most basic tools of the sheet metal trade (see *Figure 2*).

The value of metalwork was proven by the time the sheet metal trade entered the 20th century. By the 1900s the use of sheet metal had expanded to become a necessary part of the construction industry and an essential component of many manufactured products.

Today's sheet metal workers are as likely to work with special plastics as with metal. They may cut sheet metal with **tin snips** or with manual or computer-controlled cutting machines.

DID YOU KNOW?
Environmental Architecture

What is environmental architecture? We are more aware than ever that we must protect Earth's resources—air, water, green spaces, and energy—for ourselves and for future generations. Environmental architecture is sometimes called *green architecture* or *sustainable architecture*. *Green builders* are experimenting with alternative building materials, such as rammed earth or straw bales to make walls. Solar heating is one example of green architecture that you probably already know about.

Modern air distribution systems are much more energy efficient and are better able to control the indoor air environment than the systems of 20 years ago. They provide fresher air and comfortable temperatures in commercial and residential structures. There is also an increased emphasis on indoor air quality (**IAQ**). In some applications, such as in hospitals, good air quality can be critical.

Computers have become an essential part of the sheet metal trade, and sheet metal workers may be required to work with **CAD** (computer-aided design) or **CAM** (computer-aided manufacturing) systems.

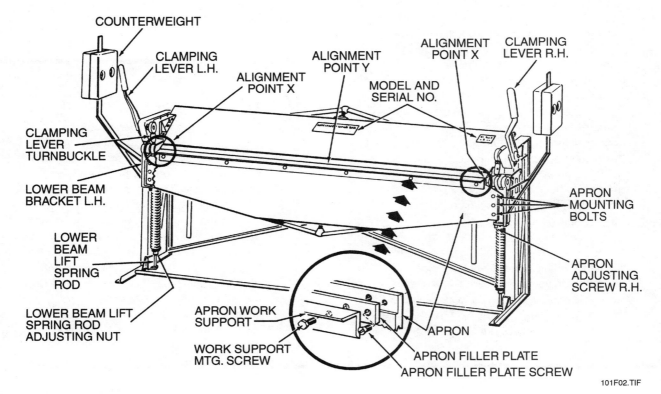

Figure 2 ◆ Hand brake and its parts.

101F02.TIF

4.0.0 ◆ THE HISTORY OF APPRENTICESHIP

Apprenticeship as a means of transferring practical knowledge from one generation to another has a long history. The first mention we have of apprenticeship is found in the Babylonian Code of Hammurabi, which was developed between 1792 and 1750 B.C.E. The code was a series of laws that governed everyday life—marriage, property, crimes, property disputes, and apprenticeship. It stated that if an artisan adopted a son and taught him his craft, he could benefit financially from his adopted son's work. But if the artisan failed to teach him a craft, the adopted son could return to his original family and owe the artisan nothing.

During the Middle Ages (300 to about 1500 C.E.), two large social classes developed: the merchants and the skilled craftsmen. Both classes established occupational **guilds**, which they formed to keep down competition and regulate training for their own apprentices.

The guilds established the indenture system. Young men were indentured, or contracted, to a master who agreed to train the apprentice in his field as well as to provide food, shelter, and clothing. The length of apprenticeship varied from two to ten years, depending on the kinds of skills to be learned.

In the 1560s, England adopted the Elizabethan Statute of Artificers, which standardized apprenticeship training and removed it from the control of the guilds. The term of apprenticeship was fixed at seven years. In colonial America, apprenticeship training tended to follow European models, with young men often serving their masters until they were 21.

4.1.0 Modern Apprenticeship Training

Nearly all trade workers learn their skills through an apprenticeship program that combines on-the-job training (**OJT**) with related class work. The organization of modern apprenticeship training has its origins in the following events:

- 1800—Apprenticeships became part of the public education system. Apprentices received wages.
- 1850s—The first graduated wage scale appeared.
- 1911—The first law regulating apprenticeship systems was enacted in Wisconsin. This law placed apprenticeship under the authority of an industrial commission.
- 1918–1919—A building boom and a decrease in the number of skilled foreign workers who could enter the United States led to higher demand for skilled apprentices.

DID YOU KNOW?

An Ancient Apprenticeship Contract

How did these old apprenticeships work? Here's one example. Historical records include a contract between a young Greek named Heracles and a weaver. In exchange for food, a tunic (a long shirt), and 20 holidays a year, Heracles worked for the weaver for five years. After two and a half years, he was paid 12 drachmas. In his fifth year, his pay was scheduled to double.

In addition to learning to become a **journeyman** weaver, Heracles most likely worked seven long days each week and had to clean the shop, build fires, pick up supplies, make deliveries, and do whatever other jobs the master weaver needed to have done. And it's also likely that any damage he caused came out of his promised pay.

So how much pay is 12 drachmas? We don't have any way of knowing for certain, but the word *drachma* means handful—not much pay for almost three years of hard work. Yet Heracles was willing to put in the time to become a skilled master in his chosen trade. As a master weaver, Heracles could look forward to a better income and a better life.

DID YOU KNOW?

From Journeyman to Master

To be considered a master, an apprentice had to produce a workpiece equal to what a master craftsman could be expected to produce. That would be the apprentice's **masterpiece**.

Masters could start their own business. Or they could choose to work as journeymen for another master for daily wages. The word *journeyman* comes from the French word *jour*, which means day. So originally, *journeyman* actually meant *day man*. Today, the word describes someone who has completed the required training and has achieved the highest skills and experience. Your goal as an apprentice is to acquire all the skills that will qualify you as a journeyman **sheet metal mechanic**.

- 1920s—National employer and labor organizations, educators, government officials, and the construction industry began work on a national apprenticeship system.
- 1937—The Bureau of Apprenticeship and Training (BAT) was established by the National Apprenticeship Act of 1937 (the Fitzgerald Act). This law ensured the safety and welfare of apprentices.

4.1.1 ATELS

ATELS (Apprenticeship Training, and Employer and Labor Services) formerly BAT, administers apprenticeship training at the federal level. ATELS also works closely with State Apprenticeship Councils (SACs), which administer apprenticeship programs at the state level. Programs administered by ATELS/SAC must follow these guidelines.

- Apprentices usually are no younger than 18. However, 16- and 17-year olds may qualify under the Fair Labor Standards Act if certain provisions are met. (Inquire at your local ATELS/SAC office.)
- There must be full and fair opportunity to apply for apprenticeship.
- There must be a schedule of work processes in which an apprentice is to receive training and experience on the job.
- The program must include organized instruction designed to provide apprentices with knowledge in technical subjects related to their trade (a minimum of 144 hours per year is necessary).
- There must be a progressively increasing schedule of wages.
- There must be proper supervision of on-the-job training with adequate facilities to train apprentices.

- Apprentices' progress, both in job performance and related instruction, must be evaluated periodically, and appropriate records must be maintained.
- There must be no discrimination in any phase of selection, employment, or training.

The apprenticeship system has grown up with the United States and, like the country, it is still growing and changing. Today this system serves a nation that is very different from the way it was in 1937 when BAT was established. Today's apprentices are more likely to use computer-aided designing and cutting tools. They can find jobs anywhere in the world. A global economy, increased competition, and an industry that needs highly skilled and able workers are all part of your future in the sheet metal trade.

DID YOU KNOW?

Apprenticeships in the United States

In 1999, more than 431,797 apprentices received registered apprenticeship training in 36,903 programs in the United States. Of these workers, 117,380 (27%) were minorities and 31,208 (7%) were women.

4.1.2 What Apprenticeship Training Means for You

For people just starting out in the construction industry, apprenticeship has important advantages. It offers an efficient way to learn skills because the training is planned and organized. The main advantage to you as an apprentice is that you *earn* as you *learn* because you are already working in your chosen trade.

A True Apprenticeship Story

An apprentice was told to go out in back of the shop and bring in a scrap 2 × 4. The apprentice went out and was gone for over an hour. Finally, the foreman went to see what had happened. He found the apprentice, tape measure in hand, faithfully but foolishly measuring every single board, looking for a piece that measured exactly 2 inches by 4 inches. Can you imagine the foreman's reaction? The term 2 × 4 designates a nominal size; the wood actually measures 1½" × 3½". Here's a case where paying attention in class or in OJT would have saved not only embarrassment but also a lot of time. And, as you'll learn in this business or any other, time is money.

An adequate supply of skilled workers is vital to industrial progress. Apprenticeship programs produce competent craftworkers who have the following qualities:

- They are well trained and understand not only how to do a task, but also why a task is done that way.
- They are flexible and can adapt quickly to the changing demands of their jobs.
- They are ready and able to work at all stages in their apprenticeship.

4.1.3 OJT + Classroom Training = Highly Skilled Workers

Professionals working in the construction industry identify the skills and knowledge that apprentices will need. They help design courses to give apprentices the necessary hands-on skills and knowledge. Many of these professionals also act as classroom instructors. Classroom instruction is an important part of your apprenticeship program because it helps you understand not only how things are done, but also why they are done.

How does the combination of OJT and classroom training work for you? Here's an example.

In OJT, you will learn and practice the basic skills of hand and machine operations. You'll work under the supervision of a journeyman who will give you specific tasks to accomplish. You'll practice good work habits and hands-on safety. You'll get experience working with others in real-life situations.

Your classroom training is designed to enhance your OJT. In the classroom, you will learn the advantages and limitations of hand and machine operations. You'll learn when and why to select certain tools. You will also learn about safety and what can happen if you don't follow safety guidelines. You'll learn why you must develop good work habits, and you'll find out more about the tools, techniques, and history of your trade. You will also get a chance to practice and learn from your mistakes. You'll be able to take time that might not be available on the job to perfect your skills.

OJT plus classroom training is a winning combination that will help you become a highly skilled craftworker.

4.1.4 The NCCER and Your Apprenticeship

This sheet metal course is part of a curriculum produced by the National Center for Construction Education and Research (NCCER). Like every course in the NCCER's curriculum, it was developed *by* the construction industry *for* the construction industry. The NCCER develops and maintains a training process which is nationally recognized, standardized, and competency based. A *competency-based* program requires you to show that you can perform specific job-related tasks safely to receive credit. This approach is unlike other apprenticeship programs that are based on a required number of hours in the classroom and on the job.

The construction industry knows that the future construction workforce will largely be recruited and trained in the nation's secondary and postsecondary schools.

Schools know that to prepare their students for a successful construction career they must use the curriculum that is developed and recognized by the industry. Nationwide, thousands of schools have adopted NCCER's standardized Construction and Maintenance curricula.

The primary goal of the NCCER is to standardize construction craft training throughout the country so that both you and your employer will benefit from the training, no matter where you or your job are located. As a trainee in an NCCER program, you will be listed in the national registry. You will receive a certificate for each level of training you complete. In addition, many technical schools and colleges use the NCCER's programs.

5.0.0 ◆ SAFETY

Construction work can be dangerous. In the sheet metal trade, you will perform tasks that involve handling different types of metals, tools, and equipment. If you handle any of these items improperly, injury or even death could result for you or for a co-worker. As you progress in your training, you'll learn safety rules that are specific to the sheet metal trade. Following are some general construction safety rules you must learn and follow:

- Wear the appropriate personal protective equipment when the task requires it (see *Figure 3*). This equipment will help protect you from a wide variety of job hazards such as being struck by objects, inhaling fumes, cutting yourself, falling, or being burned.
- If your task involves the use of a potentially hazardous substance, always read and make sure you understand the **Material Safety Data Sheet (MSDS)**. This is information provided by the manufacturer regarding safe handling of its products.

WARNING!

A Material Safety Data Sheet (MSDS) will give you complete and detailed information on a potentially hazardous substance. Don't rely only on the package label. The MSDS gives more details than the label.

Manufacturers and suppliers provide safety data sheets for their products. So when working with any potentially hazardous substance, ask your supervisor for the MSDS.

What could happen if you don't ask for the MSDS or if you ignore the information on it? Depending on the substance, here are just a few things that could happen:

- Serious burns
- Exposure to hazardous chemicals
- Blindness
- Cuts or abrasions
- Explosions or fire
- Death

Take the MSDS seriously and take the time to read and understand it.

MATERIAL SAFETY DATA SHEET

ISSUE DATE: 5/4/98
REVISED DATE: 3/15/99
Supersedes: Any Previous M.S.D.S. On This Product
EMERGENCY PHONE NUMBER: CHEM-TEL, INC. 1-800-255-3924

I. IDENTIFICATION

PRODUCT NAME: PROtack
PRODUCT CLASS: Water Based Duct Liner Adhesive

DUCTMATE INDUSTRIES, INC.
1502 Industrial Drive
E. Monongahela, PA 15063

II. HAZARDOUS INGREDIENTS

REPORTING REQUIREMENTS:
OSHA Hazard Communication Standard (29CFR1910.1200) hazard class........................None
EPA SARA Title III Section 312 (40CFR370) hazard class..None
EPA SARA Title III Section 313 (40CFR372) toxic chemicals above "de minimis" level are....None
CALIFORNIA PROP 65 substances listed by the State of California under the "Safe Drinking Water and Toxic Enforcement Act of 1986". No such substances are present in reportable amounts for occupational exposure as per OSHA's approval of the California Hazard Communication Standard, Federal Register, page 31159 ff, 6 June 1997.

III. PHYSICAL DATA

APPEARANCE: Grey Liquid
SOLUBILITY IN WATER: Dilutable
BOILING POINT: 100°C / 212°F
WEIGHT PER GALLON: 9.5 ± .2 lbs./gallon
VOLATILE BY WEIGHT: 60% ± 2% (Water)
VAPOR DENSITY: Heavier than Air.
EVAPORATION RATE: Slower than Ether.
ODOR: Mild
PHYSICAL STATE: Liquid
Ph: 8 to 9.5

IV. HEALTH AND FIRST AID

CAUTION: May cause discomfort in eyes. Prolonged or repeated contact with skin may cause dryness.
IN EYES: Flush with water for 15 minutes.
ON SKIN: Wash with soap and water.
INGESTED: Seek medical attention.
INHALATION: No effects expected. If difficulty breathing occurs remove to fresh air and consult physician.

V. FIRE AND EXPLOSION HAZARD DATA

FLAMMABILITY CLASS (OSHA/NFPA): None.
FLASH POINT: >212°F PM Closed Cup
EXTINGUISHING MEDIA: Water or dry type extinguisher.
UNUSUAL FIRE HAZARD: Containers may burst when exposed to extreme heat.
FIRE FIGHTING PROCEDURES: Firemen should wear equipment to protect against noxious fumes. Self contained breathing apparatus may be needed.
PRODUCT OF COMBUSTION: May yield Carbon Monoxide and/or Carbon Dioxide.

VI. SPILL O
Dike area to prev
absorbents. Prev
Dispose of produ

VII. SPECIA
VENTILATION
EYE PROTECT
HAND PROTE
OTHER: A clea

VIII. TRANS
Non-flammable,
U.S.A.: Regulatio
Canada: Regulati
European: EEC S
EEC Classificatio
TSCA 12(b) Exp
listed on the U.S.
Acrylic Acid resi

IX. REACTI
STABILITY: St
INCOMPATIBI
HAZARDOUS I
along with hydro
HAZARDOUS I

X. SPECIAL
HANDLING AN
vapors, ingestion,
apply to emptied
thaw completely before use.

This information is taken from sources or based upon data believed to be reliable; however, DUCTMATE INDUSTRIES, INC. makes no warranty as to the absolute correctness or sufficiency of any of the foregoing or that additional or other measures may not be required under particular conditions. Although certain hazards are described herein, we cannot guarantee that those are the only hazards that exist, as all materials may present unknown health hazards.

101SA02.EPS

- Never engage in horseplay with your tools or materials.
- Lift with your legs, not with your back. Crouch as close to the load as possible, keeping your back muscles locked and your leg muscles ready to do the work (see *Figure 4*).
- Always ask for assistance if a load is too heavy for you to lift alone.
- Immediately report any injuries. Ignoring injuries or failing to report them could lead to serious infection, brain damage, coma, or even death. Failing to report injuries that later become problems could also, in some cases, lead to a loss of **worker's compensation** benefits.
- Never carry tools in your pockets. You could accidentally sit on sharp tools. If you fall, sharp tools could cut or stab you.
- Wear snug-fitting clothing. Wear long hair tied back. Never wear wristwatches, rings, bracelets, necklaces, earrings, long scarves, or neckties when working around machinery.
- Keep tools sharp and in good repair. Dull tools can easily slip or chip and injure you or others.
- Immediately stop using damaged tools and machinery. Place a tag alerting others about the damage on the tool or machine. Then report the damage to your supervisor. You can become injured if you continue to use damaged tools or machinery.
- Always use a brush instead of your hands to remove chips from around machines to avoid cutting your hands on the sharp edges.
- Keep oily rags and other materials that can spontaneously combust in self-closing metal containers.

WARNING!

Electricity will always find and follow the shortest path to the ground. So if you are holding or using an electric tool that short-circuits, the current will pass through you. If you are standing in a puddle of water or if you are in contact with metal that is attached to the ground, the current will be very strong. The 110- to 120-volt current found in most shops can cause death.

Modern electrical tools have a third wire that provides a safe path for the current to take to the ground in case of a short circuit. Never disconnect this wire and always use a grounded outlet.

- Never remove guards from machines.
- Read and follow all the safety instructions on ladders and scaffolds to protect yourself from falling and to prevent injury to those working on the floor below.
- Always familiarize yourself with your shop's safety procedures and know the location of exits, fire extinguishers, and first-aid kits.

DID YOU KNOW?

OSHA

The Occupational Safety and Health Administration (**OSHA**) works to prevent work-related injuries, illnesses, and deaths. Since 1971, when the agency was created, occupational deaths have been cut in half and injuries have dropped by 40 percent.

OSHA publishes workplace safety standards, performs on-site inspections, and maintains information about hazards in the workplace.

All employers are required to post a federal or state OSHA poster. The poster gives employees information about their safety and health rights.

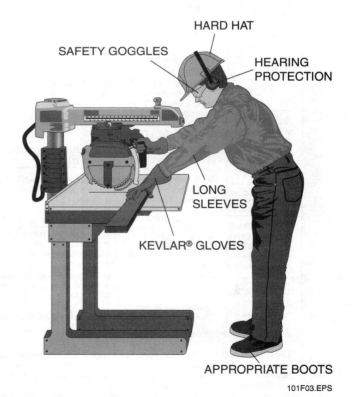

Figure 3 ◆ Appropriate personal protective equipment.

Figure 4 ◆ Lifting objects safely.

Review Questions

Sections 2.0.0–5.0.0

1. A foreman gives two apprentices several tasks and then goes to lunch. Apprentice A completes the assigned tasks carefully and checks to ensure that the work is done properly. Apprentice B takes several shortcuts, figuring the work is good enough and no one will see the sloppy work when the building is finished anyway. Worker A has demonstrated _____.

   a. ability to pay attention
   b. pride of craftsmanship
   c. skill in apprenticeship training
   d. skill in classroom training

2. Historians believe that one of the earliest metals discovered was _____.

   a. iron
   b. tin
   c. copper
   d. gold

3. The *main* advantage to you of entering an apprenticeship program is that you _____.

   a. learn from other craftworkers
   b. can start while you are very young
   c. can take courses on your own schedule
   d. can earn as you learn

4. OJT is designed to show you *how* to do a task, and classroom training is designed to help you understand _____.

   a. why you must do tasks in a certain way
   b. why you must complete tasks
   c. why you should work in task-related teams
   d. how to organize your tasks efficiently

5. Before working with any potentially hazardous substance, you must always read and understand the _____.

   a. MDSS
   b. MSDS
   c. MDDS
   d. MSSD

6.0.0 ◆ STEEL AND OTHER METALS

Steel is a combination of a metallic element, iron, and a nonmetallic element, **carbon**. Though it is the most abundant of all metals, iron is rarely found in its pure state in nature. It is usually found combined with oxygen and other elements in the form of an ore mixed with rocks, clay, and sand. About 5 percent of the Earth's crust is composed of iron compounds.

Carbon can form a great variety of compounds with other elements. Three forms of pure carbon exist: diamond, graphite, and carbon black.

Metals are classified as **pure metals** and as alloys. A pure metal is a metal that is not combined with any other metal. Iron, aluminum, copper, lead, tin, zinc, and gold are examples of pure metals. Generally, pure metals are too soft, lack high strength, or rank too low in some other desired property to be used in most construction applications. Later in this module you will learn how other elements are added to pure metals to produce alloys. This process creates materials that have the needed strength and other qualities important in the construction industry.

6.1.0 Ferrous and Nonferrous Metals

All metals are divided into two major groups:

- **Ferrous metals**
- **Nonferrous metals**

The word *ferrous* comes from the Latin word *ferum*, which means iron. Ferrous metals have a high iron content. Examples of ferrous metals include steel, alloys of steel, cast iron, and wrought or black iron. You will learn more about steel and its alloys in an upcoming section.

Cast iron is an alloy containing at least 3 percent carbon. It is a hard, brittle metal with excellent wear resistance. It is widely used in industrial applications, such as in pipe fabrication.

A nonferrous metal is one that is free or almost free of iron. This group contains many common pure metals (copper, lead, zinc, aluminum, nickel, tungsten) and a wide variety of alloys such as brass and bronze. It also includes the precious metals—gold, platinum, and silver—as well as the radioactive metals, such as uranium and radium.

7.0.0 ◆ TYPES OF SHEET METAL

Sheet metal can be divided into three basic groups:

- Basic metals
- Coated metals
- Alloy metals

WARNING!

When cutting sheet metal, it's important not to let the sheet slip through your hands. The majority of cuts suffered by sheet metal workers are slices to the hands and arms. Grip your work firmly to minimize the possibility of metal cuts.

7.1.0 Basic Metals

The common or basic metals used in the sheet metal trade are **sheet steel**, **cold-rolled steel**, hot-rolled steel, and copper. Sheet steel is an uncoated sheet with a bluish-black surface. It is commonly used to make stovepipes. Cold-rolled steel is silver-gray and has a smoother surface than regular sheet steel. The name refers to the steel mill process used to make it. The steel is compressed and rolled into the desired shape and thickness after it has cooled, giving it an improved surface finish and/or higher **tensile strength**. Hot-rolled steel is formed as it is poured out of a smelting furnace. Copper sheets usually contain a small amount of another metal as an alloy. In the construction trades, they are most commonly used as roofing and guttering materials.

7.2.0 Coated Metals

Steel is often coated with zinc to protect it from rust and corrosion. Steel treated in this way is said to be galvanized. The thickness of the coating on sheet metal may be G60 (.60 ounce per square foot) or G90 (.90 ounce per square foot). Tables that show galvanized sheet thickness tolerances provide a formula for calculating the minimum sheet thickness of metals having a G60 or G90 coating. These tables will also show the **ASTM** standard to which **lock-forming quality** grades of steel conform (see *Appendix A*).

In the United States, galvanized sheets were first produced during the 1850s. Other metals now commonly used include copper, aluminum, and **stainless steel**. Some sheet metal applications in areas exposed to corrosive fumes or high amounts of moisture require the use of plastics and fiberglass.

When the zinc coating is properly applied, galvanizing may protect the base metal from corrosion for 15 to 30 years or more. The most common uses for galvanized sheet metals are in heating and air conditioning ducts and in gutters and downspouts—applications that are exposed to atmospheric corrosion. In addition, the zinc coating provides a surface that helps retard the growth of microbes in air distribution systems.

How Metal is Galvanized

The zinc that protects metal may be applied by one of two methods: hot dipping or electroplating.

In the hot dipping method, clean, oxide-free iron or steel is placed into hot, melted zinc. This process bonds the zinc to the surface of the iron or steel.

In electroplating, a pure coating of a controlled thickness of zinc is applied without heat. This process does not have the soldering effect of the hot-dip process, so it is not suitable for articles that must be made watertight. However, with this method, the zinc coating has greater adherence.

How does corrosion take place? Here's a simple example. When an uncoated metal is placed in a corrosive atmosphere such as water, its atoms turn into ions that move into the water. This process eats away at the metal. If you place a barrier, like zinc, between the metal and the water, the corrosive process is stopped.

So how does zinc protect the base metal? Because the coating is more **electronegative** than the base metal, the zinc gives the metal what is called sacrificial protection. This means that if the base metal is scratched, the zinc is slowly consumed, or sacrificed, so that the iron or steel stays protected from corrosion. This protection will continue as long as the zinc and base metal are in contact with one another.

Tin plate is sheet metal that has been coated with a thin layer of tin to make it resistant to corrosion. Stainless steel has now replaced tin plate in most applications, however.

7.3.0 Alloy Metals

You can change the properties of a pure metal by melting it and mixing in other elements. The critical melting and burning temperatures you should become familiar with are shown in *Figure 5*. This process produces an alloy, an entirely new metal that can have characteristics very different from those of the original elements that went into it.

An alloy is named after the principal metal in its composition. When metals are added to steel, the resulting product is called alloy steel. When metals are added to aluminum, the result is an aluminum-base alloy. There are many other alloys; some common ones are shown in *Table 1*. As you have already learned, brass is an alloy of copper and zinc, and bronze is an alloy of copper and tin. Another important alloy is solder, which is an alloy of lead and tin.

Other nonmetallic elements can be alloyed with a basic metal to change their properties. The most common of these elements is carbon. When carbon is added to iron, the result is steel. Thus, steel itself is an alloy of iron and carbon.

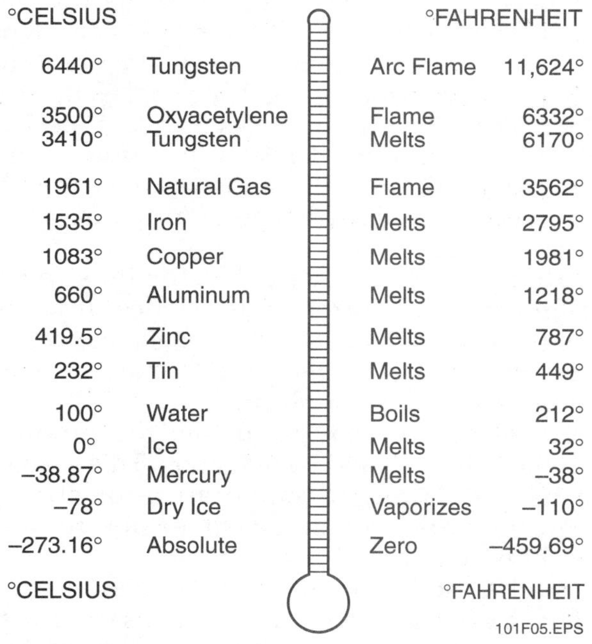

°CELSIUS		°FAHRENHEIT	
6440°	Tungsten	Arc Flame	11,624°
3500°	Oxyacetylene	Flame	6332°
3410°	Tungsten	Melts	6170°
1961°	Natural Gas	Flame	3562°
1535°	Iron	Melts	2795°
1083°	Copper	Melts	1981°
660°	Aluminum	Melts	1218°
419.5°	Zinc	Melts	787°
232°	Tin	Melts	449°
100°	Water	Boils	212°
0°	Ice	Melts	32°
−38.87°	Mercury	Melts	−38°
−78°	Dry Ice	Vaporizes	−110°
−273.16°	Absolute	Zero	−459.69°
°CELSIUS		°FAHRENHEIT	

101F05.EPS

Figure 5 ◆ Critical melt temperatures.

Table 1 Common Alloys

Alloy	Components
Brass	Copper and zinc
Bronze	Copper and tin
Stainless Steel	Iron, nickel, and chromium
Steel	Iron and carbon
Solder	Lead and tin

DID YOU KNOW?

From Galvani to Galvanized

The word *galvanized* comes from the last name of Luigi Galvani (1737–1798), an Italian scientist. While dissecting a frog near a generator, he saw that the frog's legs twitched when touched with a metal scalpel. From this he determined that animal tissues generate electricity. Another Italian scientist, Allesandro Volta, proved him wrong, but his work inspired other scientists to research electric currents. Does the name Volta sound familiar? It should. That's where we get the word *volt*.

7.3.1 Steel Alloys

Steel alloys are produced when certain other metallic elements are added to plain steel. These other metals include nickel, chromium, manganese, tungsten, and vanadium.

One of the most common of the alloy steels is stainless steel, which contains between 11 percent and 26 percent chromium. The chromium hardens and toughens steel and makes the grain finer. Chromium also makes stainless steel less likely to stain (thus *stainless*) than other metals. Sometimes nickel is also added to the chromium and steel to produce a type of nickel-chromium stainless steel.

Stainless steel is valuable for its strength, toughness, and corrosion resistance. It is often used to make counters and cabinets for hospitals and restaurants. It is also used to make ductwork for some industrial applications.

Stainless steel can be customized through a change in its chemical composition. This enables it to handle different temperature or strength requirements and makes it easier to weld, machine, and form.

High-speed steel is an alloy steel of exceptional hardness. It generally contains such metals as vanadium, molybdenum, tungsten, and cobalt. This steel is used in making cutting tools so that they can retain their hardness even at

DID YOU KNOW?

The High Cost of Rust

Rust is expensive. Experts estimate that rust and corrosion on buildings, bridges, vehicles, and aircraft cost about $300 billion a year nationally.

DID YOU KNOW?

Making Stainless Steel

Stainless steel is made in an electric arc furnace. Carbon electrodes make contact with recycled stainless scrap and alloys of chromium or other elements. A current passes through the electrodes, which increases the temperature and melts the scrap and alloys. This molten material then moves to an argon oxygen decarbonization (AOD) vessel. Here, carbon levels are reduced and final alloys are added to make the exact chemical mix wanted. Some of the material is hot rolled or forged into its final form. Some material is cold rolled to reduce the sheet thickness or to be made into rods and wire. Most stainless steels receive a final **annealing** (a heat treatment that softens the structure) and **pickling** (an acid wash that removes furnace scale).

high temperatures. Tools made from high-speed steel can make much deeper cuts at higher machine speeds than those made from regular tool steels.

There are three major groups in the family of stainless steels:

- Austenitic steel
- Ferritic steel
- Martensitic steel

Austenitic steel contains chromium and nickel. It has the following characteristics:

- Not magnetic
- Cannot be hardened by heat treatment
- Can be hardened by cold working
- Has the best corrosion resistance because it has a higher level of chromium than other steels
- Can be easily welded
- Has high resistance to both low and high temperatures

Common uses of austenitic steel include roofs and gutters, doors and windows, restaurant food preparation areas, ovens, heat exchangers, and sinks.

Ferritic steel contains chromium and no nickel, and has a low carbon content. It has the following characteristics:

- Magnetic
- Cannot be hardened by heat treatment
- Always used in a softened condition
- Has poor weldability

Common uses of ferritic steel include automotive exhaust and fuel lines, architectural trim, cooking utensils, and bank vaults.

Martensitic steel contains chromium and carbon and sometimes nickel. It has the following characteristics:

- Magnetic
- Can be hardened by heat treatment
- Has poor welding characteristics

Common uses of martensitic steel include knife blades, surgical instruments, fasteners, shafts, and springs.

Following are characteristics of stainless steel that make it an attractive material to the construction industry:

- Corrosion resistant
- Fire and heat resistant
- Hygienic
- Attractive appearance
- Light but strong
- Recyclable

7.3.2 Aluminum Alloys

Aluminum is the most plentiful metallic element in the Earth's crust. It is the most widely used non-ferrous metal, but it is never found in metallic form in nature.

Pure aluminum is soft and lacks strength, but it can be combined with small amounts of copper, magnesium, silicon, manganese, and other elements to form aluminum alloys. These lightweight metals are easily bent and formed. They are found in ductwork, siding, drainage systems, and a great many other applications.

According to the Aluminum Association, the construction industry is the third largest consumer of aluminum in the United States. (Transportation is first and packaging is second.) The following qualities make aluminum alloys attractive to the construction industry:

- Lightweight but strong
- Ductile and malleable
- Corrosion resistant
- Easily installed
- Low maintenance
- Highly durable
- Excellent conductor of heat and electricity
- Recyclable

 DID YOU KNOW?

Bauxite

Bauxite is the principal ore of aluminum. Bauxite is not found in North America; the largest deposits are found in the tropics. A steady supply of bauxite from those countries that mine it is very important to United States aluminum and construction industries.

 DID YOU KNOW?

The Aluminum Loop

More than one-third of the total United States aluminum supply is recycled every year. Aluminum travels in an endless loop from the mills to products and back to the mills where the whole process starts again.

The most common sources for recycled aluminum are castings and the sheets from which beverage cans are made. However, almost all aluminum mill products contain recycled metal—from in-plant scrap to used consumer and industrial products. In the future, automobiles will also have more recycled metal content.

You probably recycle aluminum cans. The can you recycle today could wind up as material in a sheet metal shop where you work.

8.0.0 ◆ WORK IN THE SHEET METAL TRADE

Most sheet metal fabrication is done in a sheet metal shop (see *Figure 6*). *Table 2* shows a sample of the tasks you might perform in a typical sheet metal shop. If any part of a job requires the use of preformed sheet metal, you'll measure and cut the metal for those applications on the job site. Preformed sheet metal is used for such things as roofing and siding.

Commercial sheet metal work consists of design, layout, fabrication, and installation of ductwork, housings, hoods, and HVAC systems. These systems may be fairly small and simple or large and complex—it all depends on the size of the project. The ductwork may be round, square, or rectangular. Usually engineers design the ductwork, but sheet metal mechanics with the proper experience and classroom and OJT training can also design ductwork systems.

101F06.EPS

Figure 6 ◆ Typical sheet metal shop.

Table 2 Categories and Samples of Tasks in a Sheet Metal Shop

Category	Task
Measuring and calculating	Using rules, tapes, or **gauges**. Doing calculations by hand or with electronic calculators. Doing cost estimates. Performing **layouts**.
Planning	Reading and interpreting blueprints to produce cut sheets. Coordinating with other trades.
Hand tool work	Using hammers, drills, snips, tape measures, and other tools of the trade.
Machine tool work	Operating welding machines, presses, or soldering equipment.
Computer-aided design (CAD) work	Programming and operating CAD machines and computer-guided cutting machines, presses, or other high-tech equipment.
Cutting and assembly	Cutting metal sheets into required parts. Fastening materials with bolts, screws, clips, or rivets.
Repair	Altering or repairing sheet metal structures.
Quality control	Testing, adjusting, and balancing completed work.
Administration and delivery	Ordering and purchasing parts and materials. Transporting parts and materials to job sites.
Communication	Communicating with supervisors, co-workers, and customers.
Computer Numerical Control (CNC)	Programming machine tools.

Working With Other Trades

Whether you work on the HVAC for a single-family home or install ventilation systems for a large shopping center, you will coordinate your work with workers from all the trades. The general contractor will schedule these workers so that, for example, you are not installing ductwork at the same time that plumbers are running pipe. But even with the best plans, problems can crop up. If you understand the tools and tasks of other trades, you'll be able to identify and solve problems and communicate with workers from the other trades. Doing this will help keep the job on schedule and make you a more valuable employee.

WARNING!

When cutting sheet metal, beginners often leave small slivers of metal on the cut edge. Sheet metal workers call these *fishhooks* because they resemble those needle-like hooks in shape and in the pain they can cause when run into your finger. To avoid personal injury when cutting sheet metal, be sure to examine the cut edge and trim those fishhooks away.

Private contractors, general contractors, and government contractors employ sheet metal mechanics for constructing HVAC systems, building drainage systems in new construction, remodeling, and even restoration work.

Today's sheet metal mechanics work not only with metals, but also with plastics, fiberglass, and insulation. They work not only with hand and electrical tools but also with CAD and computer-guided cutting machines. Field installations will require you to have basic skills in carpentry, masonry, plumbing, roofing, and many other trades. Even if you work on a job that does not require you to use these additional skills, you must learn about them and how they affect the work that you do.

What is a typical workday for a sheet metal worker? Because of the wide variety of jobs available in the sheet metal trade, it's not possible to describe one typical day. But the following may give you an idea of a typical day for a team of HVAC installers.

Let's say your company specializes in HVAC installations. Your work team is given the task of installing an HVAC system for a paint manufacturer. You and your team members will meet with your supervisor. You'll talk about the schedule and materials needed. In the sheet metal shop your team will follow a blueprint or cutsheet to build the pieces according to required specifications. Your team may use hand tools or computer-ized design and cutting machines to measure, layout, and cut the metal. When all the pieces are ready, they'll be loaded onto a truck and driven to the job site for assembly. You and your co-workers will consider the most efficient way to complete the installation, then your team will fasten all the pieces together and make sure that all the parts fit properly. Each of you will do a quality check on your part of the installation. The HVAC system your team installs will bring fresh heated or cooled air to the paint manufacturing shop. It also will carry away potentially hazardous fumes. So each of you will work carefully, to help ensure that the paint shop is well ventilated for those who work there.

8.1.0 Measuring Sheet Metal

Work in the sheet metal trade involves the use of metal under ⅛-inch thick, with thickness ranging from about ¼₄ inch (30 gauge) to ⅛ inch (11 gauge). Each gauge number represents a specified metal thickness: the lower the gauge number, the thicker the sheet.

Using the correct thickness of metal is important. The tool used to find the thickness of sheet metal is called a **sheet metal gauge**. Several gauge systems exist, but the one generally used for sheet steel is the United States Standard Gauge (see *Figure 7*).

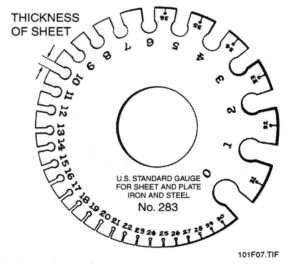

Figure 7 ◆ Sheet metal gauge.

The gauge number is next to each slot. Decimal and fractional thickness is also indicated on the tool. To measure, you simply insert the metal into the slot in which it fits best—snug, but not too tight or too loose. Then read the appropriate gauge measurement.

WARNING!

Sheet metals containing zinc, brass, bronze, cadmium, or beryllium give off toxic fumes when heated for welding or cutting. So it's important to heat these materials in a space that has an adequate mechanical exhaust system. If adequate ventilation can't be provided, you must wear a respirator designed for use in this application.

Riveting Ideas

Not Sure? Ask Questions!

There's a lot to learn in the sheet metal trade, and at first many things will be confusing to you. Remember that construction work involves using expensive equipment and materials, and that it is often dangerous, so there is no such thing as a stupid question. If you don't ask questions, you could wind up wasting time and money. Worse, you could injure yourself or a co-worker. Whenever you're not sure about which tool to use or how to perform an assigned task, ask! Even if your supervisor sometimes seems annoyed by your questions, both of you will be better off if you are sure about what you are doing and then do it well.

You must take extra care when measuring coated metals. The thickness of these metals is determined by measuring only the underlying metal itself, not the coating. The actual gauge of coated metal is one gauge thinner than that indicated by the measuring tool.

Also, be careful that the tool you're using is a sheet metal gauge and not a **wire gauge**. Some wire gauges measure differently than sheet metal gauges. You never want to confuse the two.

The thickness of most nonferrous metals, such as aluminum, is usually specified in decimal parts of an inch. Copper sheets are measured either in decimal parts of an inch or in ounces per square foot. Refer to *Appendix A* for a table of metal thicknesses.

8.1.1 Opportunities in the Sheet Metal Trade

No matter where you live and no matter what kind of sheet metal work you want to do, you can find many opportunities in the sheet metal trade.

Here's just a sample of the jobs you might find yourself doing:

- Working at a company that specializes in installing commercial HVAC systems
- Hanging ductwork in residential construction for a custom builder or large developer
- Fabricating parts for an HVAC shop
- Operating a **press brake** to fabricate duct work
- Making commercial kitchen equipment or stainless steel cabinetry for restaurants or hospitals
- Fabricating and installing ductwork, staterooms, and galleys on ships and offshore oil-drilling platforms
- Working for a company that specializes in architectural work
- Operating a **plasma arc cutting machine**
- Diagnosing and solving problems related to computer-operated machines and software

Opportunities in the construction industry are shown in *Figure 8*.

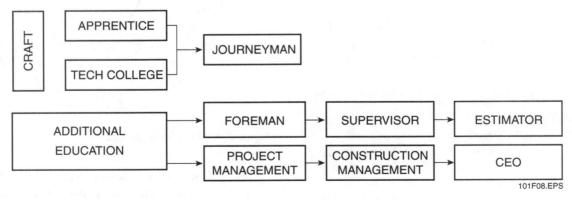

101F08.EPS

Figure 8 ◆ Opportunities in the construction industry.

Riveting Ideas

Plasma Arc Cutting

What is plasma arc cutting? Plasma arc cutting is a way of cutting metal with a special torch. This torch produces a high-speed, high-temperature jet of ionized gas, or plasma. The plasma cuts by melting and displacing material from the workpiece.

How hot can plasma get? Temperatures can range from 20,000° to 50,000°F (11,000° to 28,000°C).

Why use plasma arc cutting? The process may be used for cutting most metals, including those than can't be easily or efficiently cut with an oxyacetylene torch. It can cut aluminum alloys up to 6 inches (15 centimeters) thick and stainless steel up to 4 inches (10 centimeters) thick. The process is used for profile cutting flat plate, for cutting grooves in stainless steel, and for turning large, hardened steel rolls on lathes.

101SA03.EPS

You'll find opportunities in large cities and small towns. You could become part of a site crew and travel to a new place practically every day. You might enjoy fieldwork, or you may want to own and manage your own shop.

You can advance as far as you want to in the sheet metal trade. You can move from apprentice to journeyman to foreman to supervisor. Depending on your interests, you can work in one of the specialized areas in the trade (see *Table 3*). You might become an energy expert and specialize in air conditioning. You could invent the next revolutionary sheet metal tool. Or maybe you simply want to provide a good living for yourself and your family. It's all up to you.

Table 3 Skills of the Sheet Metal Mechanic

Job Category	Types of Tasks Performed
Sheet metal layout	This person works in a sheet metal shop and lays out patterns in sheet metal for specific products.
Sheet metal fabricator	This person lays out, cuts, forms, bends, and assembles fabricated parts.
Sheet metal installer	This person installs ductwork and air distribution system units.
Stainless steel worker	This person lays out, fabricates, and installs equipment made from stainless steel, such as sinks, tables, hoods, counters, cabinets, and carts for commercial kitchens, hospitals, and research laboratories.
Welder	A welder positions and permanently joins sheet metal components.
Architectural sheet metal worker	This person lays out, fabricates, and installs building components such as gutters, skylights, roofs, and cornices.
Production worker/power machine operator	This person operates highly specialized equipment that produces large quantities of sheet metal components in an assembly line operation.
CAM operator	This person operates computer-aided manufacturing equipment.
CAD operator	This person operates computer-aided design equipment.
Testing, adjusting, and balancing technician	This person performs quality assurance checks on new HVAC systems by measuring airflow and adjusting the systems to meet required specifications.
Estimator	This person reviews project specifications, does calculations, and estimates the overall cost based on the amount of personnel, time, and materials needed.
Sign worker	This person fabricates basic and complex sign shapes for commercial businesses. A sign worker may use an existing design or may create a design to suit the materials.
Sheet metal contractor	This person owns and manages a sheet metal shop that may specialize in any of a variety of sheet metal applications, such as HVAC.
Sales representative	This person specializes in dealing with customer sales and service for sheet-metal-related products and services.

Sample Advertisements for Sheet Metal Positions

Following are a few sample ads for positions in the sheet metal trade. As you can see, computer skills and communication skills are important. Acquire as many skills as possible and you will have more opportunities in the sheet metal trade.

SHEET METAL MECHANIC

Rewarding position in a growing, stable organization. Our company offers excellent salaries, great benefits, and a great work environment. Successful candidates will be able to do layout, read blueprints, and program and operate an Amada punch and press brake. Please apply today if you are dependable, available for overtime, and hardworking.

SHOP FABRICATOR

Must be able to read and understand blueprints. Must be capable of working without extensive supervision. Must be capable of operating the following equipment: metal shear, metal brake, cold cut and band saw, pneumatic rivet gun, forklift, spray painting equipment, and drill press. Welding ability is a plus. Must be able to do own layouts for sheet metal. Must work well with others in small shop setting.

SHEET METAL DETAILER

Must be familiar with blueprint takeoffs and Vulcan plasma cutting systems. Must have good communication skills, general administration skills, and knowledge of installation techniques for sheet metal mechanical systems. Must be computer literate (Excel/Word). AutoCAD a plus. Pay based on qualifications. Cover letter a must.

Review Questions

Sections 6.0.0–8.0.0

1. A metal that is not combined with any other metal is called a _____.
   a. base metal
   b. ferrous metal
   c. pure metal
   d. natural metal

2. The word *ferrous* means that a metal has _____.
   a. a low iron content
   b. a high iron content
   c. no iron at all
   d. a medium amount of iron

3. A precious metal is a type of _____.
   a. ferrous metal
   b. nonferrous metal
   c. cast metal
   d. basic metal

4. To prevent corrosion, steel is galvanized by coating it with _____.
   a. zinc
   b. lead
   c. copper
   d. tin

5. _____ hardens and toughens stainless steel.
   a. Zinc
   b. Chromium
   c. Manganese
   d. Vanadium

6. _____ makes stainless steel less likely to stain.
   a. Zinc
   b. Manganese
   c. Vanadium
   d. Chromium

7. _____ stainless steel is used to make roofs and gutters.
   a. Martensitic
   b. Ferritic
   c. Austenitic
   d. Carbonitic

8. _____ aluminum is soft and lacks strength.
   a. Pure
   b. Modified
   c. Alloy-based
   d. Ferritic

9. Most work in the sheet metal trade involves the use of metal under ____ thick.
   a. ½-inch
   b. ⅛-inch
   c. ¼-inch
   d. ⅙-inch

10. When measuring coated metals, you must remember that the true measure is _____.
    a. two gauges thinner than the base metal
    b. the measurement minus an industry-standard coating number
    c. the measurement shown minus ⅛ inch
    d. one gauge thinner than the measuring tool indicates

Summary

Sheet metal is an important part of the construction industry, with applications in HVAC; HVAC/R; building materials; transportation; manufacturing; environmental architecture; and countless product designs and repairs. Steel is the principal metal used in the sheet metal trade, but certain kinds of other alloy metals such as aluminum are also widely used. As a craftworker in the sheet metal trade, you will follow a long tradition of working with metals that dates from ancient times. And, you will also follow a long tradition of apprenticeship—learning while working. Today's apprenticeship programs combine learning while working with classroom training. So you will learn not only how to do a task but also why it is done that way and how to do it safely. A modern apprenticeship program will give you well-organized training that is recognized throughout the construction industry.

Mike Van Zeeland

President and CEO, Mike Van Zeeland Heating and Cooling, Inc.
Little Chute, Wisconsin

Mike Van Zeeland grew up in Little Chute, Wisconsin, and went to high school the next town over at Kaukauma High School. After spending a half-year in college, Mike decided it would be best to learn about a trade by actually being in it. Mike has demonstrated that you don't need a college degree to run a successful business. What you do need, he explains, is a plan, an interest in the field, and the ability to learn. Mike, who is fully licensed in the state of Wisconsin, is president and chief executive officer of Mike Van Zeeland Heating and Cooling, Inc.

How did you become interested in this industry?
At 10 years of age, I was working on Saturday mornings taking service calls for my father's company. By 12, I was working in the sheet metal shop—I made S-clips, drives, and connectors, all the repetitive stuff that could be made from scrap metal. I was so short they needed to make a special stool for me so I could reach the workbench.

During high school, I worked after school, on weekends, and during summers in the sheet metal shop and helping the installation crews. There was no formal apprenticeship program at the time. I learned from a talented sheet metal worker who taught me layout and installation; he became my mentor.

What path did you take to your current position?
After graduation and my short stint in college, I worked full-time for the family business with my father and his two brothers. I worked there until I was 25. Then I left sheet metal work and moved to Minneapolis, where I pursued a full-time career in music production. That was the best experience I could have had, because I worked outside the family business and realized I was capable of doing other things.

In late 1988, my father spun off the heating portion of his company and asked me to return. I came on to do sales and estimating, and took the company from $5 million to $15 million in sales. Last year, I decided to spin off the residential and service portions of the business to form yet another company, Mike Van Zeeland Heating and Cooling, Inc.

What are some things you do on the job?
I handle installation and service for residential and light commercial customers. In one year, we serve more than 500 customers. Before I started my business, my focus was on sales, estimating, and marketing. Now, I still wear those hats, but I've also added all of the other hats, including finance and operational issues, human resources, and engineering. You name it. I even sign all the bills and paychecks.

What do you think it takes to be a success in your trade?
It's very important to have a plan; you have to know when to stick with it religiously and when to deviate. And that's something I've learned a lot about in the past year. That theory applies whether you are a tradesman, supervisor, or business owner. Also, I am a continuous learner, a lifelong learner. I've taken courses in project management and executive management at the ABC Academies at Clemson University in South Carolina.

What do you like most about your job?
I like having the ability to make my own decisions and being able to mold the company into the vision I have for it. Having a broad base of experiences to draw on, I'm able to picture the end result of almost any project that we encounter. Working with the tradesmen, engineers, owners, and office professionals as they take on a new project to bring it to life is exciting. Each project has its own unique character, and it's important to share the vision with everyone who works on the project so that the end result is that customers get what they expect.

What would you say to someone entering the trade?
You have to be willing to work hard. That's the first aspect that any employer will look for. Once you have established that you'll work hard, get as many experiences as you can, and be successful in those experiences. It will round you out as an individual. Look for every training opportunity that you can throughout your career. Training is an endless process, not just a one-time, one-year, or even five-year process.

It's very important to give back to your industry. It's one of the reasons I've been involved in associations that are tied to the industry. I try to be well-rounded in what I expose myself to and to bring those experiences back to my business.

Trade Terms Introduced in This Module

Alloy: The fusing together of two or more metals to obtain desired properties.

Annealing: A heat or thermal treatment process by which a previously cold-rolled steel coil is made more suitable for forming and bending. The steel sheet is heated to a designated temperature for a sufficient amount of time and then cooled.

Appropriate personal protective equipment: Equipment or clothing designed to prevent or reduce injuries.

ASHRAE: The American Society of Heating, Refrigerating and Air-Conditioning Engineers.

ASTM: The American Society for Testing and Materials, an organization that develops and provides standards and technical information.

ATELS: The Office of Apprenticeship Training, and Employer and Labor Services administers apprenticeship programs at the federal level.

Bar folder: An adjustable machine that performs a variety of folds, such as sharp locks, open locks, flanges, double hems, and drive cleats.

Blueprint: A graphic representation of a part, a product, a building, a system, or an assembly.

CAD: Computer-aided design. Computers are used to create designs or models for buildings, air and ground transport, machine parts, and sheet metal fabrications.

CAM: Computer-aided manufacturing.

Carbon: A nonmetallic element found in nature, such as in diamonds and graphite, or as a part of coal or petroleum.

Cold-rolled steel: Metal that has been formed by rolling at room temperature, usually to get an improved surface finish or higher tensile strength.

Cornice brake: A metal-forming machine more commonly known as a hand brake.

Cut sheet: The layout and fabrications instructions to the shop fabricator.

Ductwork: Tubes that deliver the air in a heating, ventilating, or air conditioning system.

Electronegative: This describes an item that is charged with negative electricity.

Fabrication: The act of measuring, laying out, cutting, forming, and fastening sheet metal.

Ferrous metal: Any metal that has a high iron content.

Galvanized: A term that describes metal that has been coated with zinc to prevent rust.

Gauge: The thickness of a piece of sheet metal.

General contractor: The person or company who oversees the work at a construction site and may perform part of it.

Guilds: In medieval times, an association of merchants and craftsmen.

Hand brake: A metal-forming machine that forms all the depressions or bends in metal required for a particular application.

Hot-rolled steel: Plate metal that is shaped by rolling very hot slabs of metal.

HVAC: Heating, ventilating, and air conditioning.

HVAC/R: Heating, ventilating, air conditioning, and refrigeration.

IAQ: Indoor air quality.

Journeyman: A person who has completed the classroom and on-the-job training to obtain a recognized level of skill.

Layout: (1) A plan that shows how objects and spaces are to be arranged. (2) The act of planning how various parts are to be assembled.

Lock-forming quality: Said of a grade of steel that meets lock-forming quality standards. The steel is used in sheet metal forming and bending machines.

Masterpiece: In an apprenticeship system, a work that is equal in craftsmanship to what a master craftsperson would make.

Material Safety Data Sheet (MSDS): Detailed safety information on a product provided by the manufacturer.

Metalsmiths: Those who specialize in forming metal into shapes for a variety of uses such as weaponry and construction.

Nominal size: A designation used to specify the size of a pipe, piece of lumber, bolt, rivet, reinforcing steel bar, or rod, but not necessarily equal to the exact size.

Nonferrous metal: Any metal that is free or almost entirely free of iron content.

OSHA: The Occupational Safety and Health Administration, an agency of the U.S. Department of Labor.

OJT: This abbreviation stands for *on-the-job training,* which is the way many craftworkers learn their trade.

Pickling: A process using hydrochloric acid baths to clean any rust, dirt, and/or oil from steel coils that may have accumulated when the coils were stored or transported.

Plasma arc cutting machine: A machine that cuts metal with a torch that produces a high-speed, high-temperature jet of ionized gas, or plasma.

Press brake: A production machine that bends metal by pressing it into special dies, it is best suited for performing a single operation many times over.

Pride of craftsmanship: A feeling of self-satisfaction that comes from knowing that you have the job skills and ability to consistently produce high-quality work.

Pure metal: A single metal that is not combined with any other metal; for example, iron, aluminum, copper, lead, tin, zinc, or gold.

Sheet metal gauge: A measuring tool used to find the thickness, or gauge, of sheet metal.

Sheet metal mechanics: Those who specialize in measuring, laying out, cutting, forming, and fastening sheet metal.

Sheet steel: An uncoated sheet of steel with a bluish-black surface.

Solder: An alloy of lead and tin that is used to join metals by combination.

Stainless steel: A high-strength, tough, corrosion- and rust-resistant alloy that contains chromium and sometimes nickel.

Tensile strength: The resistance of a material to rupture when placed under tension.

Terneplate: Sheet metal that is coated with terne metal, an alloy of lead that contains up to 20 percent tin.

Tin plate: A sheet metal coated with a thin layer of tin to make it corrosion resistant.

Tin snips: Shears with a blunt nose used for cutting thin sheet metal.

Tinker: Historically, a man who traveled from place to place making a living by mending pewter or tin objects.

Tinners: Those who fabricate objects chiefly from tin plate. Also called *tinsmiths.*

Trades: The overall name applied to the craftworkers on a job site who represent the various construction specialties.

Weld: To unite metals by heating them, with or without applying pressure.

Wire gauge: A tool used to measure the thickness of wire.

Worker's compensation: Insurance required by law that covers an employer's liability to employees with respect to injury, sickness, disease, or death arising from employment.

Thicknesses and Weights of Metals

A chart showing decimal equivalents in inches *(Appendix B)* is provided for your convenience in working with *Appendix A*.

Galvanized			Stainless				Aluminum			Copper		
Gauge	Mfr's Thickness for Steel + .0037"	Weight per Square Foot, Pounds	Gauge	U.S. Standard Approximate Decimal Parts of an Inch Thickness	Pounds per Square Foot Chrome	Nickel	Gauge	Approximate Thickness in Inches		Ounces per Square Foot	Approximate Thickness in Inches	
										96		—
							—		0.0403	88	⅛	0.1250
							9		0.0359	72	⁷⁄₆₄	0.1080
							—		0.0320	64	³⁄₃₂	0.0972
10	0.1382	5.781	10	0.140	5.793	5.906	10	¹⁄₃₂	0.0313	56		0.0863
							—		0.0253	48	⁵⁄₆₄	0.0647
12	0.1084	4.531	12	0.109	4.506	4.593	12		0.0226	44	¹⁄₁₆	0.0647
							—		0.0201	40		0.0593
							13		0.0179	36		0.0539
14	0.0785	3.281	14	0.078	3.218	2.625	14		0.0159	32	³⁄₆₄	0.0485
							—	¹⁄₆₄	0.0156	28		0.0431
							15		0.0142	24		0.0377
16	0.0635	2.656	16	0.062	2.575	2.625	16		0.0126	20	¹⁄₃₂	0.0323
							—		0.0113	18		0.0270
							—		0.0100	16		0.0243
18	0.0516	2.156	18	0.050	2.060	2.100				15		0.0216
20	0.0396	1.656	20	0.037	1.545	1.575				14		0.0202
22	0.0336	1.406	22	0.310	1.287	1.312				13		0.0189
24	0.0276	1.156	24	0.250	1.030	1.050				12		0.0175
26	0.0217	0.906	26	0.018	0.772	0.787				11	¹⁄₆₄	0.0162
28	0.0187	0.781	28	0.015	0.643	0.656				10		0.0148
30	0.0157	0.656	30	0.012	0.515	0.525				9		0.0135
										8		0.0121

Decimal Equivalents in Inches

Fraction	Decimal	Fraction	Decimal	Fraction	Decimal	Fraction	Decimal
1/64	.015625	17/64	.265625	33/64	.515625	49/64	.76525
1/32	.03125	9/32	.28125	17/32	.53125	25/32	.78125
3/64	.046875	19/64	.296875	35/64	.546875	51/64	.796875
1/16	.0625	5/16	.3125	9/16	.5625	13/16	.8125
5/64	.078125	21/64	.328125	37/64	.578125	53/64	.828125
3/32	.09375	11/32	.34375	19/32	.59375	27/32	.84375
7/64	.109375	23/64	.359375	39/64	.609375	55/64	.859375
1/8	.125	3/8	.375	5/8	.625	7/8	.875
9/64	.140625	25/64	.390625	41/64	.640625	57/64	.890625
5/32	.15625	13/32	.40625	21/32	.65625	29/32	.90625
3/16	.1875	7/16	.4375	11/16	.6875	15/16	.9375
13/64	.203125	29/64	.453125	45/64	.703125	61/64	.953125
7/32	.21875	15/32	.46875	23/32	.71875	31/32	.96875
15/64	.234375	31/64	.484375	47/64	.734375	63/64	.984375
1/4	.250	1/2	.500	3/4	.750	1	1.000

Additional Resources

This module is intended to present thorough resources for task training. The following reference works are suggested for further study. These are optional materials for continued education rather than for task training.

Building Air Quality, 2000. U.S. Environmental Protection Agency. Washington, D.C.: Government Printing Office.

Modern Metalworking, 2000. John R. Walker. Tinley Park, IL: The Goodheart-Wilcox Company, Inc.

Sheet Metal Handbook: How to Form and Shape Sheet Metal for Competition and Restoration Use, 1989. Ron and Susan Fournier. Campbell, CA: HP Books.

Sheet Metal Hand Processes, 1974. C.J. Zinngrabe and F.W. Schumacher. Albany, NY: Delmar Publishing.

Ultimate Sheet Metal Fabrication, 1999. Tim Remus. Osceola, WI: Motorbooks International.

Figure Credits

Copper Development Association, UK	101SA01
New York State Education Department	101F07
Ricky Sonnier of Gulfside Mechanical/ Comfort Systems USA	101F06
Roper Whitney of Rockford, Illinois	101F01, 101F02
W. A. Whitney Company	101SA03

NCCER CRAFT TRAINING USER UPDATES

The NCCER makes every effort to keep these textbooks up-to-date and free of technical errors. We appreciate your help in this process. If you have an idea for improving this textbook, or if you find an error, a typographical mistake, or an inaccuracy in the NCCER's Craft Training textbooks, please write us, using this form or a photocopy. Be sure to include the exact module number, page number, a detailed description, and the correction, if applicable. Your input will be brought to the attention of the Technical Review Committee. Thank you for your assistance.

Instructors – If you found that additional materials were necessary in order to teach this module effectively, please let us know so that we may include them in the Equipment and Materials list in the Instructor's Guide.

Write: Curriculum Revision and Development Department
National Center for Construction Education and Research
P.O. Box 141104, Gainesville, FL 32614-1104

Fax: 352-334-0932

E-mail: curriculum@nccer.org

Craft _____   Module Name _____

Copyright Date _____   Module Number _____   Page Number(s) _____

Description _____

_____

_____

_____

(Optional) Correction _____

_____

_____

(Optional) Your Name and Address _____

_____

_____

Tools of the Trade

COURSE MAP

This course map shows all of the modules in the first level of the Sheet Metal curriculum. The suggested training order begins at the bottom and proceeds up. Skill levels increase as you advance on the course map. The local Training Program Sponsor may adjust the training order.

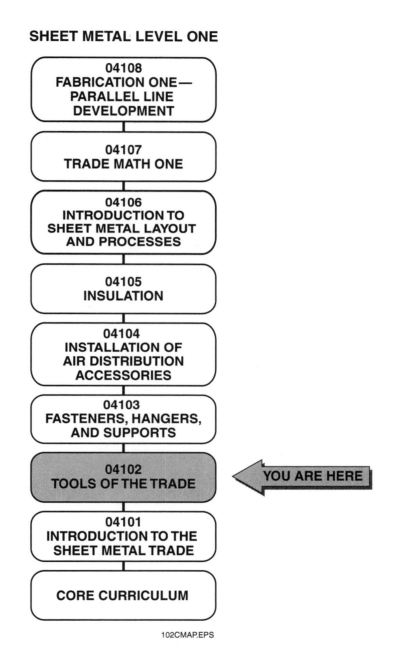

SHEET METAL LEVEL ONE

04108
FABRICATION ONE—
PARALLEL LINE
DEVELOPMENT

04107
TRADE MATH ONE

04106
INTRODUCTION TO
SHEET METAL LAYOUT
AND PROCESSES

04105
INSULATION

04104
INSTALLATION OF
AIR DISTRIBUTION
ACCESSORIES

04103
FASTENERS, HANGERS,
AND SUPPORTS

04102
TOOLS OF THE TRADE   ⬅ **YOU ARE HERE**

04101
INTRODUCTION TO THE
SHEET METAL TRADE

CORE CURRICULUM

102CMAP.EPS

Copyright © 2001 National Center for Construction Education and Research, Gainesville, FL 32614-1104. All rights reserved. No part of this work may be reproduced in any form or by any means, including photocopying, without written permission of the publisher.

MODULE 04102 CONTENTS

Figures

Tables

Tools of the Trade

Objectives

When you finish this module, you will be able to do the following:

1. Identify and describe the proper use of tools commonly used in the sheet metal trade.
2. State general rules for safety when using tools.
3. Describe proper maintenance procedures for tools.
4. Demonstrate how to properly use sheet metal tools.

Prerequisites

Before you begin this module, it is recommended that you successfully complete the following modules: Core Curriculum; Sheet Metal Level One, Module 04101.

Required Trainee Materials

1. Pencil and paper
2. Appropriate personal protective equipment

1.0.0 ◆ INTRODUCTION

Nearly every function you will perform as a sheet metal mechanic involves using tools designed to help you perform your tasks. In this module, you will learn about the hand and power tools most commonly used in the sheet metal trade. You will also learn how to use these tools safely and how to maintain them properly.

As you learned in *Introduction to the Sheet Metal Trade*, pride of craftsmanship is an important quality for craftworkers to have. Your ability to select the proper tool for the job, use it safely, and maintain it reflects your pride of craftsmanship.

As a first-year apprentice you may not use all of the tools covered in this module. The tools that you will use on the job will vary depending on where you apprentice and the work you do. Generally speaking, however, the basic tools for a first-year apprentice include the following:

- Hand crimper and hand seamer
- Left- and right-cut aviation snips
- **Riveting hammer**
- Pencils and felt-tipped markers
- Utility knife
- Tape measure
- Screwdriver (8-inch)
- Torpedo level (8-inch)
- Grip pliers and linesman pliers

You should also have a good tool belt for quick access to your hand tools.

You learned how to use a utility knife, tape measure, torpedo level, screwdriver, and pliers in the Core Curriculum. You will learn about tools specific to the sheet metal trade in this module and review the use of some other tools with which you may already be familiar.

2.0.0 ◆ HAMMERS AND MALLETS

Sheet metal workers use **ball peen hammers,** riveting hammers, **setting hammers,** the pneumatic Pittsburgh lock hammer, and mallets in their work. Each tool is made for a specific purpose. You must use the proper tool for the job and not substitute another.

2.1.0 Safety and Maintenance

No matter what type of hammer you use, you must always grip it close to the end of the handle. Hit the object you are striking squarely, and keep your other hand clear of the strike area. You use a mallet the same way you use a hammer, but with much less force. Mallets are perfect for striking objects gently but firmly. You must use a mallet when it is important to avoid damaging the object you are striking. Follow these safety and maintenance rules when using hammers and mallets:

• Always wear the appropriate personal protective equipment.
• Never use hammers as pry bars.
• Never hit a hammer with another hammer.
• Never flip, twirl, toss, or spin a hammer or a mallet.
• Always make sure the handle is set securely in the head of the hammer or mallet.
• Never use hammers or mallets with chipped, **mushroomed** (overly flattened by use), or damaged heads.
• Always set hammers and mallets carefully on the workbench. A falling tool can cause painful foot injuries or damage to other tools.

2.2.0 Ball Peen Hammer

The general-purpose ball peen hammer is sometimes called a machinist's hammer. It has a round, slightly curved face on one side of the head and a ball on the other side of the head (see *Figure 1*). You will use this hammer with chisels and **punches** (discussed later in this module). Ball peen hammers are classified by the weight of the head without the handle. Common weights are 2, 4, 8, and 12 ounces. They are also available in 1-, 1½-, 2-, and 3-pound weights.

102F01.EPS

Figure 1 ◆ Ball peen hammer.

 DID YOU KNOW?
The Art of Peening

Peening is a way to decorate the surface of mild steel. If you hit the metal uniformly with the peen end of a ball peen hammer, you can cover the surface with small overlapping indentations. This gives the metal an aged or antique look that can resemble handwrought iron.

Riveting Ideas

Safety First and Always

You know that hand and power tools can be dangerous. In this module you will learn safety guidelines for the tools discussed. But there are also some general safety rules you must always follow:

• Always wear the appropriate personal protective equipment. This equipment includes safety glasses and goggles; face shield; respiratory protection; steel-toed, steel-soled safety shoes; hearing protection; safety harness; and hard hat.
• Stay alert. Never use hand tools or operate power tools if you are drowsy, distracted, or taking medication that dulls your senses.
• The job site is no place for games. Never endanger yourself or others by playing practical jokes, tossing tools around, or doing anything that will take your own or others' attention away from the work being done.
• Pay attention to your work area. Remove obstructions and clutter that hamper your work. Don't operate power tools near flammable materials.
• Keep power cords untangled and keep your feet clear of power cords.
• Be sure to read, understand, and follow all safety and maintenance rules provided by the tool manufacturer.
• Maintain your tools in top working condition. If you find a shop tool or machine with a defect or operating problem, you must place a tag on that tool warning that it should not be used and explaining exactly what is wrong with it. You must also notify your supervisor.

You will see and hear these safety rules and many others again and again during your training. But they bear repeating. Don't ignore them. They could save your life or the life of a co-worker!

2.3.0 Riveting Hammer

The riveting hammer, sometimes referred to as the tinner's riveting hammer, is probably the most frequently used hammer in the sheet metal trade (see *Figure 2*). This hammer is designed to reduce the possibility of marring the metal. It has a square face that is slightly curved, with beveled edges. The peen is double tapered with a gently rounded end. Riveting hammers are used primarily to flatten rivets and **Pittsburgh seams**.

102F02.EPS

Figure 2 ◆ Riveting hammer.

2.4.0 Setting Hammer

The setting hammer has a square, flat face with a single tapered peen (see *Figure 3*). The flat face is used for flattening **seams** without damaging the metal, and the peen end is used for forming or flattening metal.

102F03.TIF

Figure 3 ◆ Setting hammer.

2.5.0 Pittsburgh Lock Hammer

The Pittsburgh lock hammer is a handheld pneumatic tool used for quick seaming (see *Figure 4*). This rapid-fire hammer can seam at the rate of about 15 feet per minute. It is made of hardened steel and is lightweight. This hammer can be used with 18- to 30-gauge steel.

102F04.EPS

Figure 4 ◆ Pittsburgh lock hammer.

2.6.0 Mallets

Dead-blow mallets (see *Figure 5*) and rawhide mallets are used whenever using steel hammers would deface the work. Other types of mallets are made of lead, brass, wood, leather, plastic, or rubber (see *Figure 6*). Never use your mallet to drive nails. It is not designed for this purpose. Mallets used to drive nails won't work properly for delicate forming tasks.

102F05.EPS

Figure 5 ◆ Dead-blow mallet.

102F06.EPS

Figure 6 ◆ Rubber mallet.

 DID YOU KNOW?
Dead-Blow Mallet

The head of the dead-blow mallet is encased in plastic. Hidden inside the head is a small piece of steel, which provides the striking power. Unlike other mallets, the dead-blow mallet will not rebound after striking an object; that is how it got its name.

Mallet faces are designed to shape, bend, or force metal parts together and to form light-gauge metals without marring or damaging them. Whenever you form metal on **stakes**, you should use a mallet. Never use steel hammers on sheet metal stakes.

3.0.0 ◆ COLD CHISEL

You will use a **cold chisel** to cut cold metal (hence the name), to break rivets, and to split nuts. It is made of tool steel and comes in a variety of sizes and shapes. The cutting edge is hardened and **tempered** and will cut any material softer than itself. Cold chisels are classified by the shape of their cutting edges. Shapes include the following:

- Flat
- Cape
- Round-nose
- Diamond-point

The flat cold chisel is the one used most often by sheet metal mechanics (see *Figure 7*). It has a wide cutting edge and is slightly convex (ground outward) so that the center portion receives the greatest shock, thus protecting the corners. The cutting angle is usually ground at 60 to 70 degrees for most purposes.

102F07.EPS

Figure 7 ◆ Flat cold chisel.

The cape chisel is similar to the flat chisel except that it has a narrower cutting edge. You will use it to cut grooves.

The round-nose chisel has a tapering point that is rounded. You can use this chisel to cut a radius and round grooves.

The diamond-point chisel has a square-shaped tapered point. You will use this type of chisel mainly to square corners.

3.1.0 Safety and Maintenance

Hold chisels loosely between the thumb and first fingers about an inch from the head of the chisel. Always select a chisel big enough for the job and a hammer to match. A good rule of thumb to follow: the larger the chisel, the heavier the hammer. Follow these safety and maintenance rules when using chisels:

- Always wear the appropriate personal protective equipment.
- Never use a chisel that has a mushroomed head or is otherwise damaged.
- Never use a chisel to cut or split stone or concrete.
- Make sure the chisel blade is beveled at a 60- to 70-degree angle so that it will cut well.

- When grinding a chisel, avoid holding it against the grinding wheel for a long time. Dip the chisel in water frequently to keep it cool and prevent the temper from being drawn from the cutting edge.
- Sharpen the chisel's cutting edge on an oilstone to produce a keen edge.
- Remove sharp edges from the workpiece after making a cut by grinding or filing the metal smooth.

WARNING!

After being continually pounded, the head of a chisel flattens out or mushrooms. This creates a rough edge that makes it easy for the chisel to slip and cut your hand. In addition, pieces may break off the mushroomed edge. Flying pieces of metal can cut you, lodge in your eyes, or fly into other tools or at co-workers. Keep the chisel head properly ground and sharp to cut properly and safely.

4.0.0 ◆ PUNCHES

A punch is made of tool steel and comes in various sizes and shapes. You must select the proper punch for the task. You will use a punch to knock out rivets or pins, line up parts to be assembled, mark locations, and cut holes.

4.1.0 Safety and Maintenance

Follow these safety and maintenance rules when using punches:

- Always wear the appropriate personal protective equipment.
- Never use prick punches or center punches to punch holes. They are designed to make indentations, not holes.
- Never use a punch that has a mushroomed head.
- Never exceed the load capacity of a punch.

4.2.0 Prick Punch or Awl

The prick punch or awl has a tapered point that is ground to approximately 60 degrees (see *Figure 8*). You will use this punch primarily for marking the location of points for **dividers** and **trammels**. You can also use it to punch an indentation in a workpiece as a starter hole for a drill. Indenting the workpiece in this way gives the drill a secure place to start and keeps it from skipping over the surface of the workpiece.

Figure 8 ◆ Prick punch or awl.

4.3.0 Center Punch

The center punch is similar to the prick punch except that the tapered point is ground to an angle of about 90 degrees (see *Figure 9*). The center punch has a blunter point than the prick punch. You will use the center punch mainly to punch an indentation in a workpiece as a starter place for a drill.

Figure 9 ◆ Center punch.

4.4.0 Aligning Punch or Drift Pin

The aligning punch or drift pin is similar in shape to the prick punch and center punch, but it is much longer, with a machine-ground gradual taper for most of its length (see *Figure 10*). This punch may also have a point ground on the end at about the same angle as a center punch. You will use an aligning punch to line up holes for the assembly of fabricated parts.

Figure 10 ◆ Aligning punch or drift pin.

4.5.0 Hollow Punch

With the development of power-driven cutting devices, the hollow punch is not used very often. It can be used to make circular holes in sheet metal large enough so that bolts, thin cables, and pipes can pass through the opening (see *Figure 11*). The holes are usually ¼-inch wide or slightly larger. To minimize damage to the hollow point of the punch, the sheet metal is usually placed over a block of lead or against the end grain of a piece of hardwood. However, many of the holes punched in this way have burred edges. You can smooth this burred edge with a mallet.

Figure 11 ◆ Hollow punch.

4.6.0 Hand Punch

The hand punch looks a little like a handheld paper punch. You will use it to punch holes in light- and medium-weight sheet metal (see *Figure 12*). Most sheet metal workers carry this punch in their toolboxes. It is also used in the shop to punch holes on large pieces of sheet metal that would be difficult to move to a large shop punch.

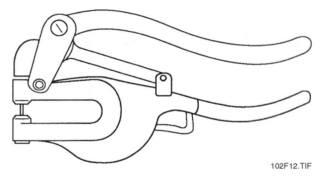

Figure 12 ◆ Hand punch.

Hand punches come with changeable punches and dies so you can punch a hole ranging in size from ¹⁄₁₆ inch to ⁹⁄₃₂ inch. When using a hand punch, you must make sure that the punch and die are the same size. Do not exceed the load capacity given on the punch.

5.0.0 ◆ HAND-CUTTING TOOLS

You will use various types of hand-cutting tools to cut thin sheets of brass, aluminum, copper, black and galvanized iron, and stainless steel. These tools allow you to make straight cuts, left cuts, right cuts, and angled cuts. Generally, you can use hand-cutting tools such as **snips** to cut light-gauge metals, and snips with a compound-lever design, such as aviation snips, to cut medium-gauge metals. You cannot use hand-cutting tools to cut tempered steel. You must use power shears for this purpose. You must cut 18-gauge or heavier metals with appropriate power tools.

Sheet Metal Gauge

Most sheet metal work involves the use of metal under ⅛-inch thick, with metal in thicknesses ranging from about ¹⁄₆₄ inch (30 gauge) to ⅛ inch (11 gauge). The lower the gauge number, the thicker the sheet.

5.1.0 Safety and Maintenance

Follow these safety and maintenance rules when using hand-cutting tools:

- Always wear the appropriate personal protective equipment.
- Never force snips by placing all your weight on the handles.
- Never pound on the backs of the blades.
- Keep the blades free of oil to prevent metal from slipping out of the blades.
- Never cut wire or anything other than sheet metal with snips.

5.2.0 Snips

Snips are used like scissors to cut thin, soft metal. The blades of snips come in two basic types: straight blade (see *Figure 13*) or combination blade (see *Figure 14*). Snips can cut metal that is up to 18-gauge thick.

102F13.EPS

Figure 13 ◆ Straight-blade snips.

102F14.EPS

Figure 14 ◆ Combination-blade snips.

On straight-blade snips, the face of the blade runs straight up from the cutting edges. Straight-blade snips are very strong and have fairly long blades.

On combination-blade snips, the blade curves back from the cutting edge. This curve allows the metal to slide over the top blade when you cut curves. This feature gives you greater control over the cutting.

5.2.1 General-Purpose Snips

General-purpose snips are made with either straight blades or combination blades. The combination blade is the type most commonly used by sheet metal workers. You can use general-purpose snips to cut 26-gauge or lighter metal.

5.2.2 Aviation Snips

Aviation snips have a compound-lever design that enables them to cut thicker metal than the general-purpose snips. You can use them to cut small, irregular curves and even inside 90-degree corners. Aviation snips are available in straight, left-cut, or right-cut cutting models. The right-cut snips cut tight curves to the right and the left-cut snips cut tight curves to the left. The blades are serrated so that they grip the metal tightly. Aviation snips can cut metal up to 18-gauge thick.

Aviation snips have color-coded plastic handles. Straight-cut snips have yellow handles (see *Figure 15*); left-cut snips have red handles (see *Figure 16*); and right-cut snips have green handles (see *Figure 17*). These handles are *not* insulated.

NONINSULATED
YELLOW HANDLES

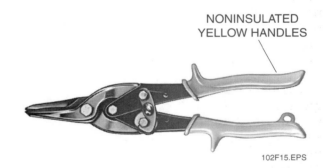

102F15.EPS

Figure 15 ◆ Straight-cut aviation snips.

UPPER BLADE

NONINSULATED
RED HANDLES

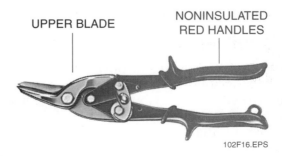

102F16.EPS

Figure 16 ◆ Left-cut aviation snips.

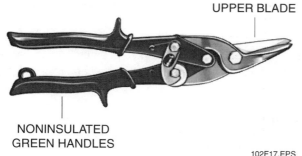

Figure 17 ◆ Right-cut aviation snips.

102F17.EPS

WARNING!
Never let sheet metal slip through your hands. Always keep a firm grip on your workpiece to avoid being sliced by the sharp edge of the metal.

Always snip sharp points off scrap metal when cutting out a pattern to avoid being jabbed by these scraps.

When cutting curves, check the cut edges and trim off any curved slivers of metal. These sharp projections, called fishhooks, can run into your hands or fingers, and they are difficult and painful to remove.

You can also see the difference between right-cut and left-cut snips by looking at the position of the upper blade when you hold the snips ready to cut the metal. If the upper blade is on the right, it is a right-cut snip. If the upper blade is on the left, it is a left-cut snip.

DID YOU KNOW?
Aviation Snips

How did aviation snips get their name? During the early days of airplane manufacturing, snips were used to cut thin-gauge sheets of stainless steel for the wings and fuselage of aircraft.

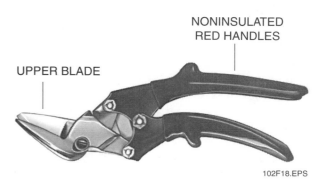

Figure 18 ◆ Left-cut offset snips.

102F18.EPS

5.2.3 Offset Snips

Offset, or lever, snips have the distinct advantage of allowing you to keep your operating hand *above* the sheet as you cut the metal. This means you do not run the risk of cutting yourself on the sheared metal. Offset snips will cut 18-gauge and lighter metal, and their compound-lever design makes difficult cuts relatively easy.

Like aviation snips, offset snips have color-coded handles—red for left (see *Figure 18*) and green for right (see *Figure 19*)—that indicate in which direction they will cut. They can make sharp 90-degree cuts in the direction indicated by the handle color. But if the cutting diameter is 5 inches or more, they can also cut straight and in the opposite direction.

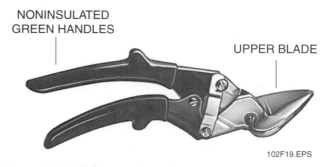

Figure 19 ◆ Right-cut offset snips.

102F19.EPS

Deburring Tools

Most metal- and plastic-cutting operations create rough edges called burrs. To remove burrs, you will use a hand- or machine-operated deburring tool. Although it is possible to use a file, filing burrs is time consuming and does not produce a smooth edge. Most hand-operated deburring tools are made of heat-treated high-speed steel. They are available in a variety of shapes and cutting angles. Deburring tools made for use with pipes feature an inside cutting edge as well as an outside cutting edge.

Avoid Sprung Blades

If you try to force snips by extending the handles, putting all your weight on the blades, or pounding on the blades, you will put more pressure on the blades than they are designed to take. These actions will cause the blades to spring. There will be too much clearance between the blades. If you try to trim small pieces of sheet metal with sprung blades, you will bend the edge instead of cutting it. Because the tips of sprung blades do not meet, you will not be able to make notches with the tip of the blade. Keep your snips in top operating condition—don't force them to do tasks they are not designed for. Sprung blades can be repaired, but it may be less expensive to replace them.

Review Questions

Sections 2.0.0–5.0.0

1. Riveting hammers are used primarily to _____.
   a. raise rivets
   b. smooth rivets
   c. flatten rivets
   d. pop rivets

2. Prick punches and center punches are designed to make _____.
   a. holes
   b. indentations
   c. grooves
   d. die cuts

3. You can easily identify left-cut aviation snips by their _____ handles.
   a. yellow
   b. green
   c. blue
   d. red

4. You must cut 18-gauge or heavier-gauge metals with _____.
   a. appropriate power tools
   b. red-handled snips
   c. green-handled snips
   d. a hacksaw, chisel, or snips

5. If you try to trim small pieces of sheet metal with sprung blades, you will wind up with _____ edges.
   a. curved
   b. serrated
   c. bent
   d. crooked

6.0.0 ◆ CUTTING MACHINES

Cutting machines are used in the sheet metal trade to square and cut metal. Some of these machines are manually operated. Some are operated by electric motors or pneumatic or hydraulic power.

6.1.0 Safety and Maintenance

Follow these safety and maintenance rules when using cutting machines:

- Always wear the appropriate personal protective equipment.
- Stay alert! Never operate cutting machines if you are drowsy or distracted.
- Never operate cutting machines if you are taking medication that dulls your senses.
- Keep your fingers away from the cutting blades at all times.
- Never place your fingers under the **hold-down bar** of a cutting machine.
- When operating a treadle-powered shear, use only one foot and keep the other clear of the treadle to avoid crushing your toes.
- Always check to ensure that the gauge of the metal is within the rated capacity of the machine.
- Cut only one thickness of metal at a time.
- Always lock shears when they are not in use.
- Never remove guards from machines.
- Never reach behind the shear blade to hold small pieces being cut off. The metal pieces can tip up and force your fingers into the cutting blade.

6.2.0 Squaring Shear

The **squaring shear** is used to cut, trim, and square large sheets of metal to required sizes (see *Figure 20*). The treadle-squaring shear is foot operated. You can use it to cut many pieces of metal of the same size. You can usually cut 16-gauge or thinner metal on the manual-squaring shear; however, you must always check the manufacturer's capacity specifications for the shear you intend to use. For thicker-gauge metal you must use a power-squaring shear.

WARNING!

Never horseplay around cutting machines. These machines are dangerous. Fooling around near the machines could result in damage to the equipment. You could also cause injury to the machine operator, to co-workers, or to yourself. Work safely. Stay alert and focused on the job when working around cutting machines.

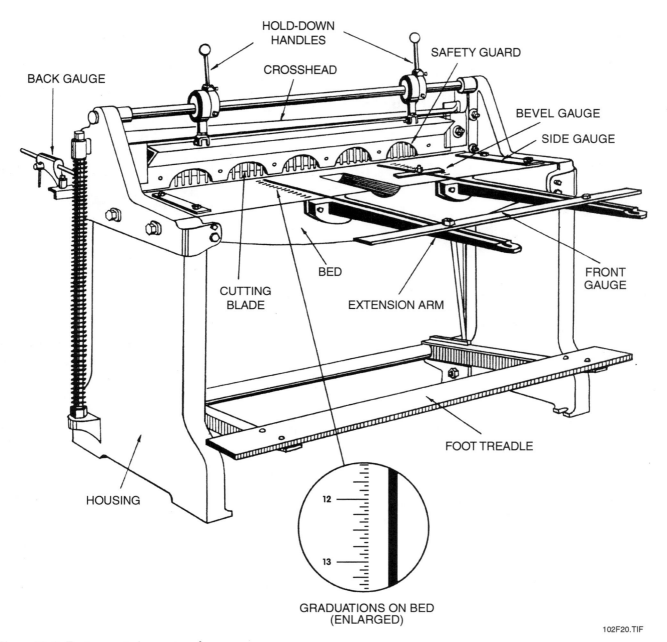

Figure 20 ◆ Foot-operated squaring shear.

Machine Capacity

Before using any sheet metal machine, you must know its capacity. How much can this machine handle? The answer to this question is stamped on the manufacturer's specification plate on the front of the machine. If you cannot locate these specifications, you can contact the manufacturer. Many manufacturers maintain Web sites with downloadable specifications, answers to frequently asked questions, or customer contact telephone numbers.

Checking the capacity is important for several reasons. Using a higher capacity machine than the job requires is wasteful. On the other hand, if you exceed the machine's capacity, you could damage it. If you damage a machine because you ignored or weren't aware of the manufacturer's specifications, you could void any warranties on the machine.

6.3.0 Notcher

The manual or power-operated **notcher** can make angled cuts in a sheet metal workpiece (see *Figure 21*). It enables sheet metal workers to quickly lay out and assemble rectangular trays, boxes, or pans. Notching allows a worker to cut away parts of metal to prevent overlapping and bulging on seams and edges. A tab notcher is a production unit that forms tabs for corner fastening.

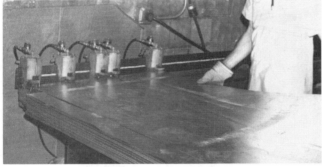

102F21.EPS

Figure 21 ◆ Production power notcher.

6.4.0 Hand Notcher

The hand notcher is used for quick and easy notching on the job site (see *Figure 22*). This tool, which works with a lever action, will make a crisp V-shaped notch in light-gauge sheet metal without much strain. The hook at the tip of the cutting jaw helps you make your notch at the required position without slipping.

6.5.0 Ring and Circle Shear

You will use the power- or hand-operated **ring and circle shear** to cut disks or rings (see *Figure 23*). This machine can also be used for irregular cutting to a line. The cutting head includes cutters of various diameters to handle different thicknesses of metal. The upper cutter is adjustable.

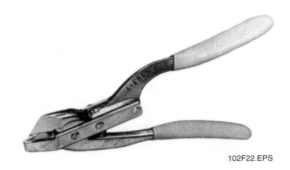

102F22.EPS

Figure 22 ◆ Hand notcher.

6.6.0 Nibbler

A **nibbler** may be electrically or pneumatically powered and can be either bench-mounted or portable (see *Figure 24*). It can make straight or circular cuts. A hardened steel cutter punches out metal notches against a die as either the sheet metal is moved over the nibbler or the portable nibbler is applied to the sheet metal. Nibblers cut irregular shapes and usually don't leave a straight, finished edge. The width of the cut is usually in excess of ⅛ inch.

A nibbler can cut around tight corners. Chips produced by the cutting are ejected downward, away from the worker.

6.7.0 Uni-Shear

The **uni-shear** is a power-operated tool with both an upper and a lower blade (see *Figure 25*). Its cutting capacity ranges from 18 to 14 gauge. The tool has a unique steel yoke that allows cut metal to pass under and over, allowing continuous cutting and burr-free edges. The powered blades move at about 4,000 strokes per minute.

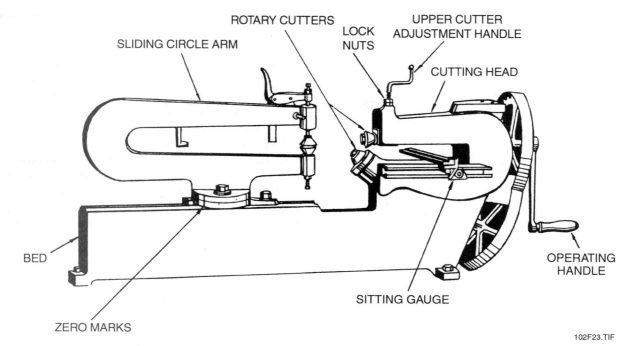

Figure 23 ◆ Ring and circle shear.

Figure 24 ◆ Nibbler.

Figure 25 ◆ Uni-shear.

7.0.0 ◆ SAWING TOOLS

Some of the saws used to cut metal are found only in the shop. Others are portable, and you can take them to the job site with you. The saws used in sheet metal work include the hand hacksaw, the reciprocating saw, the portable band saw, the saber saw, the horizontal band saw, and the vertical band saw.

7.1.0 Safety and Maintenance

Follow these safety and maintenance rules when using power saws:

- Always wear the appropriate personal protective equipment.
- Never operate a power saw until you have read and understood the proper operating procedures and guidelines provided by the manufacturer.
- Stay alert! Never operate a power saw if you are drowsy or taking medication that dulls your senses.
- Grip power saws firmly with both hands.
- Never wear loose clothing or jewelry. Tie back long hair.
- Always make sure the power to the saw is properly disconnected before changing or replacing the blade.
- Make sure your power saw is properly grounded before you turn it on.

- Never remove metal chips while the saw is running. Clear them away with a brush after the saw has completely stopped. Never blow chips away and never use your bare hand to sweep them away.
- Follow the manufacturer's instructions for setting proper blade tension.
- Stop the saw completely before adjusting the workpiece.
- Always keep your hands clear of the moving blade.
- Never force a saw into the work. Let the saw do the cutting.
- Never remove guards or other safety features from the saw.
- Make sure that you read, understand, and follow the manufacturer's guidelines for cleaning and maintaining your power saws.

WARNING!
Keep minor injuries from turning into major ones. Quickly treat all scratches and cuts, no matter how minor. An untreated cut can become seriously infected, which could lead to further complications.

7.2.0 Hacksaw

Hacksaws are used to cut heavier-gauge metal than snips or shears can, and they can cut practically all types of metals except tempered steel (see *Figure 26*). An effective hacksaw is equipped with an adjustable frame to allow it to accept blades of different lengths.

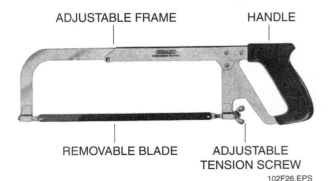

ADJUSTABLE FRAME   HANDLE

REMOVABLE BLADE   ADJUSTABLE TENSION SCREW

102F26.EPS

Figure 26 ◆ Hacksaw.

Hacksaw blades may be made of carbon steel, molybdenum alloy steel, tungsten steel alloy, or high-speed steel with either tungsten or molybdenum alloy contents.

WARNING!
It is almost a natural reaction to blow away the metal chips that appear when you saw or drill, just as you blow away eraser dust. Don't do it! Flying chips can land on other machines, where they could create a jam or other damage. These small, sharp metal pieces can also land on and cut you or other workers. And, because these pieces are sharp, you must not brush them away with your bare hand. Use a brush or wear gloves to carefully remove metal chips from the work area.

Hacksaws are available with different numbers of teeth per inch, called **pitch**, to accommodate different metals. For example, you would use a blade pitch of 14 teeth per inch to cut soft iron or steel, aluminum, brass, bronze, copper, and other soft metals that are 1 inch or more thick (see *Table 1*). As a general rule, blades selected for cutting thin metal should have at least three teeth in contact with the surface to be cut.

Table 1 Blade Pitches and Uses

Pitch (Teeth per Inch)	Used to Cut
14	Soft iron or steel, aluminum, brass, bronze, copper, and other soft metals that are 1 inch or more thick
18	Steel, angle iron, drill ends, untempered tool steel, aluminum, and other nonferrous metals less than 1 inch thick
24	Metals ⅟₁₆-inch to ¼-inch thick
32	Metals less than ⅟₁₆-inch thick, such as tubing and sheet metal

DID YOU KNOW?
Types of Steel

Steel is a combination of a metallic element—iron—and a nonmetallic element—carbon. Carbon steel is a type of steel that contains carbon as its main alloy.

Molybdenum is an alloying element that is added to any steel that must withstand high temperatures. It strengthens and hardens steel.

Tungsten is an alloying element added to steel to make it self-hardening. Tungsten has a higher melt temperature (6200°F, 3429°C) than any other metal.

Tooth set refers to how blade teeth are set to provide clearance or **kerf** for the blade to pass easily through the metal without binding. Two kinds of set are used: a *wavy set* and a *raker set*. In a raker set, each sawtooth alternates—one left, one right, and so on. In a wavy set, several teeth in a row alternate—one row of teeth left, one row right, and so on. Generally, coarse blades of 18 or coarser pitch are raker set; finer-toothed blades are wavy set.

Before starting to cut with a hacksaw, you must first notch the workpiece with a file. The action of notching is similar to making a starter indentation for a drill. It gives your saw a firm place to start. Begin sawing with a backward stroke. Always press down on the forward stroke and lift up on the backward stroke. This technique reduces wear on the blade so it will not dull quickly. Proper cutting speed is about 40 to 50 strokes per minute with long (full-blade-length), steady strokes. Most hacksaws have an arrow scribed on the side that indicates the cutting direction.

 WARNING!

When cutting with a hacksaw, always wear hand and eye protection. Remove all jewelry and keep long hair tied back.

To cut with a hacksaw, first select the right blade for the task, then follow these steps:

Step 1 Place the blade in the frame with the teeth pointing away from you.

Step 2 Tighten the blade snugly in the frame with the wing nut. Do not overtighten. You could cause the blade to buckle or break. Overtightening can also shear (cut off) the holding pins or bend the frame.

Step 3 Clamp the workpiece in a vise and make sure that you can easily see the cut line.

Step 4 Use a file to make a starting point for the blade and to break away any sharp area on the metal that could strip the teeth from the blade.

Step 5 Place the front end of the blade on the metal, apply a little pressure, and push the saw down to start the cutting. Gradually increase pressure on each forward stroke.

Step 6 When the metal is nearly cut through, relieve the pressure a bit to prevent the saw's teeth from catching. Remove burrs and jagged edges with a smooth-cut file.

7.3.0 Reciprocating Saw

Reciprocating saws can make straight and curved cuts (see *Figure 27*). They are used to cut irregular shapes and holes and are handy for cutting in tight spaces. The straight metal saw blades are interchangeable and can measure up to 6 inches long and ¾ inches wide with matching thickness. The blades cut by moving back and forth, with the cut being made on the backstroke. On the forward stroke, a cam lifts the blade to prevent it from rubbing against the metal. Reciprocating saws can cut at low and high speeds. The low-speed setting is best for metal work.

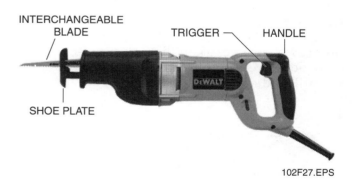

102F27.EPS

Figure 27 ◆ Reciprocating saw.

 *Cutting Soft-Finished Surfaces*

If the metal has a soft-finished surface (such as aluminum or copper) you must line the jaws in the vise with copper or other suitable soft material to avoid marring the metal. Place the cut line at right angles to the vise face and about ¼ inch from the vise jaws to eliminate vibration.

7.4.0 Portable Band Saw

The portable band saw is used on the job site and whenever it makes more sense to move the saw to the metal rather than to move the metal to the saw (see *Figure 28*). The band blade is a thin, flat piece of steel that runs in one direction. It is especially good for cutting heavy metal, but you can also use it for fine cutting work.

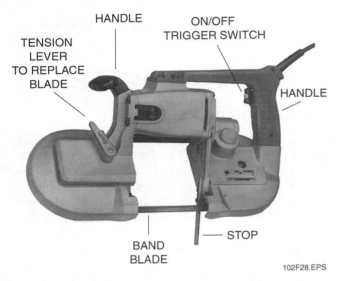

Figure 28 ◆ Portable band saw.

7.5.0 Saber Saw (Jigsaw)

Saber saws (also called jigsaws) are electrically driven and handheld (see *Figure 29*). The most common use for this type of saw is at the job site where internal openings must be cut in existing ductwork. Saber saws vary in size and configuration. The light-duty saw, sometimes called a bayonet saw, resembles a handheld electric mixer. The heavy-duty version resembles a heavy-duty electric drill and must be operated with both hands.

Figure 29 ◆ Saber saw (jigsaw).

Saber saw blades are short, with the metal-cutting version having a pitch of 32 teeth per inch. Bayonet saws will accommodate a blade 3 inches long, ¼ inch wide, and .032 inch thick. Unlike the reciprocating saw, the blades on a saber saw cut by moving up and down.

7.6.0 Horizontal Band Saw

The horizontal band saw is a shop unit with a continuous band-saw blade that runs in one direction. It is used for the same purpose as a power hacksaw but usually cuts faster. The saw blade is horizontal when in the cutting position. Horizontal band saws may be either dry cutting or wet (coolant) cutting.

7.7.0 Vertical Band Saw

The vertical band saw is also a shop unit and is often classified as a contouring machine. Like the horizontal band saw, it has a continuous blade that runs in one direction. Unlike the horizontal band saw, however, the vertical band-saw blade is in a fixed position and the workpiece is moved into it. The blade can cut many thicknesses of sheet metal stacked in a pile (see *Figure 30*).

Figure 30 ◆ Vertical band saw.

You can attach various accessories to this tool for contour filing, cutting, and polishing. Band saws of this type are classified as dry-cutting machines.

8.0.0 ◆ DRILLS AND DRILL PRESSES

Drills and drill presses are important tools that are used often in the sheet metal industry. Drills may be powered by electricity, a rechargeable battery, or an air hose (pneumatic drill). The drill press can be used for **reaming**, **counterboring**, and **spotfacing**, but it is used chiefly for cutting round holes.

8.1.0 Safety and Maintenance

Follow these safety and maintenance rules when using drills or drill presses:

- Always wear the appropriate personal protective equipment.
- Always check to make sure that the drill is the correct size, that it is sharp, that the bit is properly mounted in the chuck, and that the angle is proper for the material to be drilled.
- Accurately locate holes and make an indentation for the drill with a center punch.
- Make sure the workpiece is properly secured to the worktable and adjust the workpiece so that the drill bit does not bore into the table.
- Keep your hands clear of the spinning drill. If you must make adjustments, allow the drill to completely stop.
- Hold the drill firmly by the handle and apply steady pressure while drilling. Don't force the drill. Let the drill do the work.
- Use a sharp drill bit that produces even chips. Resharpen dull drill bits. Doing so is more economical than replacing them in some cases.
- Check the chuck capacity for proper sizing. The small handheld drill may have a chuck size from ¹⁄₆₄ inch to ¼ inch in diameter. The capacity of heavier, portable handheld drills can be ⅜ inch, ½ inch, or more.
- Never operate electric drills without proper ground-fault protection.
- Before connecting an electric drill to the power source, make sure the trigger is turned off. Never use the trigger lock.
- Always disconnect the power source to an electric drill *before* you change bits or work on the drill.
- Always use the right bit for the job.
- Before you start the drill, tighten the drill bit in the chuck and be sure to remove the chuck key. Attach the chuck key to the holder on the power cord to avoid losing it.
- Never touch the workpiece with your bare hands. The metal will be hot.

- Always use a brush to remove metal chips. Never use your bare hands. Never blow chips clear of the work area. The chips are sharp and can damage equipment or cause injury.
- Never ram the drill.
- Keep the drill's air vent clean with a small brush or stick.
- Lubricate when necessary. Some drills never need to be lubricated. Other drills do. These drills have a small hole in the case for lubricating the motor bearings. Apply about three drops of oil. Don't overlubricate. Extra oil can leak onto electrical contacts and burn the copper surfaces.

8.2.0 Twist Drill Bit

The common drill bit is called a **twist drill bit** because of its spiral configuration (see *Figure 31*). Twist drill bits come in a variety of shanks, the most common of which is the straight shank. The parts of the bit are as follows:

- The body into which the flutes are cut
- The shank, which is held by the drill chuck
- The cutting end or point
- The margin (the narrow edge alongside the flute)
- The cutting edge or lip

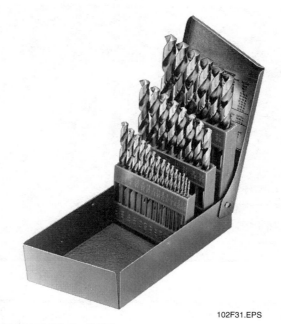

102F31.EPS

Figure 31 ◆ Twist drill bits.

Twist drill bits are made with two, three, or four cutting lips. The two-lipped or two-fluted bit is used to drill holes in solid metal.

Cutting in the Right Spot

Sometimes the drill won't cut in the right spot. If this happens, center punch a deeper hole in the metal.

The size of a twist drill bit is marked on the shank. The size may be shown by letters or by whole numbers or fractions (either by the American system, the metric system, or both). Twist drill bits are available in a range of sizes, as shown in *Table 2*. Be sure to choose the proper size bit for the hole you need to drill.

Twist drill bits are made of either carbon tool steel or high-speed tool steel. Bits made of carbon tool steel lose their temper if excessively heated and then cooled. High-speed tool steel can become very hot and will not lose its temper when allowed to cool.

You will use twist drill bits in portable drill guns. Use bits made of carbon tool steel for low-speed, slow-feed drilling. Use bits made of high-speed tool steel when drilling harder or heavier metals. Use tungsten carbide-tipped or solid tungsten carbide bits to drill very hard or very abrasive material.

WARNING!

Never touch a spinning drill bit. Allow the drill to stop completely before making any adjustments or changing the bit.

Follow these steps when drilling metal:

Step 1 Clamp the work securely to prevent the metal from moving around when you start drilling.

Step 2 Back up light metal with a piece of wood. (Sometimes it is faster and more cost-effective to back up the workpiece with a workbench. You should do this only when you can easily and cheaply resurface the workbench.)

Table 2 Twist Drill Bit Sizes

CATALOG NUMBER (PACKAGE)	SIZE	QUANTITY PER PACKAGE	OVERALL LENGTH (INCHES)	CATALOG NUMBER (PACKAGE)	SIZE	QUANTITY PER PACKAGE	OVERALL LENGTH (INCHES)
48-89-0064	1/16"	12	1-5/8	48-89-0220	7/32"	12	2-3/8
48-89-0080	5/64"	12	1-11/16	48-89-0236	15/64"	12	2-7/16
48-89-0095	3/32"	12	1-3/4	48-89-0252	1/4"	12	2-1/2
48-89-0111	7/64"	12	1-11/16	48-89-0267	17/64"	12	2-5/8
48-89-0127	1/8"	12	1-7/8	48-89-0283	9/32"	12	2-11/16
48-89-0142	9/64"	12	1-15/16	48-89-0298	19/64"	12	2-3/4
48-89-0158	5/32"	12	2-1/16	48-89-0314	5/16"	6	2-13/16
48-89-0173	11/64"	12	2-1/8	48-89-0330	21/64"	6	2-15/16
48-89-0189	3/16"	12	2-3/16	48-89-0345	11/32"	6	3
48-89-0205	13/64"	12	2-1/4	48-89-0361	23/64"	6	3-1/16

102T02.EPS

Riveting

Machinist's Handbook

When you drill certain materials (such as stainless steel), you must consult a machinist's handbook for the correct twist drill type and drilling procedures. This handbook is available from the drill bit manufacturer.

 **Riveting**

Cool Off Hot Metal

When drilling metal, lubricate the bit to help cool the cutting edges and produce a smoother finished hole. A very small amount of noncombustible cutting oil is a good lubricant for drilling softer metals.

Step 3 Mark the holes to be drilled by making an indentation with a center punch. This indentation gives the drill bit a secure place to start and keeps it from skipping over the surface of the metal.

Step 4 Select a drill bit that is the right size for the task and secure it in the drill chuck. Be sure to tighten the chuck securely around the bit, but do not overtighten.

Step 5 Start drilling. After the drill point has enlarged the mark slightly but before the entire point has entered the metal, check to make sure that the hole is correctly centered. Feed the bit into the workpiece with a steady, even pressure.

Step 6 When the hole is almost made, relieve your pressure on the drill slightly and continue drilling until the hole is completed.

Step 7 Using a brush, carefully brush away metal chips from the workpiece.

When drilling large holes, you must usually first drill smaller pilot holes. However, if you use a **step drill** (uni-bit), pilot holes are not necessary (see *Figure 32*). With a step drill you can gradually increase the size of the same hole without having to stop and change drill bits.

 **WARNING!**

You must use three-wire cords for portable power tools and make sure that they are properly connected. The three-wire system protects you from accidental electrical shock. Here is how it works. When an electric tool shorts or the insulation fails, electricity in the tool will naturally travel to the ground through the shortest route. Without the third wire to act as a conductor, the electricity will pass through you. Less than 1 amp of electrical current can kill. Because the third wire in a three-wire system is connected to the ground, the electricity will take that path to the ground and won't pass through you.

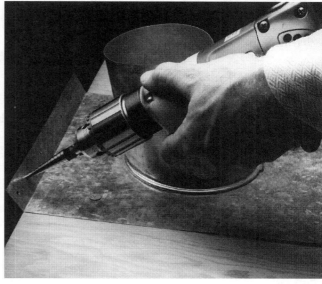

102F32.EPS

Figure 32 ◆ Step drill (uni-bit).

Tools and Temper

What does it mean when a tool loses its temper? To understand how this happens, you must first understand how the tempering process works. Steel is heat-treated to make it less brittle and to improve its toughness. Different temperatures are applied depending on the type of steel and its intended use. Once the metal reaches the right temperature, it is held at that temperature for a specified time and then quenched to cool it. If a carbon steel tool is excessively heated and then cooled, this tempering process can be reversed and the steel can become less tough and more brittle.

8.3.0 Drill Presses

Several types of drill presses are used in the sheet metal industry. Common drill presses include the floor drill press, the bench drill press, and the multihead drill press used for gang drilling.

8.3.1 Floor Drill Press

The floor drill press is mounted at the top of a support column that rests on a sturdy base. Because this tool is heavy, it usually does not have to be fastened to the floor, so you can move it to different locations in the shop if necessary. A worktable is fastened on the column between the drill press and the base. You can move this table up and down the column to adjust the working height. You can also vary the speed of the drill press with drive belt placements or gear changes, and you can adjust the speed to suit the metal being drilled.

8.3.2 Bench Drill Press

The bench drill press is similar to the floor drill press. Generally, it is smaller than the floor drill press and its work size is limited. It is used for drilling small workpieces.

8.3.3 Multihead Drill Press

The multihead drill press consists of a number of floor drill presses, each mounted on its own column, that are connected to a long, common worktable. Each press is fitted with a different cutting tool. The workpiece is held in a drill jig and moves from one press to another for each operation. This type of press is also called a gang-drilling machine because the different cutting operations can be ganged together on one machine.

8.3.4 Speed and Feed

The time it takes to drill a hole into metal depends on two things:

- The *speed* at which the drill rotates
- The distance the drill is fed into the work (*feed*)

The distance the drill travels in one minute is called its cutting speed. Drill cutting speed, which is also called **peripheral speed,** is measured in feet per minute.

The pressure you apply to a drill feeds the drill through the metal. Feed is measured in decimal fractions of an inch. It will vary with the type of workpiece material and size of the drill.

Many variables affect the feed and speed you must select for the drill press. Drill feed and speed tables contain recommended, not exact, feeds and speeds. As you gain experience, you will be able to determine how to set the correct feed and speed. And you will become aware of things that will alert you to problems, such as irregular chip size or a chattering (vibrating) drill. If you have any doubts about the correct feed and speed, you must ask your supervisor before you start drilling.

9.0.0 ◆ FORMING MACHINES

You will use the **bar folder** and the **brake** in the sheet metal shop. These forming machines fold and form straight pieces of sheet metal and make flanges, locks, and seams. You will also use the **slip-roll forming machine** to form cylinders and conical shapes.

9.1.0 Safety and Maintenance

Follow these safety and maintenance rules when using forming machines:

- Always wear the appropriate personal protective equipment.
- Be sure to read, understand, and follow the manufacturer's safety recommendations for safe operation of these machines.
- Never disable any of the manufacturer's safety features.
- Never deface or cover up any safety stickers on the machines.
- Never place your hand in a brake when someone is operating the handle.
- Never put your hand in the dies of a brake unless the main switch is off and locked.
- Make sure that the area around the counterbalance balls on the brake is clear before operating the brake.
- If you stand in front of the brake, be sure to stand back far enough so that you won't be hit by the handles that project from the leaf when it is swung up.
- Never bend a rod or wire on a sheet metal brake. You will damage the blade and the bending leaf.
- Never use a steel hammer to start a bend on a sheet metal brake. You could miss the metal and damage the brake beyond repair. Always use a mallet.

Riveting Ideas

Cutting Fluids

High-speed drilling produces a lot of heat at the drilling point. Too much heat will destroy the drill's temper and dull it quickly. Cutting fluids (also called cutting compounds) are oils that will absorb this heat and cool the drill. These oils also help reduce friction at the cutting edges.

Because there are many kinds of cutting fluids, you must read and follow the manufacturer's recommendations for your drill about how much fluid to apply and when or whether to apply it. You cannot use cutting fluids at all with some brittle materials such as cast iron.

Always wash your hands thoroughly after applying cutting fluids.

9.2.0 Bar Folder

The bar folder is used for making limited folds in sheet metal (see *Figure 33*). You will use it to form edges of 20-gauge or lighter metal sheets, to pre-pare folds for lock seams, to make **wired edges**, and to form double right-angle folds or channels. The bar folder is generally hand operated and ranges in length from 21 inches to 42 inches. Bar folders used in mass production are machine operated. Another type of metal folding machine is the cheek bender, which is used to make bends on 20-gauge or lighter metal sheets (see *Figure 34*). On the cheek bender, a two-way **trunnion** keeps the bending bar in position at the starting point. This trunnion ensures consistent bends through-out the entire length of the metal sheet. The cheek bender can be adjusted for bends from ¼ inch to ⅞ inch.

102F34.EPS

Figure 34 ◆ Cheek bender.

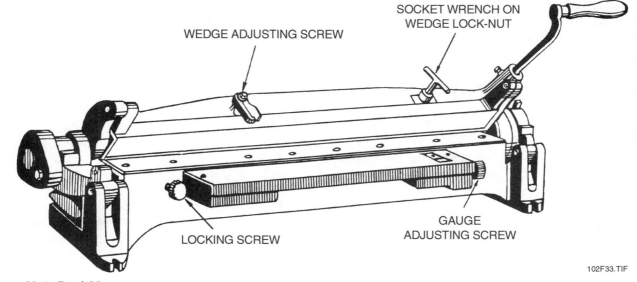

WEDGE ADJUSTING SCREW

SOCKET WRENCH ON WEDGE LOCK-NUT

LOCKING SCREW

GAUGE ADJUSTING SCREW

102F33.TIF

Figure 33 ◆ Bar folder.

To use a bar folder, follow these steps:

Step 1 Set the gauge to the width you need.

Step 2 Tighten the lock screw to set the gauge.

Step 3 Loosen the wedge lock nut on the back of the bar folder.

Step 4 Adjust the wedge screw to the fold wanted and tighten the wedge lock nut.

Step 5 Set the stop of the adjustable collar to the angle you need.

Step 6 Adjust the screws on each side of the folder to the thickness of the metal. Make sure the settings on both sides are identical.

Step 7 Slide the metal between the blades and the jaw and rest it against the gauge fingers.

Step 8 Hold the metal in place with one hand and pull the handle completely forward.

Step 9 Carefully return the handle to the upright position. Don't let the handle fly out of your hand or slam back.

Step 10 Place the metal back on the beveled part of the blade and as close to the wing as possible.

Step 11 Hold the metal with one hand and quickly pull the operating handle to flatten the seam.

9.3.0 Brake

The brake is used for making numerous folds in sheet metal. A brake is basically a horizontal vise with a movable front **apron** that allows you to permanently change the shape of whatever the rest of the brake is holding.

The brake consists of a sturdy base that supports a large, heavy hold-down bar; left- and right-hand clamps that lower and raise the hold-down bar; a movable apron; and left and right counterweight bars that raise and lower the apron.

To use a brake, follow these steps:

Step 1 Start with the hold-down bar in the raised position so that you can slide the sheet metal onto the work bed.

Step 2 Pull on the clamps to lower the hold-down bar.

Step 3 Push either one of the counterweight bars forward. This lifts the apron and forces the metal to move with it. The permanent bend or fold is then made in the metal.

There are several types of brakes that are designed for various jobs. They include the cornice brake, the box and pan brake, and the press brake.

9.3.1 Cornice Brake

The standard hand brake, or cornice brake, is a versatile machine. You will use it to make sharp and rounded-angle bends or folds. By using a mold, you can also make curved shapes. The shapes that can be formed with a cornice brake resemble the decorative cornices found on some buildings. Hand-operated or power brakes can be from 3 to 10 feet long.

9.3.2 Box and Pan Brake

It is usually not possible to bend all four sides of a box at one time on a conventional brake. The box and pan brake, however, can fold boxes, pans, or trays from one sheet of metal (see *Figure 35*). The upper leaf holds box fingers. These box fingers come in different sizes so that you can form different sizes of duct.

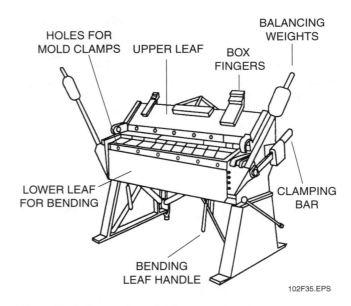

Figure 35 ◆ Box and pan brake.

9.3.3 Press Brake

The press brake is a production machine generally used in large-volume manufacturing (see *Figure 36*). It forms metal by pressing it into specially formed dies. The press brake is capable of forming either light sheet metal or heavy metal plate into a variety of production shapes and fittings.

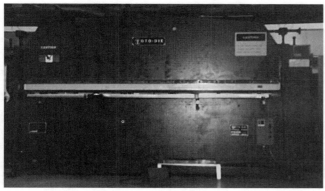

Figure 36 ◆ Press brake.

Press brakes operate on hydraulic or electric power, and they exert much more force on a workpiece than a hand brake can. They are therefore extremely dangerous unless proper safety precautions are practiced. Manufacturers of press brakes provide several types of safety devices for the operator. Safety devices include the following:

- Controls located above the work area that require both hands.
- Pullback restraints that automatically yank the operator's hands back from danger if an accidental pressing occurs.

Press brakes are available in many lengths from 4 feet up to 35 feet, and they can handle many different sheet metal forming operations.

9.4.0 Slip-Roll Forming Machine

You will use a slip-roll forming machine (see *Figure 37*) to form cylindrical parts. This machine consists of three long rolls (solid metal cylinders) that can be set various distances apart. To form a cylinder, place the metal between the rolls and turn the handle. The two front rolls will grip the metal and force it against the rear roll, which forces it up, curving the sheet.

The position of the rear roll in relation to the front upper roll will determine the curve radius or cylinder diameter. There is no specific rule for setting the position of the rear roll. As you gain experience you will learn how to set the roll properly. Until then, observe experienced sheet metal workers, ask questions, and work to perfect your skills.

9.5.0 Turning Machines

Bench-mounted turning machines use rolls that can produce different edges and other shapes on a metal workpiece. Various roll sizes are available, and they should be carefully matched to produce the desired end result. One type of turning machine called the easy edger turns out perfect 90-degree flanges on elbows and other curved sheet metal fittings. You can adjust the roll's equipment vertically, and you can raise the upper roll to remove a closed flange. The easy edger also can be moved around the shop because it installs easily on any workbench with a hand clamp. The turning machines used most often in the sheet metal trade are described in the following sections.

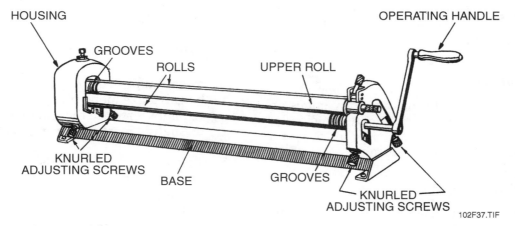

Figure 37 ◆ Slip-roll forming machine.

 **Riveting Ideas**

Plan Bend Sequence

When bending metal on a brake, you must plan the sequence of bends. If you don't make the bends in the right order, you may find it impossible to make all the bends that are needed.

9.5.1 Thin Edge Rolls

Thin edge rolls are used to form a thin bead or flange around the circumference of a pipe or the circular edge of other fittings (see *Figure 38*). Notice the threaded crank for adjusting the rolls and the hand crank for turning them.

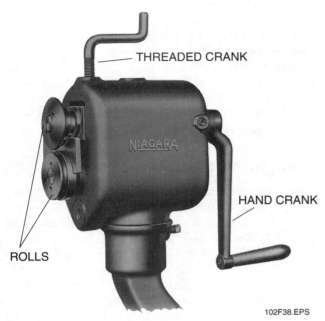

THREADED CRANK

HAND CRANK

ROLLS

102F38.EPS

Figure 38 ◆ Thin edge rolls.

9.5.2 Wiring Rolls

Wiring rolls are used to make rounded edges in a workpiece, into which wire can be inserted for added strength. The roll size must match the thickness of the wire. The roll turns the edge of the metal over the wire.

9.5.3 Burring Rolls

Burring rolls are used to make narrow edges on disks. They are also used to prepare the circular edges of the tops and bottoms of cylindrical and round containers for double seaming.

9.5.4 Setting-Down Rolls

Setting-down rolls are used as a follow-up to the burring machine. These rolls make it possible to form double seams on cylindrical workpieces.

9.5.5 Double-Seaming Rolls

Double-seaming rolls are used for the final operation in forming a double seam on cylinders and round containers. They form the seams or edges up against the side of the container.

9.5.6 Crimping and Beading Rolls

Crimping and beading rolls are designed to make it possible to connect sheet metal pipes. Like hand crimpers, these rolls crimp (slightly reduce) the end of one pipe so that it can fit into another pipe of the same circumference.

When the crimp is formed, an **ogee bead** is formed next to it. This keeps the overlapping pipe from slipping beyond the bead when the pipes are connected.

Review Questions

Sections 6.0.0–9.0.0

1. You use _____ to cut disks.
   a. ring and circle shears
   b. uni-shears
   c. hand notchers
   d. treadle shears

2. Hacksaws are available with different numbers of teeth per inch, called _____.
   a. slant
   b. pitch
   c. rows
   d. rank

3. It is best to use _____ when drilling hard or heavy metals.
   a. carbon tool steel drills
   b. bench-mounted twist drills
   c. straight shank drills
   d. high-speed tool steel drills

4. Crimping and beading rolls are designed to _____.
   a. split pipe evenly
   b. galvanize metal pipes
   c. slightly reduce the end of a pipe
   d. slightly increase the end of a pipe

5. To make numerous folds in sheet metal, you must use a(n) _____.
   a. bar folder
   b. brake
   c. slip-roll forming machine
   d. easy edger

10.0.0 ◆ ROLL-FORMING MACHINES

Roll-forming machines create shapes in metal sheets and strips. These shapes make it possible for you to join the sheet metal edges together.

10.1.0 Safety and Maintenance

Follow these safety and maintenance rules when using roll-forming machines:

- Always wear the appropriate personal protective equipment.
- Be sure to read, understand, and follow the manufacturer's safety recommendations for safe operation of these machines.
- Never disable any of the manufacturer's safety features.
- Never deface or cover up any safety stickers on the machines.
- Keep your hands clear of the rolls.

10.2.0 Pittsburgh Lock Machine

The **Pittsburgh lock** (or seam) is used often in sheet metal work (see *Figure 39*). This seam consists of two parts: a single flange and a pocket, which also has a flange. The single flange is inserted into the pocket, and then the pocket flange is hammered over to lock the single flange permanently in place. The advantage of the Pittsburgh lock is that it can be formed on a flat sheet and rolled to fit curved sections.

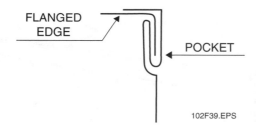

Figure 39 ◆ Pittsburgh lock.

The Pittsburgh lock machine (see *Figure 40*) has been designed especially to form the pocket lock. The metal sheet is inserted into one end of the machine and runs through a series of rolls that form the pocket lock.

10.3.0 Button Lock Machine

A button lock machine uses a series of rolls to produce button locks or snap locks in ductwork. This equipment generally handles metal of 20 gauge or lighter and is capable of making both receiver locks and button-punched right-angle flanges. It

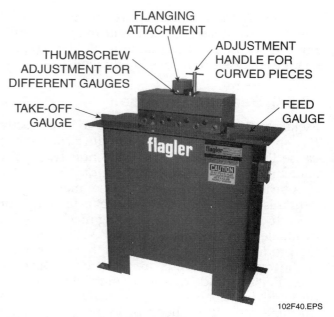

Figure 40 ◆ Pittsburgh lock machine.

can produce these locks at the rate of 60 feet per minute or better. The button or snap lock is a faster method for assembling sheet metal parts because you don't need to hammer over edges to complete the seam, as in the case of Pittsburgh locks. The button lock is limited as to pressure and duct size, and it should not be used on aluminum duct.

10.4.0 Slip and Drive Machine

This roll-forming machine makes all types of connectors, such as flat slips, standing slips, and reinforced standing slips, and various types of drives for connecting duct sections (see *Figure 41*). It subjects the metal strips to a continuous series of rolls that make all the required folds needed to produce various types of S-shapes and drives. A slip and drive machine can make slips at the rate of 100 feet per minute, using metal of 22 gauge or lighter. These machines are also known as cleat-forming machines.

Figure 41 ◆ Slip and drive machine.

Generally these machines are ordered to fulfill a specific roll-forming need, and the tooled rolls remain set inside the machine. A shop rarely changes the rolls to form something else.

10.5.0 Beading Machine

Metal sheets are not manufactured to be perfectly flat, so when air rushes through ductwork, it can cause the sheet metal to vibrate noisily. This is sometimes called *bellying* or the *oilcan effect*.

A beading machine stiffens sheet metal to prevent this vibration. If a metal sheet is too large for a beading machine or if a beading machine is not available, you must use a cross brake. Cross braking produces a slight indentation that looks like a shallow pyramid. Beads are made using beading rolls. Beading adds rigidity to metal and also can be used for decorative purposes. A beading machine can stiffen sheets of 16 gauge or lighter metal up to 5 feet wide.

11.0.0 ◆ HAND-FORMING AND HAND TOOLS

When you are on a job site, you probably will not have ready access to shop machines or facilities. That is why knowing how to use sheet metal hand-forming and hand tools is a necessary skill.

11.1.0 Safety and Maintenance

Follow these safety and maintenance rules when using hand tools and stakes:

- Always wear the appropriate personal protective equipment.
- Always use a mallet for forming sheet metal over stakes.
- Never use a stake to back up work when prick-punching or cutting with a cold chisel.
- Take care of your stakes to ensure that your finished work looks smooth and well crafted. If stakes are marred by punch or chisel marks, your completed work will look rough.
- Keep your hand tools clean and stored properly.
- Never use a hand tool for any job except the one it is designed to do.
- Never flip, toss, or spin hand tools.
- When using a duct jack, always be sure to lock the wheels on the portable platform before loading or lifting duct.

11.2.0 Hand Seamer

The hand seamer is also called *hand tongs*. You will use a seamer to form and flatten metal when hand brakes are not available or when it is impossible to use a hand brake to form the seam. The hand seamer is not effective on heavy-gauge metal. The top jaw of the seamer is ruled off in ¼-inch increments to help you make accurate bends and flanges (see *Figure 42*).

102F42.EPS

Figure 42 ◆ Hand seamer.

11.3.0 Folding Tool

The folding tool, like the seamer, forms and flattens metal (see *Figure 43*). To form bends and flanges in sheet metal, insert the metal into the slot and lift the tool with a lever action. This tool is most effective on lighter gauge metals.

½" SLOT

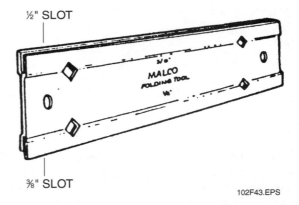

⅜" SLOT

102F43.EPS

Figure 43 ◆ Folding tool.

This tool is available in different lengths and comes premeasured, or slotted, for a ½-inch or ⅜-inch drive or fold. This tool is sometimes called a *cleat bender* or *hand drive turner*.

11.4.0 Locking Hand Seamer

The locking hand seamer has the added advantage of lock-grip pliers (see *Figure 44*). This tool gives you a more secure grip on the metal edge, and it serves as an extra clamp when you need it. You can also use it to straighten out or flatten sheet metal that may have been damaged or incorrectly formed.

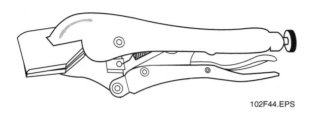

102F44.EPS

Figure 44 ◆ Locking hand seamer.

11.5.0 Stakes

You will use various types of forming and bending anvils or stakes to bend, form, seam, and rivet metal objects. The bottom of each stake has a tapered point or shank that fits into a flat, rectangular iron plate. This plate is pierced with a number of square, tapered holes called bench plates, which are designed to hold the stake firmly. The more common types of stakes include the blowhorn, the beakhorn, the candlemold, the needlecase, the hollow mandrel, the double-seaming, and the hatchet.

11.5.1 Blowhorn Stake

The blowhorn stake has two tapered horns: a short one at one end and a long one at the other end (see *Figure 45*). This stake is used mostly to form, seam, and rivet metal into tapered objects such as funnels.

102F45.EPS

Figure 45 ◆ Blowhorn stake.

11.5.2 Beakhorn Stake

Like the blowhorn stake, the beakhorn stake also has two horns: a thick, tapered horn at one end and a rectangular horn at the other end (see *Figure 46*). It is used to form, seam, and rivet workpieces when the blowhorn stake won't form the desired shape.

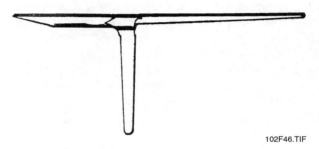

102F46.TIF

Figure 46 ◆ Beakhorn stake.

11.5.3 Candlemold Stake

The candlemold stake has two long tapered horns of differing lengths and angles (see *Figure 47*). It is used to form, seam, and rivet metal into long shapes with flaring ends.

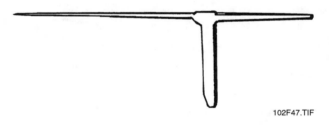

102F47.TIF

Figure 47 ◆ Candlemold stake.

11.5.4 Needlecase Stake

The needlecase stake is similar in design and purpose to the candlemold stake. However, the needlecase stake is used for very fine handwork such as forming small pipes and tubing (see *Figure 48*).

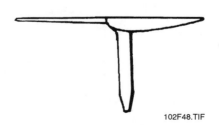

102F48.TIF

Figure 48 ◆ Needlecase stake.

DID YOU KNOW?

Stake Names

Those strange-sounding names for some stakes are based on what they were first used to make. Here are just a few examples:

Blowhorn stakes were originally designed to make horns for food peddlers who sold their wares from carts. These peddlers announced their arrival in the neighborhood by blowing a horn.

Beakhorn stakes were designed to make containers called beakers to hold gunpowder.

Candlemold stakes were designed to create molds that were then used to make candles of various sizes and shapes for everyday use.

11.5.5 Hollow Mandrel Stake

The hollow mandrel stake has a slot running through it the full length (see *Figure 49*). A bolt slips into the slot and allows the stake to be fastened to the bench at any length or angle. It has a rounded surface on one end and a rectangular surface on the other end. The rounded end is used to seam and rivet pipes. The rectangular end is used to form **laps**, to double-seam corners, and to rivet.

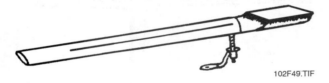

102F49.TIF

Figure 49 ◆ Hollow mandrel stake.

11.5.6 Double-Seaming Stake

The double-seaming stake has two tube-shaped horns with knobs at each end (see *Figure 50*). This stake is used to double-seam metal that is shaped into cylinders. Another type of double-seaming stake has accessory heads for double-seaming large workpieces.

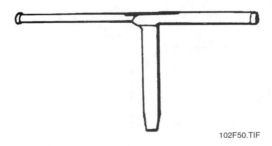

102F50.TIF

Figure 50 ◆ Double-seaming stake.

11.5.7 Hatchet Stake

The hatchet stake has a sharp, straight edge beveled along one side (see *Figure 51*). It is used to make sharp bends and to form boxes and pans.

102F51.TIF

Figure 51 ◆ Hatchet stake.

11.6.0 Groover

The most common join, or seam, is the grooved seam. To make this seam, you fold the edge of one piece of metal down and fold the edge of a second piece of metal up. These folds, which are called locks, are of equal size on both pieces of metal. You hook the down-turned fold over the up-turned fold. Then you use a groover to lock the pieces in place.

The recessed end of the hand groover fits over the lock to form the grooved seam. You will groove, or set, the ends of each groove before finishing the rest of the seam. Groovers are made of tool steel. They come in widths ranging from $\frac{3}{32}$ inch to $\frac{19}{32}$ inch and are always $\frac{1}{16}$ inch wider than the finished lock.

11.7.0 Crimper

You often will have to insert one pipe into another pipe. But if both pipes have the same circumference, you must slightly reduce, or **crimp**, the edge of one pipe so that it will fit into the other. You will use the crimper to do this.

Crimpers are made in single-, three-, and five-blade varieties. You will probably use the single-blade crimper most often (see *Figure 52*).

CAUTION

Be careful not to overcrimp pipe. Overcrimping will make the piece too small for a proper fit.

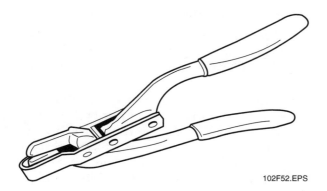

Figure 52 ◆ Single-blade crimper.

11.8.0 Snap Lock Punch

With the snap lock punch, you can create a raised area or button on a metal edge. Then you can snap one fitting into another. This tool is especially handy when you must cut off a premade snap lock fitting. With the snap lock punch, you can quickly fabricate a new edge to be snapped into place after the old edge has been cut away.

11.9.0 Duct Stretcher

Installing **drive slips** can sometimes be rather difficult because duct sections often resist coming together. The duct stretcher will help you make the proper fit (see *Figure 53*).

HANDLE   BARS   WHEELS

Figure 53 ◆ Duct stretcher.

Here is how the duct stretcher works. Slip the two wheels on the bar inside the drive flanges of each duct. Pull on the bar with one hand. This creates a lever action that draws each duct section closer together. When the two sections are together, use your other hand to install the drive slip. You can change the position of the wheels on the bar to handle different duct sizes.

Another useful tool is a locking duct stretcher. A wheel centered over the tool's arm produces a self-locking action. This tool leaves both hands free to align and install the duct.

11.10.0 Duct Holder

A duct holder keeps the duct in place between two joists while you install the duct hangers. It consists of two clamps with an adjustable length of beaded chain in between. Adjust the chain to the length you need and clamp the holder onto the joists bordering the duct. Duct holders can help you hold other installations in place, such as piping or conduit. You can also use the clamps for other clamping applications.

11.11.0 Duct Jack

A duct jack is used to lift sections of duct from the floor into place near the ceiling. It consists of a tabletop or platform mounted on a pole that can be extended to the desired height (see *Figure 54*). The duct jack is portable; the unit sits on a wheeled base. The pole may be manually operated or power operated. You must check the manufacturer's specifications for weight and height to ensure that you select the right jack for the application.

Figure 54 ◆ Duct jack.

12.0.0 ◆ WELDING TOOLS

As you have learned, sheet metal edges may be joined by mechanical methods, such as with a Pittsburgh lock machine. Sheet metal edges also may be joined by riveting or by welding. You will determine which method to use based on the thickness of the metal, fabrication cost, and available equipment. Generally, you will use mechanical seams to join light- and medium-gauge metal and welding to join heavier metal. Rivets are used on sheet metal that is too heavy for machine forming or whenever it is not practical to weld.

12.1.0 Safety and Maintenance

Follow these safety and maintenance rules when spot welding:

- Wear the appropriate personal protective equipment.
- Never work with welding equipment until you have received the proper training.
- Always follow the manufacturer's specifications and safety guidelines when setting up and operating welding equipment.
- Heated metals can give off toxic fumes. Make sure that your work area is properly ventilated. If the area cannot be ventilated, you must wear a protective respirator.
- Do not wear rolled-up sleeves, cuffs in trousers, or clothing with front pockets. Sparks may fall into and remain in these areas.
- Make sure your hands and clothing are free of grease, oil, or other flammable substances before operating welding equipment.

 WARNING!
Do not weld a workpiece on a concrete floor. Doing this can cause the concrete to explode with enough force to injure you.

12.2.0 Spot Welder

The electrically powered spot welder is designed to weld metal parts together very quickly at a single spot (see *Figure 55*). To operate this machine, you must clamp the metal pieces to be joined between the welder's two electrodes. When you turn the welder on, an electric current will attempt to pass from one electrode to the other. Because the metal between the electrodes acts as a resistor, heat is generated at the point of contact. For this reason, spot welders are also called *resistance welders*. The heat generated by the electrodes causes the metal to melt and fuse together.

 WARNING!
Spot welding produces heat and sparks. Be sure to always wear eye protection and heatproof gloves when spot welding.

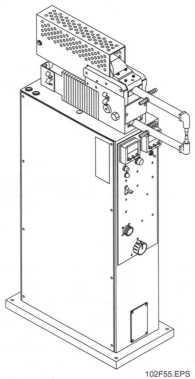

Figure 55 ◆ Spot welder.

102F55.EPS

 *Standing Seams*

It is not always necessary to spot weld standing seams. Standing seams can be locked using a button punch instead of a spot welder.

Spot welders are useful for such operations as attaching chimney caps to their mounting brackets, or wherever you must attach metal parts in places that are impractical for riveting or other joining methods.

12.3.0 Other Types of Welders

Other types of welding commonly used in sheet metal include **oxyacetylene welding**, **arc welding**, and **inert gas welding**. Each type requires a different tool and different techniques.

An oxyacetylene welder, also called a *gas welder*, consists of two tanks: one containing oxygen, the other containing acetylene. These two gases are fed into a torch that produces a high-temperature flame to melt the metal. Gas welding is used chiefly to heat and bend heavy steel.

Arc welding works quickly compared with other welding techniques. An arc welder consists of two cables, one positive and one negative. A sheet metal worker connects one cable to the workpiece and the other cable to an arc-welding rod. An electric current moves through the rod, then jumps over a small gap to the workpiece, creating a spark that is hot enough to melt the metal and create a welded seam. Arc welding is used for almost all sheet metal welding applications.

The term *inert gas welding* describes a welding technique that combines arc welding and the use of an inert gas such as helium. The inert gas covers the arc and protects the metal from oxidation during the welding process. There are two common types of inert gas welding: TIG (tungsten inert gas) and MIG (metallic inert gas). Inert gas welding is used chiefly for stainless steel and aluminum welding.

You will learn more about these other types of welding tools and techniques as you progress in your apprenticeship training.

13.0.0 ◆ PRODUCTION AND COMPUTER-AIDED MACHINES

As you progress in your career, you also may work with production machines or computer-aided machines. These machines are used in large commercial and industrial applications. Examples of some of these machines are covered in this section.

13.1.0 Safety and Maintenance

Because many high-tech machines are designed for high-speed, high-volume production, safety is an important issue. These types of machines come with safety and maintenance instructions from the manufacturer. As you progress in your career and learn how to operate these machines, you will learn more about how to maintain them and operate them safely.

13.2.0 Coil Line

A **coil line** is a mechanical assembly line. It is used mainly for high-volume manufacturing or other heavy industrial applications (see *Figure 56*). The coil line works something like a newspaper printing press. If you have ever seen one of these printing presses in operation, you know that large rolls of paper get fed through a machine where articles and illustrations are imprinted. Rolls and gears inside the press align the pages to allow printing on both sides. By the time the paper reaches the end of the press, it has been printed, trimmed, and folded and is ready to be sent out to readers.

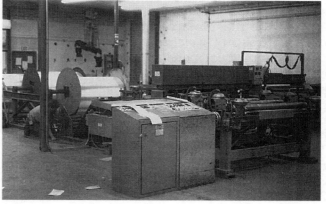

102F56.EPS

Figure 56 ◆ Coil line.

In the coil line, the bulk sheet metal rolls off a coil through a series of specialized machines and comes out as completely fabricated individual sections or fittings. A common use of coil lines is the fabrication of galvanized pipe.

Your tasks as a sheet metal apprentice might include handling the raw or finished materials that are processed by a coil line. But you will not be responsible for engineering, operating, or repairing the line.

13.3.0 Plasma Arc Cutting Machine

Today's sheet metal mechanics might use a computer to fabricate workpieces instead of using a shear or a brake. The plasma arc cutting machine may be found in shops that use high technology to reduce time and waste during fabricating operations (see *Figure 57*).

Figure 57 ◆ Plasma arc cutting machine.

These machines do for sheet metal fabrication what the computer-aided design (CAD) plotter does for drafting and engineering. A CAD system operator uses a computer to make drawings that a plotter prints onto blueprint-size paper. The CAD system's plotter looks like a plasma arc machine. In fact, the plasma arc machine is sometimes referred to as an *x-y plotter*.

In modern sheet metal applications, a standard or customized fitting is computer-generated. The plasma arc machine reads the design and cuts the fitting from a large sheet of metal using a rapidly moving torch. This torch produces a high-speed, high-temperature jet of ionized gas or plasma. The plasma cuts by melting and displacing material from the workpiece. The plasma temperature can range from 20,000°F to 50,000°F (11,000°C to 28,000°C).

One advantage of the plasma arc cutting machine is that it eliminates human error during the cutting process. It cuts the sheet metal exactly as shown on the computer layout. Of course, the computer layout must be carefully done and all dimensions correctly drawn because the computer will reproduce exactly what is programmed, mistakes and all.

Another advantage of the plasma arc cutting machine is that it can optimize the layout of the sheet, which saves material and reduces scrap. It moves directly from the design in the computer's memory to the cutting. It does not need scribed lines to make cuts.

13.4.0 Spiral Duct Machine

This machine produces circular duct to exact lengths. The main part of the machine is made of welded steel. Special steel alloys are used for other parts. Sheet metal is fed into the machine from a large coil. This process is similar to the way thread is fed into a sewing machine but on a much larger scale. The metal then passes through a series of rollers made from high-grade tempered steel. Forming heads made of aluminum shape the metal into spiral duct. The machine can produce smooth, corrugated, or ribbed duct.

Depending on the type of machine, the spiral duct machine can cut, deburr, form, crimp, or seam the duct in one continuous operation. The operator uses an instrument panel to set up the machine for the length, thickness, and finished effect desired. As with most automated machines, the spiral duct machine is a time- and money-saver for large commercial and industrial applications.

14.0.0 ◆ MEASURING TOOLS

Measuring tools allow you to perform highly accurate measurements for close tolerances. Most modern measuring tools include both American and metric scales. Others may contain only one scale specific to the measurement task.

14.1.0 Safety and Maintenance

Used properly, measuring tools are not dangerous. However, you should handle them carefully. After all, a steel square that is carelessly set down could fall on your foot and the sharp corner can cause a lot of pain. So follow your basic common sense for safety and follow these maintenance rules when using measuring tools:

- Avoid dropping your steel rule. Never bang it on any surface or use it as a pry bar or hammer or for any purpose other than the one it is designed for.
- Keep your measuring tools clean and free of dirt and oil.
- Store your measuring tools neatly to keep them from getting nicked or damaged.
- Replace any measuring tools that have been damaged to the point that you can no longer use them properly.
- Always check to make sure that you have chosen a sheet metal gauge and not a wire gauge to measure sheet metal thickness.

14.2.0 Steel Rule

The flexible steel rule is sometimes also called a machinist's rule. Because it is used to measure close dimensions in layout and development, you should handle it carefully to keep the edges from being nicked or worn. The types in common use are the pocket-size 6-inch rule, the 12-inch rule, and the 48-inch rule. For lengths greater than 48 inches, steel tapes are used.

The edges of the steel rule are divided by fine lines into different parts of an inch such as 8ths, 16ths, 32nds, and 64ths. Some rules are divided into 10ths and 100ths of an inch.

14.3.0 Circumference Rule

You can use the upper edge of a circumference rule (see *Figure 58*) in the same way that you would use an ordinary rule. You use the lower edge to quickly see the circumference of any circle. For example, a circle with a diameter of 6 inches would be 18⅞ inches in circumference.

The reverse side of the rule contains tables that show sizes of containers, dry and liquid measures, and container capacity computing rules. The circumference rule is available in 36-inch or 48-inch lengths.

14.4.0 Steel Square

The steel square is shaped like the letter L (see *Figure 59*). The two sides of the L, called the blade and the tongue, form a right angle. Both are marked off in inches and fractions of inches. The square is made of hardened steel. You will use it to measure right angles and to check squareness. It is available in various sizes and is a useful tool for layout and pattern drafting.

14.5.0 Combination Square

The combination square is a steel rule with attachments that greatly increase its versatility (see *Figure 60*). In addition to the rule, it has a sliding try square head that combines a miter and a level. A combination square can serve as a rule, square, miter, depth gauge, level, or height gauge.

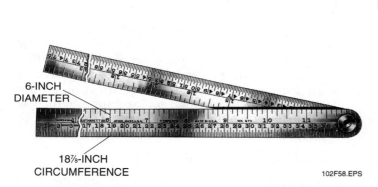

6-INCH DIAMETER

18⅞-INCH CIRCUMFERENCE

102F58.EPS

Figure 58 ◆ Circumference rule.

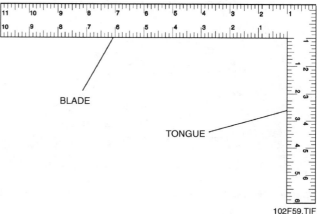

BLADE

TONGUE

102F59.TIF

Figure 59 ◆ Steel square.

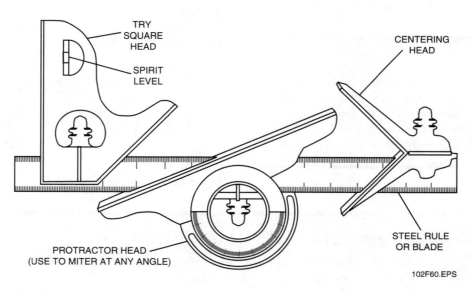

TRY SQUARE HEAD

SPIRIT LEVEL

CENTERING HEAD

STEEL RULE OR BLADE

PROTRACTOR HEAD (USE TO MITER AT ANY ANGLE)

102F60.EPS

Figure 60 ◆ Combination square.

A centering head that can replace the try square head is also available. Thus, the combination square can be used for indicating the centers of shafts and cylindrical pieces and for measuring the diameter of cylinder bores.

Another accessory is the variable head protractor (bevel protractor). This accessory further increases the versatility of the combination square because it allows any angle to be measured. The variable head protractor is divided into degrees; once you have fastened the rule to it, you can lay out or measure any angle.

14.6.0 Basic Protractor

You will use the basic protractor to measure and lay out angles (see *Figure 61*). The protractor is divided into 180 degrees with every 10 degrees designated by two figures. The outer figure shows the angle measures starting at the left, and the inner figure shows the angle measures starting at the right.

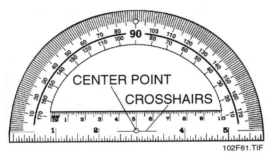

Figure 61 ◆ Basic protractor.

The swinging blade protractor is a modification of the basic protractor. You set the blade with a lock nut. You can use this protractor as a small T-square and for setting bevels and transferring angles.

CAUTION

Always check the gauge you're using to be sure it is a sheet metal gauge and *not* a metal gauge designed to measure wire thicknesses. Some wire gauges measure differently than sheet metal gauges do. Be careful not to get the two confused.

14.7.0 Feeler Gauge

You will use the feeler gauge to measure small gaps or clearances between objects that you cannot measure in any other way (see *Figure 62*). It is most often used for machine setup. The feeler gauge, also called a thickness gauge, contains many thin steel blades that fan out from a handle. To use it, try blades of various thicknesses until one (or more) snugly fills the gap you are measuring.

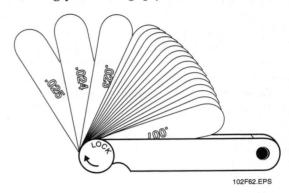

Figure 62 ◆ Feeler gauge.

A number on each blade shows the blade thickness in thousandths of an inch, in millimeters, or both. If you must use more than one blade to fill a gap, add the measures of all blades to arrive at your total measurement. A modification of the feeler gauge is a stepped feeler gauge, which is often called a **no-go gauge.**

14.8.0 Sheet Metal Gauge

The thickness of metals you use is designated by a series of numbers called gauges. Often, the thickness of the metal is marked on the metal sheet. When it is not, you must use a sheet metal gauge to determine the thickness. The United States Standard Gauge is most commonly used for iron and steel sheets (see *Figure 63*).

Figure 63 ◆ Sheet metal gauge.

Riveting **Ideas**

Sheet Metal and Plate Metal

Metal is considered sheet metal when its thickness is less than ⅛ inch. When its thickness is ⅛ inch or greater, it is considered plate metal.

The thickness of each gauge in decimal equivalents of an inch is marked on the back of the gauge. The U.S. Standard Gauge numbers are marked opposite the series of slots on the front of the gauge.

To determine the gauge of sheet metal, slide each slot over the sheet until you get a snug fit. When you measure galvanized or other coated metals, remember that the reading will be 1 gauge thicker because of the coating. Therefore, the gauge of coated metal is always 1 gauge less than the gauge shown on the slot where it fits most snugly.

15.0.0 ◆ LAYOUT TOOLS

When you lay out sheet metal, you will mark lines, circles, and arcs on the surface. You get the pattern from a working drawing and transfer it to the metal. The layout shows how much metal to cut away and where to cut it. Laying out a pattern on sheet metal is a lot like making a mechanical drawing on paper. The tools you will use to mark the lines are the **straightedge**, scratch awl, scriber, and trammel.

15.1.0 Safety and Maintenance

Follow these safety and maintenance rules when using layout tools:

- When grinding the points of a scriber, always wear safety goggles.
- Avoid dropping your straightedge. Never bang it on any surface or use it as a pry bar or hammer or for any purpose other than the one it is designed for.
- Never carry scribers, scratch awls, dividers, or trammels in your pockets. The sharp points can jab you.
- Never toss a layout tool to a co-worker.
- Always hand a tool to a co-worker with the pointed end facing you so that your co-worker can grasp the tool by the handle.

- Never jab the ends of scratch awls or scribers into any material.
- Sharpen the points of scribers and scratch awls on an oilstone.
- Store your tools carefully to prevent them from becoming damaged.
- Place a piece of cork on the end of sharp tools for safe storage.

15.2.0 Straightedge

You will use a straightedge to lay out straight lines on flat metal surfaces. A straightedge is a steel strip that has been hardened, tempered, and ground to a fine degree of accuracy. It is unmarked (that is, not graduated with measurements), may be either beveled or unbeveled, and comes in lengths ranging from 12 inches to 72 inches.

15.3.0 Scratch Awl

You will use a scratch awl to mark guidelines on pieces of metal for layout work (see *Figure 64*). The awl is a piece of hardened steel from 6 inches to 10 inches long, usually with a ball handle. To use an awl to scribe straight lines, lay the straightedge flat or on its edge on the metal. Draw the awl across the surface of the metal, using the straightedge to guide you. This process is similar to drawing a straight line with a sharp pencil and a ruler. You must put enough pressure on the straightedge to hold it firmly in place, but not so much pressure that you force the straightedge out of alignment.

102F64.EPS

Figure 64 ◆ Scratch awl.

Layout Dye

Metal has a shiny surface that can make it hard to see layout lines. To make the lines easier to see, you can coat the metal with a dye specially made for this purpose. Be sure to carefully clean the metal first to remove dirt, grease, or oil. Other types of coatings are also available, such as one made of chalk that is applied when working with hot-rolled steel.

15.4.0 Scribers

A sheet metal scriber is a convenient tool for scratching a line parallel to and equally distant from the straight perimeter of a metal sheet (see *Figure 65*). This scriber is adjustable for a variety of distances from the edge of the metal sheet—up to the maximum extension of the tool. You can use the locking cap to tighten down and hold the extension for as long as you need it.

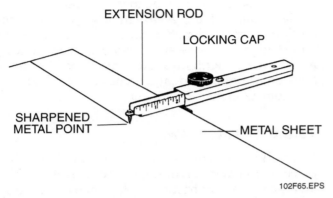

Figure 65 ◆ Sheet metal scriber.

A carbide-tipped scriber works like an awl and is often held and used like a pencil (see *Figure 66*). But instead of lead, it contains a sharp carbide-tipped rod designed to scratch layout lines on sheet metal. Retractable models are available that can be clipped inside your shirt pocket.

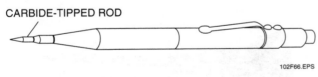

Figure 66 ◆ Carbide-tipped scriber.

15.5.0 Trammel

You can lay out large circles or areas with a large radius by using a trammel (see *Figure 67*). The trammel is made of two steel points attached to heads. You can adjust each head to slide along a trammel beam that may be made of wood or metal. The heads are held in place by thumb-screws. You can replace either one of the points and heads with a pencil holder and pencil for layout work on paper. You can use the small locknut on one of the points for more accurate settings.

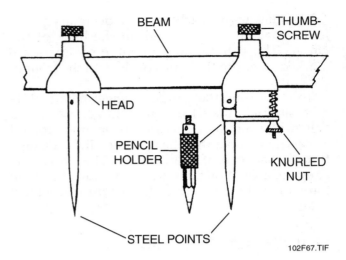

Figure 67 ◆ Trammel.

You also can use the trammel to measure extended distance. The size of the circle or arc you want to scribe, or the distance you want to measure, depends only on the length of the beam.

16.0.0 ◆ DRAFTING TOOLS

Computer-generated drawings have replaced drafting by hand for large commercial and some residential projects. However, some drawings are still made with drafting tools. It will be helpful to learn what tools are used and how to use them. The basic drafting equipment can be found at an art store or an office supply store (see *Figure 68*).

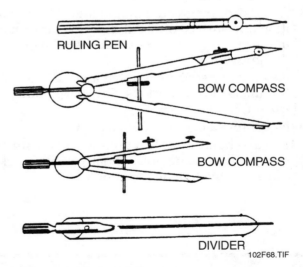

Figure 68 ◆ Basic drafting equipment.

Use tracing paper for rough sketching or to work out designs. You can then lay fresh sheets of tracing paper over your base drawing to make refinements. To control proportions, use cross section or graph paper.

16.1.0 Safety and Maintenance

Used properly, drafting tools are not dangerous but you should treat these tools as you would any other tool. Don't toss them to co-workers or use them for anything except for what they are designed to do. Follow these maintenance rules for drafting tools:

• Protect the surface of your drawing board from knife cuts.

• Don't use your T-square as a hammer or lever. Keep the edges from becoming nicked or worn.

• Store your drafting tools in the case provided by the manufacturer and periodically clean them.

16.2.0 Drawing Board

A drawing board is designed to hold paper, cloth, or film flat and to allow you to draw straight lines. The guiding edges of a good drawing board have metal, hardwood, or plastic strips to provide a true guiding edge. Drawing boards are available in portable, tabletop, and floor models.

16.3.0 T-square

T-squares are made of stainless steel, hard aluminum, plastic, or a combination of wood and plastic (see *Figure 69*). You should use T-squares with blades made of stainless steel or hard aluminum when making precision drawings. The

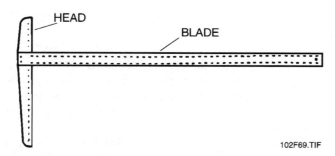

102F69.TIF

Figure 69 ◆ T-square.

hard metal resists wear and will allow you to draw fine lines. To use a T-square, line up the head along the edge of your drawing board. This will give you a base for drawing straight horizontal lines.

16.4.0 Wing Divider

The wing divider is a handheld steel instrument with two pointed legs. These points can be adjusted with a small screw set between the legs. Wing dividers are used to scribe circles and parts of circles and to measure distances.

16.5.0 Compass

Most of the curved lines in drawings are circles or parts of circles (arcs), which you can draw with a compass. Like a wing divider, a compass has two legs. You can adjust the point on one leg to hold a sharpened piece of graphite or a ruling pen point. You hold a compass by pinching it between your thumb and index finger (see *Figure 70*). To draw a circle, set the compass to one-half of the diameter of the circle. For example, if you want to draw a circle with a diameter of 4 inches, set the compass to 2 inches.

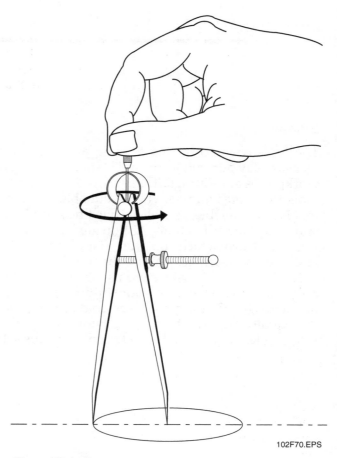

102F70.EPS

Figure 70 ◆ Compass.

1. A seam in which a single flange is inserted into a pocket is called a _____.
   a. Pittsburgh lock
   b. snap lock
   c. button lock
   d. New York lock

2. The _____ is a faster method for assembling sheet metal parts because you don't need to hammer over edges to complete the seam.
   a. Pittsburgh lock
   b. inverted lock or reverse lock
   c. button lock or snap lock
   d. New York lock

3. A _____ stiffens sheet metal to keep it from noisily vibrating.
   a. slip and drive machine
   b. beading machine or cross brake
   c. roll-forming machine or slip-roll machine
   d. turning machine

4. The feeler gauge is also called a _____.
   a. wire gauge
   b. sheet metal gauge
   c. metal coating gauge
   d. thickness gauge

5. You can lay out large circles or areas with a large radius by using a _____.
   a. trammel
   b. scriber
   c. protractor
   d. compass

Summary

The tools covered in this module will help you measure, lay out, cut, form, and install sheet metal workpieces and fittings. These tools include hand tools that you will use when a suitable machine tool is not available, as well as machine shop tools and computer-aided tools. As you gain experience you will learn which tools to select for the task and you will learn how to use them properly.

Knowing how to select and use the right tool is only one part of your responsibility as a sheet metal mechanic. Many tools can be dangerous, so it is equally important for you to know and follow safety rules in the machine shop and on the job site. You must think safety first—and always. Take the time to learn how to use your tools safely to prevent injury to you and to your co-workers by reading and following the manufacturer's safety instructions.

Finally, the quality of your finished workpiece will be affected by the condition of your tools, so taking good care of your tools is important. You will get plenty of advice on how to maintain your tools from the companies that make them. It is your responsibility to read, understand, and follow those guidelines. Remember: If you take care of your tools, they will take care of you.

Robert T. Monastra

Owner
Sheet Metal Duct Inc.
Clifton Heights, Pennsylvania

Robert Monastra grew up in Drexel Hill, a suburb of Philadelphia, and attended Upper Darby High School. Rob entered the sheet metal field at the age of 16, while attending the HVAC Vocational/Technical School at Folcroft Vocational School and doing side jobs. After completing high school, Rob took trade-related courses at night. At the age of just 21, he started his first residential heating and air conditioning company. Rob holds heat pump, refrigerator recovery, and auto-CAD certifications. Today, he is owner of Sheet Metal Duct Inc.

How did you become interested in this industry?
Various members of my family had been involved in the heating and air conditioning industry. I took an immediate liking to it and enjoyed a sense of accomplishment. Shortly after finishing my apprenticeship, I started my own company, doing residential work. Once I mastered that, I began to seek out commercial work to expand my business. My first large project was a high school. I fabricated duct by hand during the day and installed it at night. As the company grew, I purchased advanced cutting machinery, hired more mechanics, and began to take on larger projects. Now my company also manufactures specialty duct for resale to other contractors and suppliers.

What do you think it takes to be a success in your trade?
It takes hard work, patience, and pride in workmanship, as well as an ability to stay current with technology, and the desire to continue to reinvest in your company.

What are some things you do on the job?
I do a little bit of everything, including estimating, purchasing, supervising, design, layout, and engineering.

What do you like most about your job?
I appreciate the rewards of a job done right. I hate going on a job and seeing that it wasn't done properly. Financial success is important, but it's more important that a job be done right and look right. This industry is never stagnant, so I am always growing and learning. That's what keeps my interest strong. There's always another hurdle. I like to continue to accomplish new things, and this industry has allowed me to do that.

What would you say to someone entering the trade today?
Stay focused, be patient, be willing to learn, and work hard. Put the quality of your work first. Financial gains will follow once you have mastered your trade. You can never stop learning and growing in this industry. True craftsmen are hard to find and, therefore, will always be rewarded.

Trade Terms Introduced in This Module

Apron: A covering plate that encloses and protects a machine.

Arc welding: A technique used to join metal; it uses an electric current to produce heat that makes the metal melt and fuse together.

Ball peen hammer: A striking tool with a round, slightly curved face and round ball part.

Brake: A machine used in sheet metal work to make bends and folds on metal edges.

Coil line: A mechanical assembly line used for high-volume production manufacturing.

Cold chisel: A metal tool with a sharp, beveled edge that is used to cut cold metal.

Counterboring: The process of enlarging a hole to receive the head of a bolt or a nut.

Crimp: To reduce the end of a round pipe so that it can be slid into another pipe of the same circumference.

Dead-blow mallet: A mallet that conceals a small steel shot in its head that provides the striking power or dead blow.

Divider: A layout tool used to draw circles and arcs on metal.

Drive slip: The strip of metal that slips between two pieces of metal, acting as a connector, and is driven into place.

Hold-down bar: On a machine, a heavy bar that holds down the work to be cut or folded.

Inert gas welding: Any welding technique that uses a combination of arc welding and an inert gas (for example, helium, neon, or argon).

Kerf: The slot or opening made by a saw blade.

Lap: To overlap or partly cover one surface with another, as in roof shingles.

Mushroom: The general shape of the head of a tool that is overly flattened by use.

Nibbler: A machine that punches out metal notches against a die.

No-go gauge: A measuring tool that is used to check the diameter of a hole.

Notcher: A tool that makes angled cuts. It is used to cut out trays, boxes, and pans.

Ogee bead: A double curve resembling an S-shape.

Oxyacetylene welding: A method used to join metal; it combines acetylene and oxygen to produce heat that melts the metal and fuses it together.

Peripheral speed: The speed at which a drill rotates. It is measured in feet per minute.

Pitch: The number of teeth per inch in a saw blade.

Pittsburgh lock: A seam that consists of two parts: a single lock and a pocket lock. Also called a *Pittsburgh seam.*

Pittsburgh seam: See *Pittsburgh lock.*

Punch: A tool used to make indentations or holes in sheet metal.

Reaming: The process of improving the accuracy and finish of a drilled hole.

Ring and circle shear: A machine designed to cut circles in sheet metal.

Riveting hammer: A striking tool designed to reduce the possibility of marring the metal. The head has a square face and beveled edges.

Seam: Where two pieces of sheet metal join at the edges.

Setting hammer: A hammer with a square, flat face that is used to flatten seams without damaging the metal.

Slip-roll forming machine: A machine that uses three rolls to form sheet metal into cylindrical or conical shapes.

Snips: A hand tool used for cutting a layout from sheet metal.

Spotfacing: The process of machining a circular spot on the surface of a workpiece to provide a flat surface to support a bolthead or nuthead.

Squaring shear: A machine that is used to cut sheet or plate metal. It is also used to square and trim large metal sheets.

Stake: A metal tool that allows a sheet metal worker to make many different kinds of bends by hand.

Step drill: A drill that can drill a large hole in one pass, eliminating the need for pilot holes.

Straightedge: A tool used to lay out straight lines on flat surfaces.

Temper: The hardness and strength of rolled metal.

Tooth set: A term that describes how the teeth in a saw blade are set. Individual teeth may alternate from side to side or rows of teeth may alternate from side to side.

Trammel: A layout tool with two scriber points, used to draw large circles and arcs.

Trunnion: A pin or pivot on which something, such as a handle, can be rotated or tilted.

Twist drill bit: A bit with one or more cutting grooves that spiral around the shank; used for drilling holes in metal and wood.

Uni-shear: A power-operated cutting tool that allows continuous cutting of metal with burr-free edges through a two-blade design.

Wired edges: These edges provide more strength and rigidity to a sheet metal edge.

Additional Resources

This module is intended to present thorough resources for task training. The following reference works are suggested for further study. These are optional materials for continued education rather than for task training.

Build Your Own Metalworking Shop from Scrap, 1982. David J. Gingery. Bradley, IL: Lindsay Publications.

The Drill Press, 1982. David J. Gingery. Bradley, IL: Lindsay Publications.

Working Sheet Metal, 1993. David J. Gingery. Bradley, IL: Lindsay Publications.

Acknowledgments/Figure Credits

Sheet Metal, 1995. Leo A. Meyer. Homewood, IL: American Technical Publishers, Inc.

American Tool Companies, Inc.	102F13, 102F14, 102F15, 102F16, 102F17, 102F18, 102F19, 102F32
Chicago Heights Furnace Supply Co.	102F21, 102F30
DeWalt Industrial Tool Company	102F27, 102F29
The Flagler Corporation	102F40, 102F41
Klein Tools, Inc.	102F01, 102F02, 102F05
The L. S. Starrett Co.	102F58, 102F62
The Lockformer Company	102F34
Malco Products, Inc.	102F53, 102F69
Miller Electric Manufacturing Company	102F55

Milwaukeee Electric Tool Corp.	102F24, 102F25, 102F28
New York State Education Department	102F20, 102F23, 102F33, 102F37, 102F63, 102F65, 102F67
Niagara Machine and Tool Works	102F38
Ricky Sonnier of Gulfside Mechanical/Comfort Systems USA	102F36
Parrott Mechanical, Inc.	102F56
Roper Whitney of Rockford, Illinois	102F22, 102F42, 102F45
Stanley Tools	102F06, 102F07, 102F08, 102F09, 102F10, 102F11, 102F26, 102F31, 102F64
Superior Pneumatic Company	102F04
Vermette Machine Company, Inc.	102F54
W. A. Whitney Company	102F57

NCCER CRAFT TRAINING USER UPDATES

The NCCER makes every effort to keep these textbooks up-to-date and free of technical errors. We appreciate your help in this process. If you have an idea for improving this textbook, or if you find an error, a typographical mistake, or an inaccuracy in the NCCER's Craft Training textbooks, please write us, using this form or a photocopy. Be sure to include the exact module number, page number, a detailed description, and the correction, if applicable. Your input will be brought to the attention of the Technical Review Committee. Thank you for your assistance.

Instructors – If you found that additional materials were necessary in order to teach this module effectively, please let us know so that we may include them in the Equipment and Materials list in the Instructor's Guide.

Write: Curriculum Revision and Development Department
National Center for Construction Education and Research
P.O. Box 141104, Gainesville, FL 32614-1104

Fax: 352-334-0932

E-mail: curriculum@nccer.org

Craft _____ Module Name _____

Copyright Date _____ Module Number _____ Page Number(s) _____

Description _____

_____

_____

_____

(Optional) Correction _____

_____

_____

(Optional) Your Name and Address _____

_____

_____

Fasteners, Hangers, and Supports

COURSE MAP

This course map shows all of the modules in the first level of the Sheet Metal curriculum. The suggested training order begins at the bottom and proceeds up. Skill levels increase as you advance on the course map. The local Training Program Sponsor may adjust the training order.

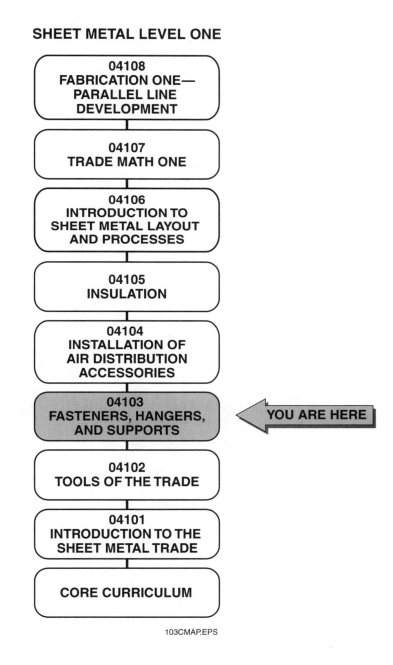

SHEET METAL LEVEL ONE

04108
FABRICATION ONE—
PARALLEL LINE
DEVELOPMENT

04107
TRADE MATH ONE

04106
INTRODUCTION TO
SHEET METAL LAYOUT
AND PROCESSES

04105
INSULATION

04104
INSTALLATION OF
AIR DISTRIBUTION
ACCESSORIES

04103
FASTENERS, HANGERS,
AND SUPPORTS   ◁ **YOU ARE HERE**

04102
TOOLS OF THE TRADE

04101
INTRODUCTION TO THE
SHEET METAL TRADE

CORE CURRICULUM

103CMAP.EPS

Copyright © 2001 National Center for Construction Education and Research, Gainesville, FL 32614-1104. All rights reserved. No part of this work may be reproduced in any form or by any means, including photocopying, without written permission of the publisher.

Figures

Tables

Fasteners, Hangers, and Supports

Objectives

When you finish this module, you will be able to do the following:

1. Identify and describe the various kinds of fasteners used in the sheet metal trade.
2. Select and use the right fastener for the task.
3. Describe some of the more common methods of supporting air system components.
4. Install duct fasteners, hangers, and supports.

Prerequisites

Before you begin this module, it is recommended that you successfully complete the following modules: Core Curriculum; Sheet Metal Level One, Modules 04101 and 04102.

Required Trainee Materials

1. Pencil and paper
2. Appropriate personal protective equipment

1.0.0 ◆ INTRODUCTION

Concealed in the walls and ceilings of residential and commercial buildings is a system of ducts that delivers heated and cooled air and provides ventilation. These systems can be fairly simple or highly complex.

All of the components of an air distribution system must be held together and fastened properly in place to withstand various loads and stresses. Sheet metal mechanics use a wide variety of fasteners (screws, nuts, bolts, and rivets) to join sheet metal parts and to fasten those parts into place. In this module, you will learn about the characteristics of these fasteners so that you can decide which fastener will work best for the task at hand.

Air distribution system components (ducts, fans, and diffusers) are held in place by a system of hangers and supports. In this module, you will also learn about proper spacing of hangers, load ratings, and how to install hangers and support systems.

2.0.0 ◆ BOLTS AND SCREWS

You will use bolts and screws to fasten parts that need to be able to be quickly unfastened and reassembled for repairs or adjustments. Bolts are tightened with wrenches or screwdrivers and require a nut and a washer to hold them in place. Usually, screws are tightened in place with a screwdriver; however, some types of screws have heads that require **Allen wrenches**.

Semi-finished and rough-finished screws and bolts are pressed, hammered, rolled, or punched from hot or cold metal. Finished screws are cut from a bar of steel by an automatic lathe.

Screws and bolts consist of a head and a shaft that is partly or totally threaded with external (outside) threads. External threads are also called *A threads*. Internal (inside) threads, which are found on nuts, are called *B threads*. Screws and bolts (see *Figure 1*) are classified by the following characteristics:

- Length
- Diameter
- Pitch
- Length of thread
- Size of fastening tool required
- Tensile strength

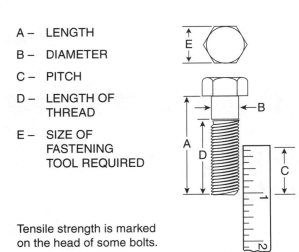

A – LENGTH

B – DIAMETER

C – PITCH

D – LENGTH OF THREAD

E – SIZE OF FASTENING TOOL REQUIRED

Tensile strength is marked on the head of some bolts.

103F01.EPS

Figure 1 ◆ Characteristics of fasteners.

Except for flat-head screws and bolts, the fastener head is not included when measuring length. Diameter, or thickness, is expressed in fractions of an inch. Pitch refers to the number of threads per inch. The length of the thread refers to the total distance covered by the threaded shaft. The size of the fastening tool required refers to the size of screwdriver or wrench needed to fasten the bolt or screw in place. Tensile strength refers to the amount of stress a fastener can withstand before breaking.

2.1.0 Thread Pitch Measurement

You can measure thread pitch with a standard rule or with a thread pitch gauge. There are two thread measurement designations: **National Coarse (NC)** and **National Fine (NF)**. See *Table 1* for a sample of how this designation looks. It is possible to have two fasteners of the same diameter with different thread designation numbers. Fasteners with a lower number of threads per inch are designated *coarse*, and fasteners with a higher number of threads per inch are designated *fine*.

Table 1 National Coarse and National Fine Thread Designations

Fastener	National Coarse Threads per Inch	National Fine Threads per Inch
1/4 inch	20	28
1/2 inch	13	20
3/4 inch	10	16

DID YOU KNOW?
A Brief History of Fasteners

Archimedes, a famous mathematician and inventor, invented the concept of the screw in the third century B.C.E. But you could not use his invention to fasten anything. It was a motion device used to pump water or to raise heavy weights. In fact, his concept for the water pump is still used today in low-lift industrial applications.

Around the first century B.C.E., people started using wooden screws to put pressure on objects—for example, to press grapes into wine or to operate a clothes press. A worker placed a spike in the head of the screw to turn it. This type of screw is most like the fastening devices used today. The external thread was made by hand filing. The internal thread, which would have made nuts possible, had not yet been developed.

Metal screws and nuts appeared around the 15th century. A worker could use a box wrench to turn the screw head, which had a square or hexagonal shape. Many fastening devices were used to create weapons and armor. The next time you visit a museum, take a closer look at a suit of armor. Study how those metal pieces were formed and fastened together.

2.2.0 Bolt Thread Class

In addition to the fastener designations noted earlier, bolt threads are further classified by series, which indicate the closeness of the fit between a bolt and a nut. There are three series:

- Class 1: loosest fit between threads
- Class 2: intermediate fit
- Class 3: very close fit

2.3.0 Tensile Strength

Tensile strength, which is measured in pounds per square inch, is the pull in pounds that a rod with a 1-inch cross section can withstand before it breaks. High-strength fasteners are very expensive and are used only where additional strength is required. For example, bolts used to attach wings to jet aircraft can cost several thousand dollars each.

2.4.0 Types of Screws and Bolts

A wide variety of bolts and screws is available for construction work. These different types of fasteners have been developed to suit specific job requirements. The job may require that wood be fastened to wood, that metal be fastened to metal, or that wood be fastened to metal. Strength requirements, cost of materials, and the finished look desired are additional factors in choosing the right fastener. Generally, the job specifications will indicate the types and sizes of fastener to be used. The types of screws and bolts commonly used in sheet metal work are described in the following sections.

2.4.1 Carriage Bolt

The carriage bolt (see *Figure 2*) has a round head. The unthreaded area immediately below the head is square. The square area is designed to sink into the wood when the bolt is tightened and prevent the bolt from turning as the nut is attached. Carriage bolts usually have a coarse thread and are used chiefly to fasten wood to metal.

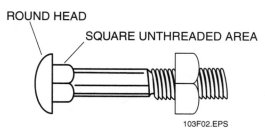

ROUND HEAD
SQUARE UNTHREADED AREA

103F02.EPS

Figure 2 ◆ Carriage bolt.

2.4.2 Machine Bolt

The machine bolt is made of low-carbon steel (see *Figure 3*). It comes in a wide range of sizes and can be as large as ⅜ of an inch in diameter. The bolt shaft may have either a coarse or a fine thread.

Machine bolts are used chiefly to attach parts and fixtures that do not require bolts with high-tensile strength. They are also used to assemble parts that do not require close **tolerances.**

2.4.3 Stove Bolt

The stove bolt (see *Figure 4*) may have either a round or a flat head that includes a screwdriver slot. Stove bolts are commonly used in the sheet metal shop.

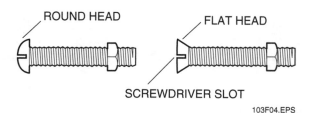

ROUND HEAD   FLAT HEAD

SCREWDRIVER SLOT

103F04.EPS

Figure 4 ◆ Stove bolts.

2.4.4 Stud Bolt

The stud bolt (see *Figure 5*) is headless and is threaded on both ends. One end is threaded into a fixture. You can place a nut on the other end to fasten fabricated assemblies to a fixture.

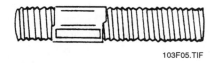

103F05.TIF

Figure 5 ◆ Stud bolt.

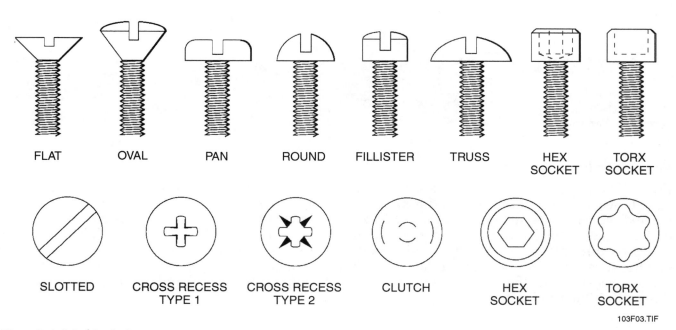

FLAT   OVAL   PAN   ROUND   FILLISTER   TRUSS   HEX SOCKET   TORX SOCKET

SLOTTED   CROSS RECESS TYPE 1   CROSS RECESS TYPE 2   CLUTCH   HEX SOCKET   TORX SOCKET

103F03.TIF

Figure 3 ◆ Machine bolts.

2.4.5 Cap Screw

The cap screw (see *Figure 6*) usually has a hex head, although other head shapes are available. Cap screws are used chiefly to hold parts onto a fixture with internal threads. You insert the screw through a hole in one piece and screw it into a threaded hole in the other piece. Cap screws are also used when both sides of a workpiece are not easily accessible. Cap screws can be either coarse thread or fine thread and range in size from ¼ inch to 2 inches.

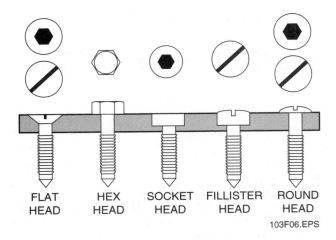

FLAT HEAD   HEX HEAD   SOCKET HEAD   FILLISTER HEAD   ROUND HEAD

103F06.EPS

Figure 6 ◆ Cap screw and available heads.

2.4.6 Lag Screw

The lag screw (see *Figure 7*) is shaped and threaded like a wood screw, but it is heavier and usually has a square head. Lag screws are used chiefly for heavy work such as attaching machines to floors or walls.

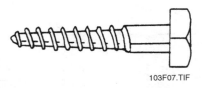

103F07.TIF

Figure 7 ◆ Lag screw.

2.4.7 Self-Tapping Screw

The self-tapping screw, one of the most widely used fasteners in the sheet metal industry, has a tapered end with slots cut into it (see *Figure 8*). This design allows the screw to cut its own threads as it is driven through the metal. One kind of self-tapping screw is called the drill-and-tap screw. It drills its own hole and then cuts its own thread. So it is a self-drilling and self-tapping screw.

Self-tapping screws are also called sheet metal screws. They are chiefly used to join parts that cannot be riveted. Self-tapping screws are sized by gauge (larger screws are sized in fractions). They are made with various types of heads, including the round head, binding or pan head, flat head, oval head, and hex head. Some self-drilling and self-tapping screws are fitted with sealing or lock washers to provide watertight joints.

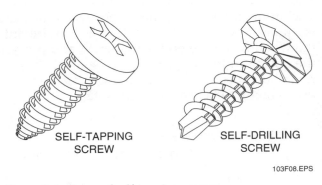

SELF-TAPPING SCREW   SELF-DRILLING SCREW

103F08.EPS

Figure 8 ◆ Types of self-tapping screws.

2.4.8 Setscrew

The setscrew (see *Figure 9*) may be headless or have a round or square head. Headless setscrews have either a hexagonal socket head or a screwdriver slot machined into them. Setscrews with heads may have socket, slotted, fluted, or square tops. You can turn socket-head setscrews with an Allen wrench.

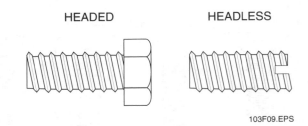

HEADED   HEADLESS

103F09.EPS

Figure 9 ◆ Headless and headed setscrews.

Setscrews are **case hardened** and are chiefly used to hold pulleys and keep them from slipping on shafts. They also hold collars on shafts and hold shafts in place. They are available with flat, oval, cone-shaped, half-dog, full-dog, or cup points. The half- and full-dog points are flat, rectangular points of slightly different lengths.

2.4.9 Wood Screw

The wood screw (see *Figure 10*) may have a flat, round, or oval head. The heads are machined so that they can be turned with a screwdriver. The screw shaft is tapered, which allows the screw to cut its own threads as it is driven through the workpiece. Wood screws are used chiefly to fasten metal parts to wood or to fasten wood to wood.

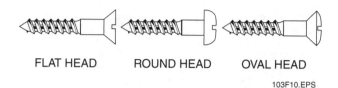

FLAT HEAD   ROUND HEAD   OVAL HEAD

103F10.EPS

Figure 10 ◆ Wood screws with various heads.

Wood screws may be made of steel, brass, or aluminum. They come in a wide variety of lengths and are sized by gauge. The gauge number indicates the thickness of the screw. The higher the gauge number, the thicker the screw—for example, a Number 12 screw has a larger diameter than a Number 8 screw.

3.0.0 ◆ NUTS

Machine bolt nuts are designed for speedy fastening and for locking parts together. The size of the nut you select is determined by the diameter of the bolt, not by the diameter of the tightening tool. For example, a ½-inch nut fits on a bolt that is ½ inch in diameter even though you may need to use a ¾-inch wrench or socket for tightening.

Square nuts are used with stove bolts, carriage bolts, and machine bolts. Hex-head nuts are used with hex-head bolts.

There are several types of nuts. Each works in a slightly different way to fasten a unit. The interference nut has a soft metal or fiber collar that jams the threads of the bolt, which prevents the nut from working loose. The jam nut has vertical cuts in its upper section that narrow or taper the upper portion of the nut. Thus, the upper bolt threads jam tightly against the nut threads and lock the nut into place. The pal nut is a spring-steel threaded nut that provides a locking action when turned down on the companion nut. The castellated nut has machined slots that allow you to insert a **cotter pin** through the slots into the bolt and out the other side. The cotter pin, made of soft steel, is then bent around the nut. Doing this holds the cotter pin in place and prevents the nut from turning.

3.1.0 Self-Locking Nuts

Stress or vibration can cause fasteners to loosen over time. In applications where stress or vibration are factors, you must use a self-locking nut. The chief purpose of all lock-type nuts is to prevent a fastened unit from loosening so that parts will not fall off.

Some of these nuts have a built-in locking fixture. This is a slot cut in the side so that, when the nut is tightened, the separated sections of the thread pull together and lock the nut on the bolt. Other types of self-locking nuts have machined slots to allow you to insert pins.

4.0.0 ◆ WASHERS

Washers, also called lock washers, hold or lock nuts or bolts in place. A split-ring washer is shown in *Figure 11*. Like nuts, washers help prevent a fastened unit from being loosened by vibration. There are two types of locking washers: the *helical spring type* and the *tooth type*. The helical spring type resembles a coil spring. It acts as a take-up device between the screw or nut and the workpiece. Spring-type washers are available in light, regular (medium), heavy, and extra-heavy types. They are made of hardened steel and are available for screws and bolts, ranging in size from .086 inches to 3 inches in diameter.

103F11.TIF

Figure 11 ◆ Split-ring washer.

Tooth-type washers (see *Figure 12*) are also made of hardened steel and are designed to wedge into the bearing surface between nuts, bolts, cap screws, and the workpiece. Commonly used tooth-type washers include the external, internal, internal-external, and countersunk types.

EXTERNAL   INTERNAL   INTERNAL-EXTERNAL   COUNTER-SUNK

103F12.EPS

Figure 12 ◆ Tooth-type washers.

Preassembled screw and washer assemblies called **prems** have a washer that fits loosely beneath the screw head. An expanded thread diameter on these assemblies keeps the washer from falling off. Sheet metal workers frequently use prems to quickly assemble sheet metal parts and metal buildings.

5.0.0 ◆ STRUCTURAL FASTENERS

You often will have to fasten metal or ductwork to concrete, steel, or wood structures. One way to do this is by using a powder-actuated fastening tool. This tool can be a time saver on large commercial projects. You will learn more about this tool and its fasteners later in this module. Other ways to fasten metal or ductwork to structures are discussed in this section.

5.1.0 Concrete Inserts

Concrete inserts are used mainly on projects where the duct layout is simple and where there is enough lead time in which to determine accurate placement. Lead time is needed because the insert must be placed before the concrete is poured. The simplest insert is a flat bar with an L-shaped bend (see *Figure 13*).

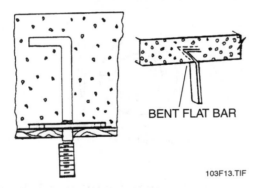

BENT FLAT BAR

103F13.TIF

Figure 13 ◆ Concrete inserts.

5.2.0 Concrete Fasteners

Concrete fasteners are installed after the concrete has been poured. Because of this, you have more flexibility in working with these than with concrete inserts. Concrete fasteners include powder-actuated fasteners, expanding concrete anchors, threaded masonry anchors, and expansion shields. Expansion shields are light-duty fasteners that are used on small ducts. See *Figure 14* for an explanation of how masonry anchors work and for a description of loading conditions. See *Figure 15* for a partial list of the many different types of fasteners available from one manufacturer.

HOW MASONRY ANCHORS WORK

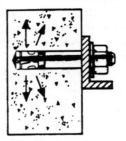 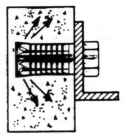

EXPANSION against the wall of the drilled hole.

UNDERCUTTING the masonry material at the base of the drilled hole.

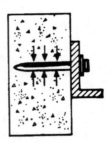 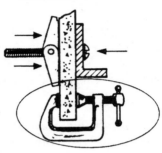

FRICTION between the fastener and the masonry material.

CLAMPING the item to be fastened to the masonry material.

LOADING CONDITIONS

STATIC or Dead Load . . . constant and unchanging.

DYNAMIC or Vibratory Load . . . intermittent and of varying intensity.

IMPACT or Shock Load . . . periodic load of substantial intensity.

TENSILE Load . . . direct axial load applied to installed anchor.

SHEAR Load . . . a load applied at a right angle to the installed anchor.

COMBINED Load . . . a load applied to the anchor at any angle between 0° and 90°.

CEILING . . . usually a direct axial (tensile) load.

WALL . . . usually either combined or shear load.

FLOOR . . . may be tensile, shear or combined load.

103F14.TIF

Figure 14 ◆ How masonry anchors work and loading conditions.

	ANCHOR TYPE	USE IN	USE WITH	MADE OF	SIZE RANGE	GENERAL INFORMATION
ONE/STEP ANCHORS						
	Rawl-Bolt®	Concrete, block, stone	No other fastener needed	Steel (grade 5 bolt)	¼"x1¾" to ¾"x8¼"	Finished hex head, removable, vibration-resistant.
	Rawl-Stud	Concrete, stone	No other fastener needed	Steel, 303 & 316 S.S., galvanized	¼" × 1¾" to 1¼" × 12"	Heavy duty one-piece expansion bolt. Custom lengths on special order.
	Lok/Bolt	Concrete, block, brick, stone	No other fastener needed	Steel	¼"x⅝" to ¾"x7½"	Pre-assembled, all-purpose anchor. 7 head styles, 6 diameters, 20 lengths.
	Rawl-Drive	Concrete, stone	No other fastener needed	Steel	³⁄₁₆" × 1" to ½" × 6"	One-piece expansion bolt. Heat-treated for maximum shear strength, 4 head styles.
	Spike®	Concrete, dense brick, stone	No other fastener needed	Steel	³⁄₁₆"x1" to ¼"x16"	Easy "Drill 'n Drive" installation. Vibration-resistant. Zinc plate or Perma-Seal®.
	Tapcon®	Concrete, block, brick	No other fastener needed	Steel	³⁄₁₆" × 1¼" to ¼" × 6"	Fast, easy to install. No hole spotting, removable, 2 head styles, 30 sizes.
	Zamac Nailin	Concrete, block, brick, stone	No other fastener needed	Zinc alloy and steel	³⁄₁₆" × ⅞" to ¼" × 2"	Pin drive anchor in mushroom or flat head styles. Available with S/S nails.
	Nylon Nailin	Concrete, block, brick, wallboard	No other fastener needed	Nylon and steel	³⁄₁₆" × 1" to ¼" × 6"	Pin drive anchor in 3 head styles. Available with S/S nails.
BOLT ANCHORS						
	Chem-Stud™	All solid masonry	Threaded rod, reinforcing bar	Polyester resin capsule, steel	⅜"x5⅛" to 1¼"x15"	Self-contained unit, shock resistant. Rapid curing.
	Calk-In	Concrete, brick, stone	Machine screw or bolt	Zinc alloy and lead	6-32 to ¾"-10	Single unit calking anchor, can be set shallow (flush) or deep in hole.
	Multi-Calk	Concrete, brick, stone	Machine screw or bolt	Zinc alloy and lead	½" to 1"	Heavy duty multi-unit calking anchor. Use with bolt head down for stud applications.
	Single	Concrete, brick, stone	Machine screw or bolt	Rustproof zinc alloy	¼" to ¾"	Non-calking bolt anchor, easy to install. Tightening bolt sets anchor.
	Double	Concrete, brick, stone	Machine screw or bolt	Rustproof zinc alloy	¼" to 1"	Heavy duty non-calking bolt anchor. ⅞" and 1" sizes in malleable iron.
	Saber-Tooth	Concrete	Machine screw or bolt	Steel	¼" to ⅞"	Self-drilling anchor, installed by power or manually.
	Steel Drop-In	Concrete, stone	Machine screw or bolt	Steel, Stainless Steel	¼" to ¾"	Heavy duty use in solid masonry. Internal plug cannot be lost.
SCREW ANCHORS						
	Rawlplug	All masonry material	Sheet metal, wood, lag screws	Jute fiber w. lead liner	#6 × ¾" to ⅜" × 3"	All-purpose screw anchor. 26 sizes. No hole spotting. Vibration-resistant.
	Lag Shield	Mortar joint, concrete	Lag bolt	Rustproof zinc alloy	¼" to ¾"	Available in short and long styles. Long style recommended for weaker masonry.
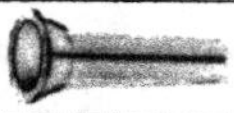	Scru-Lead	Concrete, block, brick	Sheet metal, wood, lag screws	Lead alloy	#6-8 × ¾" to # 16-18 × 1½"	Light duty, multi-size anchor. Use with static loads.
	Bantam Plug	Concrete, block, tile, brick	Sheet metal, wood, lag screws	Corrosion-resistant plastic	#6-8 × ¾" to #14-16 × 1½"	Light duty, multi-size anchor. Has collar for hollow materials.
HOLLOW WALL ANCHORS						
	Toggle Bolt	Block, wallboard, plaster	No other fastener needed	Steel, Stainless Steel	⅛" × 2" to ½" × 6"	Fully threaded machine screw. Four head styles.
	Rawly	Wallboard, plaster, paneling	No other fastener needed	Steel	⅛" extra short to ¼" extra long	Single unit, light duty anchor for use in hollow walls.
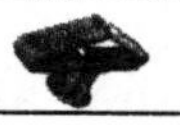	Rawl Poly-Toggle®	Wallboard or solid masonry	Sheet metal screws	Polypropylene	⅜" to ¾"	Fast, easy, economical. Medium duty application for hollow walls.
SPECIAL FASTENERS						
	Cad-Screw®	Steel (18, 20, 22 gauge) and wood	Big Fella or little guy tool	Steel	12-11 × 1⅝" to 12-11 × 4"	Fast, gimlet point. High thread. Phillips head. Cadmium plated.
	Hammer Drive Pin	Concrete, block, brick	No other fastener needed	Steel	¼" × ½" to ¼" × 3"	Lightweight anchor requiring no drilling. Use 2 lb. hammer with Drive Tool.
	Rawl Twin-Fast™ Screws	Metal to metal	No other fastener needed	Steel	6-20 × ⅜" to ¼-14 × 1"	Drills and taps own hole. 4 head styles. Removable.

Figure 15 ◆ A sample of types of fasteners available from one manufacturer.

103F15.TIF

5.3.0 Structural Steel Fasteners

Structural steel fasteners include several types of beam clamps. These clamps are driven onto a **flange** (see *Figure 16*). Other types of fasteners, such as the master clamp, the beam clip, and the clip, will support rods or other hangers (see *Figure 17*). Powder-actuated fasteners and welded studs also may be used on structural steel. Powder-actuated fasteners are attached by a trained operator using a powder-actuated fastening tool. Welded studs are attached with welding equipment.

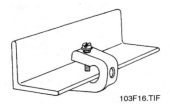

103F16.TIF

Figure 16 ◆ Beam clamp on a flange.

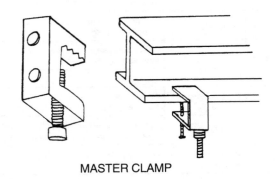

MASTER CLAMP

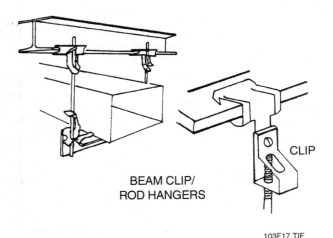

BEAM CLIP/
ROD HANGERS

CLIP

103F17.TIF

Figure 17 ◆ Three types of structural steel fasteners.

WARNING!

A powder-actuated fastening tool works like a gun and, used incorrectly, can be just as dangerous. Instead of bullets, a stud bolt or a specially designed fastener is loaded into the tool. A metal-shell cartridge or a powder pellet provides the energy to propel the fastener forward. The tool is highly effective, but only those workers who have received the manufacturer's training and hold an operator's card certifying that they have been trained may use this tool.

Review Questions

Sections 2.0.0–5.0.0

1. To fasten parts that you want to be able to unfasten and then quickly reassemble, you must use _____.
   a. bolts and screws
   b. nuts and washers
   c. welded studs
   d. temporary supports

2. The number of threads per inch on a bolt or screw is called the _____.
   a. standard thread measurement
   b. class
   c. pitch
   d. thread length

3. The two thread measurement designations are _____.
   a. National Standard Thread and International Standard Thread
   b. National Coarse and National Fine
   c. National Variable Pitch and National Standard Pitch
   d. National American Measure and International Metric Measure

4. Prems are _____.
   a. premium setscrews
   b. preassembled self-locking nut assemblies
   c. preassembled screw and washer assemblies
   d. premeasured thread assemblies

5. You must place concrete inserts _____.
   a. before the concrete is poured
   b. after the concrete is poured
   c. after the concrete is poured but before it cures
   d. no more than 15 minutes after the concrete is poured

DID YOU KNOW?
Rosie the Riveter

During World War II, many men left their jobs to go into military service. To fill those jobs, the United States government created a marketing campaign centered on a fictional woman named Rosie the Riveter. Even though women were needed for all sorts of manufacturing and production jobs, the idea of riveting captured the public imagination. In posters and films, Rosie was shown as strong, smart, patriotic, and feminine. The fictional Rosie inspired women, many who had never held a paying job, to go to work. Motivated by patriotism, a chance to earn money, and the freedom of the working world, more than 6 million women entered the workforce between 1942 and 1945.

6.0.0 ◆ BLIND RIVETS (POP RIVETS)

In many installations, the worker is not able to see both sides of the workpiece and so must use **blind rivets** (also called pop rivets), which can be inserted and set from one side of the workpiece. The blind rivet consists of a hollow body that contains the rivet head attached to a **mandrel** (stem). The rivet and mandrel assembly is inserted into the workpiece with a **blind riveter** (a tool that resembles a hand punch). When the handles of the blind riveter are squeezed together, the rivet head and mandrel assembly is pulled upward. Because the rivet head is wider than the hollow rivet, it forces the base of the rivet to widen. The widening base causes the rivet head to fit snugly into place for a tight connection as the mandrel snaps off. Power-operated riveters are available for production riveting.

Blind rivets may be used for fastening metal to metal or for fastening fiber or plastic to metal. They are made from aluminum, steel, copper, **monel** (an alloy), or stainless steel and may have either a dome or a countersunk head.

Other types of blind rivets include the drive-pin and explosive-type rivets. Drive-pin rivets are clinched by striking a pin that forces the small end to expand or lock on the inside of the workpiece. Explosive-type rivets have a hollow space in the shank that contains a small charge of heat-sensitive chemicals. When sufficient heat is applied to the head, an explosion takes place that expands the rivet shank tightly into the hole. Most explosive rivets are aluminum, but they are available in stainless steel as well.

Molded nylon rivets are also available. They are used to fasten plastic to plastic, plastic to metal, and fiberglass to fiberglass.

Blind rivets are available in several head styles. The dome head is the most commonly used and is suitable for many applications. The large flange head has a larger bearing surface than the dome head does. In other words, the spread of the flattened head is wider. The large flange head is used to join compressible or brittle materials to structures. When the application requires a flush surface, a countersunk head is used.

Blind rivets are measured by diameter and length of the body excluding the head (except for the countersunk rivet, which includes the head in the length measurement). Rivets come in diameters from ⅛ inch to ⅜ inch and in lengths from ¼ inch to 3 inches.

7.0.0 ◆ SPECIAL-PURPOSE FASTENERS

Most fasteners depend on the material into which the fastener is driven to provide the gripping power—for example, the way wood grips a screw. Other fasteners are designed so that the gripping power is in the fastener itself. Hollow-wall anchors, for example, are designed with wings or arms that grip the inside of a hollow wall. When choosing special-purpose fasteners, you must consider the weight and size of the item to be fastened and the material into which the fastener will be inserted. The many types of special-purpose fasteners fall into four classifications:

- Toggle bolts
- Expansion shields
- Threaded masonry anchor system
- Studs and pins

Choosing the Right Rivet

The blind rivet must be compatible with the materials being joined. If dissimilar materials are used, the rivet may fail because of corrosion.

Blind rivets are designed to meet a specific range of material thickness in which they will be effective. This work thickness is called the rivet's *grip range*. You must read the manufacturer's recommendations for grip range, proper hole size, and choice of materials.

7.1.0 Toggle Bolts

Toggle bolts are ideal for attaching brackets, hangers, and fixtures to hollow walls and ceilings (see *Figure 18*). These bolts are strong because the weight they hold is distributed over built-in wings. Among the most commonly used toggle bolts are the tie-wire toggle bolt, the fixture hanger toggle bolt, the spring-wing toggle bolt, the tumble toggle bolt, the riveted-head stud toggle bolt, and the hollow-wall screw anchor.

REGULAR TOGGLE BOLT

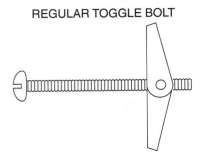

TIE-WIRE TOGGLE BOLT

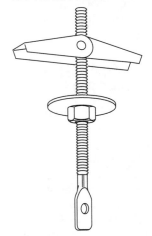

FIXTURE HANGER TOGGLE BOLT

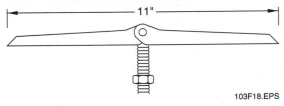

103F18.EPS

Figure 18 ◆ Toggle bolts.

7.1.1 Spring-Wing Toggle Bolt

The spring-wing toggle bolt has spring-loaded wings that automatically deploy after passing through a pre-drilled hole. After you insert this bolt, you tighten it—an action that draws the wings flat against the inside wall surface. Thus, the holding power of the bolt is distributed over the area of the wings.

7.1.2 Tumble Toggle Bolt

The tumble toggle bolt is pivoted off-center. Gravity causes the toggle to fall into a cross position. The toggle head bears against the inside surface of the wall, distributing the load on the wings.

7.1.3 Riveted-Head Stud Toggle Bolt

The riveted-head stud toggle bolt is similar to the tumble toggle bolt except that it is headless. It works as a stud with a hex-head nut tightened against the fixture.

7.1.4 Hollow-Wall Screw Anchor

The hollow-wall screw anchor (see *Figure 19*) is used to fasten the workpiece to drywall, wallboard, plaster, or hollow walls faced with tile. This type of anchor is commonly called a molly bolt. The advantage of this fastener is that fixtures can be removed without removing the anchor. To install this anchor, follow these steps:

Step 1 Drill a hole the size of the anchor.

Step 2 Insert the anchor and tighten the screw to expand the anchor.

Step 3 Remove the tightening screw.

Step 4 Put the fixture in place.

Step 5 Reinstall the tightening screw to hold the fixture.

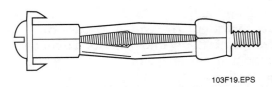

103F19.EPS

Figure 19 ◆ Hollow-wall screw anchor (molly bolt).

There is usually already a hole in the fixture to accommodate the tightening screw. You can use a washer, if necessary.

7.2.0 Expansion Shields

You can use expansion shields to attach fixtures and workpieces to concrete, brick, block, and other masonry. The size and type of fastening device used depends on the fastening strength required.

The expansion shield gets its holding power when its sides expand firmly against the sides of a hole. The tapered fastener forces the external ribs outward into the surrounding masonry. Almost all of the many types of expansion shields work on this same principle. Commonly used expansion shields include the three-way expansion shield, the general-purpose expansion shield, the self-drilling expansion shield, and the lag-screw expansion shield.

7.3.0 Threaded Masonry Anchor System

This system enables you to screw a threaded anchor directly into masonry or concrete. To use this system, follow these steps:

Step 1 Fit a special extension tool to the chuck of a standard hammer drill.

Step 2 Drill a pilot hole.

Step 3 Retract the twist drill bit into the tool and insert a threaded masonry anchor into the drill's chuck.

Step 4 Drill the anchor to drive it permanently into place.

7.4.0 Studs and Pins

Some masonry fastenings require the use of studs and nail-like pins. Because studs and pins are difficult to drive into place, you may have to use a power tool such as the powder-actuated fastening tool.

One advantage of the powder-actuated fastening tool is that no drilling is required. You can use this tool to set threaded studs into steel or concrete for removable installations or to drive pins into concrete for permanent installations.

8.0.0 ◆ HANGERS AND SUPPORTS

Many parts of a structure's mechanical systems such as heating, ventilating, and air conditioning (HVAC); plumbing; and electrical conduits and fixtures require hanging and support systems. The HVAC hanging system is composed of three elements:

- The upper attachment to the structure
- The hanger
- The lower attachment to the duct

8.1.0 Construction Code Specifications

When planning the installation of hangers and supports, you must consider such things as proper spacing, materials, and installation practices. The following sections present some construction code specifications for hanging straight ducts, fiberglass duct hangers, fiberglass **risers**, riser supports, and flexible ducts. In addition, you will find specifications for minimum fasteners for **lap-joined** straps in *Appendix A*, maximum loads for single metal hangers in *Appendix B*, and strap sizes and spacings in *Appendix C*.

8.1.1 Hanger Spacing: Straight Duct

In straight duct sections the joints are the weakest points, so support must be provided. Standards published by the **Sheet Metal and Air Conditioning Contractors National Association** (SMACNA) specify the allowable loads and maximum spacing for hangers. These specifications vary according to hanger and duct type and size and type of installation.

Your task as a sheet metal mechanic is not to redesign the ductwork, but to hang it according to the building plans. However, you should know that SMACNA standards exist. And you should check with your supervisor whenever you have questions about the installations on which you are working.

8.1.2 Riser Supports

You must support rectangular risers (vertically running ducts) with angle irons or **channels** secured to the sides of the ducts with welds, bolts, sheet metal screws, or blind rivets. Place riser supports at one- or two-story height intervals (every 12 to 24 feet). Some risers are supported from the floor (see *Figure 20*). Reinforcing for the riser support is located below the duct joint. It may be necessary to install vibration isolators to eliminate duct-borne noise. These isolators keep vibration noise from transferring through the riser supports to surrounding walls, floors, or ceilings, which might act like sounding boards and amplify the noise.

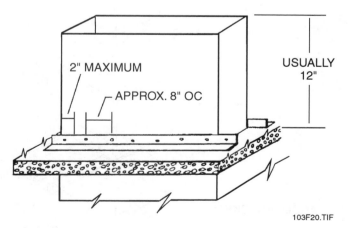

Figure 20 ◆ Floor-supported risers.

Air Pressure

On ducts more than 30 inches wide, internal air pressure generated by the fan will cause the sheet metal to expand. The larger the duct, the greater the pressure, and the greater the pressure, the more support you will have to install.

Some risers are supported from the wall (see *Figure 21*) and may be held in place by a band or by **angle brackets**. The allowable load per fastener and the number of fasteners to be used depend on the duct gauge and duct size. You must locate ducts against the wall or a maximum of 2 inches away from the wall. Each wall anchor must satisfy both the **tensile load** and the **shear load** of the supported member.

8.1.3 Fiberglass Duct Hangers

Trapeze hangers (see *Figure 22*) are recommended for supporting fiberglass ducts. These hangers should be made from channels with minimum dimensions of 3" × 1½" × 24-gauge metal. The 1-inch supporting metal strap should be 22 gauge or heavier. Rods ¼ inch in diameter may be used in place of hanger straps; when local codes permit, 12-gauge hanger wire may be substituted.

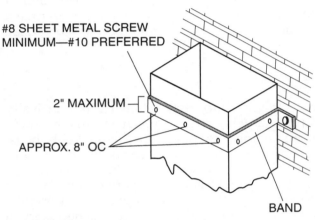

ALLOWABLE LOAD PER FASTENER:

25 Lbs. – 26 to 28 Gauge

35 Lbs. – 20, 22, 24 Gauge

50 Lbs. – 16, 18 Gauge

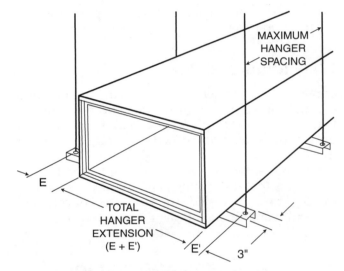

HANGER SPACING AND EXTENSION
3" Wide Channels

STANDARD 3" WIDE HANGERS
Hanger extension is defined as the sum of the distances between the hanging wires and the duct walls (both sides).

CHANNEL SELECTION		
If Total Extension Is Not Greater Than:	Minimum Channel Gauge	Minimum Channel Profile
6"	24	3" × 1½"
18"	22	3" × 2"
30"	18	3" × 2"

103F22.EPS

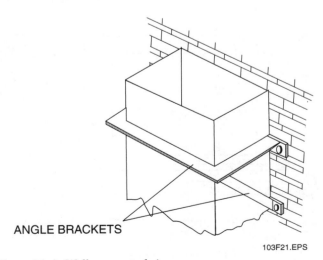

Figure 21 ◆ Wall-supported risers.

Figure 22 ◆ Trapeze hangers for fiberglass ducts.

The maximum on-center spacing for trapeze hangers on fiberglass ducts is shown in *Table 2* and *Figure 23*.

In addition, reinforcement of pressurized fiberglass air duct systems is often necessary to reduce sagging of larger panels and to eliminate excess stress.

Table 2 Maximum On-Center (OC) Spacing for Trapeze Hangers on Fiberglass Ducts

Duct Size (Width)	Maximum OC Spacing
49" or greater	4' OC
48" or less and less than 12" high	6' OC
48" or less and from 12" to 24" high	8' OC
24" wide or less and more than 24" high	8' OC
More than 24" wide and more than 24" high	6' OC

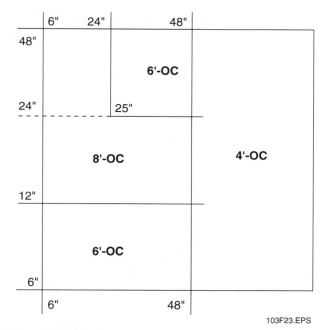

Figure 23 ◆ Maximum on-center spacing for trapeze hangers.

8.1.4 Fiberglass Duct Risers

Fiberglass duct risers 8 feet long or longer require the use of special support (see *Figure 24*). This support does not reinforce the duct for deflection (deformation of the duct from loads placed upon it). Vertical riser supports should be installed at maximum spacing intervals of 12 feet.

The **National Fire Protection Association (NFPA)** limits riser height for vertical risers in air duct systems serving buildings with more than two stories.

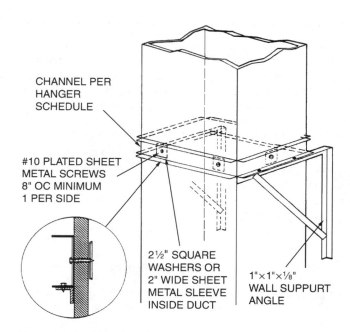

Figure 24 ◆ Fiberglass duct riser support.

8.1.5 Flexible Duct and Round Duct

When supporting flexible duct, you should never place supports more than 10 feet apart (see *Figure 25*) or as recommended by the manufacturer. The most sag that is allowed is ½ inch per foot between supports. Note that connections to other ducts or equipment are also considered to be flexible duct supports.

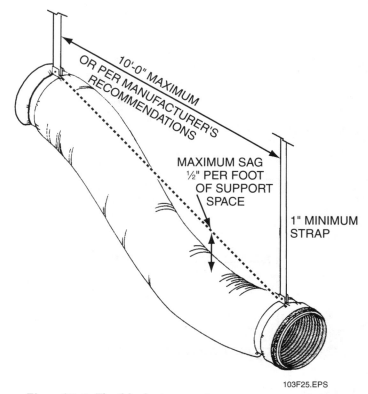

Figure 25 ◆ Flexible duct supports.

You must ensure that the straps used to wrap around and hang the duct do not pinch the duct diameter (see *Figure 26*). Unless you use a **sheet metal saddle** underneath the duct, the strapping material must never be less than 1 inch wide. To avoid tearing any vapor barrier—especially during installation—never support the entire weight of the duct on one hanger. You must always avoid contact between flexible duct and sharp metal edges. You may sometimes be permitted to repair damage to the vapor barrier with the proper kind of tape. But if the internal core is punctured, you must replace that section of flexible duct or else cut it completely and treat it as a connection.

8.1.6 *Rectangular Duct Hangers*

Rectangular duct hangers include strap hangers (see *Figure 27*) and trapeze hangers (see *Figure 28*). Duct up to 60 inches wide must be supported with strap hangers. Duct more than 60 inches wide must be supported with trapeze hangers.

DID YOU KNOW?

For Lack of an Anchor

An old quotation, which has been repeated and modified many times, reads, "For lack of a nail, the horseshoe was lost; for lack of its shoe, the horse was lost; without a horse, the rider was lost; without a rider, the message was lost; without the message, the battle was lost; with the loss of the battle, the war was lost."

Much the same thing could be said about anchors. If even one anchor fails, an air handling system can potentially fall apart. That is because the stress that should have been carried by that one anchor must now be handled by nearby anchors, which, in turn, may fail under the added stress.

When an entire system fails, there will be damage to the equipment and possibly the structure itself. People might be injured or even killed. All this for the lack of an anchor.

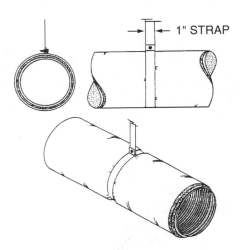
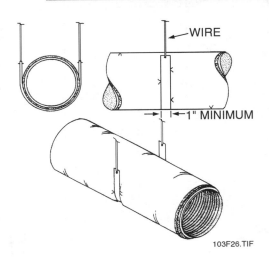

Figure 26 ◆ Hanging flexible duct.

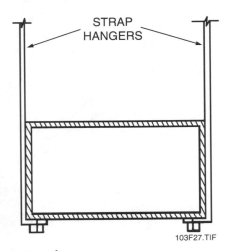

Figure 27 ◆ Strap hangers.

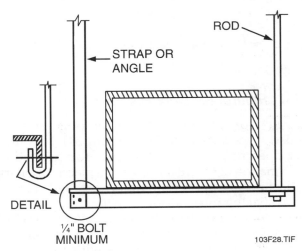

Figure 28 ◆ Trapeze hanger.

You also can use stacked trapeze hangers for stacked ducts (see *Figure 29*). However, whatever method you use, you must ensure that you have not exceeded the load rating. Minimum recommended sizes of hangers for rectangular duct are shown in *Table 3*.

8.2.0 Special Hanging Methods

Earlier in this module, you learned how to fasten duct to concrete and masonry. Some structural systems—such as a cellular metal deck—require special hanging methods.

Cellular metal deck is used in many contemporary buildings. The structure allows wiring to be placed in the cells that make up the deck but prohibits the use of fasteners that would pierce the deck.

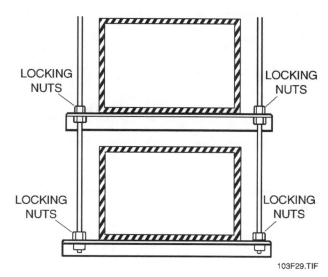

Figure 29 ◆ Stacked trapeze hangers.

Table 3 Types, Sizes, and Spacing of Hangers

Rectangular Metal Duct at 16-Gauge Maximum With Allowance for Insulation			
P/2*	Hanger Pair Spacing	Strap Width Inches × Thickness	Wire or Rod
30" maximum	10' apart	1" wide × 22 gauge	10 gauge (.135")
30" maximum	8' apart	1" wide × 22 gauge	10 gauge (.135")
30" maximum	5' apart	1" wide × 22 gauge	12 gauge (.106")
30" maximum	4' apart	1" wide × 22 gauge	12 gauge (.106")
72" maximum	10' apart	1" wide × 18 gauge	⅜" diameter
72" maximum	8' apart	1" wide × 20 gauge	¼" diameter
72" maximum	5' apart	1" wide × 22 gauge	¼" diameter
72" maximum	4' apart	1" wide × 22 gauge	¼" diameter
96" maximum	10' apart	1" wide × 16 gauge	⅜" diameter
96" maximum	8' apart	1" wide × 18 gauge	⅜" diameter
96" maximum	5' apart	1" wide × 20 gauge	⅜" diameter
96" maximum	4' apart	1" wide × 22 gauge	¼" diameter
120" maximum	10' apart	1½" wide × 16 gauge	½" diameter
120" maximum	8' apart	1" wide × 16 gauge	⅜" diameter
120" maximum	5' apart	1" wide × 18 gauge	⅜" diameter
120" maximum	4' apart	1" wide × 20 gauge	¼" diameter
168" maximum	10' apart	1½" wide × 16 gauge	½" diameter
168" maximum	8' apart	1½" wide × 16 gauge	½" diameter
168" maximum	5' apart	1" wide × 16 gauge	⅜" diameter
168" maximum	4' apart	1" wide × 18 gauge	⅜" diameter
192" maximum	10' apart	No straps allowed	½" diameter
192" maximum	8' apart	1½" wide × 16 gauge	½" diameter
192" maximum	5' apart	1" wide × 16 gauge	⅜" diameter
192" maximum	4' apart	1" wide × 16 gauge	⅜" diameter
193" and greater	Special analysis required		

The limits are for duct, insulation, and normal reinforcement and trapeze weights. No external loads are allowed in addition to this total weight.

* P = Total perimeter of the rectangular duct. P/2 = ½ of the duct perimeter.

Hangers for Special Uses

For installations in corrosive atmospheres, you must use hangers made of noncorrosive, stainless steel plating. Wire (12, 10, or 8 gauge) should be galvanized black annealed steel. Examples of corrosive atmospheres include wastewater treatment plants and chemical plants.

Some manufacturers of this type of deck offer an integral hanging system. When no integral hanging system is available, you can install rod or strap hangers in a cellular metal deck before the concrete is poured (see *Figure 30*).

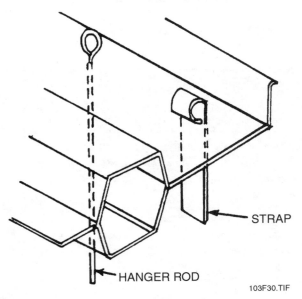

STRAP

HANGER ROD

103F30.TIF

Figure 30 ◆ Hangers in a cellular metal deck.

You can attach welded studs directly to the underside of the metal deck after the concrete has been poured and cured (hardened) on the top side. You must follow underside attachment methods correctly, and you must include a safety factor, or safe working load (SWL), of four or five times what is necessary to support the suspended ductwork.

DID YOU KNOW?
Seismic Restraints

In some parts of the United States, building codes require the installation of seismic restraints to help building fixtures withstand the vibrations and shocks from tremors and earthquakes. A seismic restraint system may include deflection springs, duct supports, and acoustical panels.

8.3.0 Hanging Systems

For large commercial construction or industrial applications, the Unistrut® system or a similar system may be used. An alternative to conventional support methods, the Unistrut® system eliminates welding and drilling and is easily adjustable and reusable. The system is made up of a series of slotted channels made from low-carbon strip steel, spring nuts, and bolts. The nuts and bolts have coarse screw threads.

The rectangular case-hardened nuts have ends shaped to permit a quarter turn clockwise into the slotted channel. Two toothed grooves in the top of the nut engage the turned-in edges of the channel and prevent movement of the bolt and nut within the frame. The fittings are punch-pressed from hot-rolled, pickled, and oiled steel plates. Fittings can be placed anywhere along the channel opening.

9.0.0 ◆ AIR HANDLING EQUIPMENT NOISE

The vibration of air handling equipment (such as fans, compressors, vanes, or blowers) creates noise that can penetrate into occupied spaces. To reduce or prevent this noise, mount or suspend such equipment and its associated ducts on rubber pads or isolation hangers.

The following section deals with air handling equipment concerns that are generally taken care of by architects or engineers. However, you should know what these concerns are and how they are dealt with. Learning all that you can about every aspect of the sheet metal trade will make you a more valuable employee and will help you to do a first-class, professional job.

Air handling equipment is selected with these considerations in mind:

- Lowest possible sound and vibration levels
- Engineering concerns
- Budget constraints
- Product life

Architects or engineers will specify the maximum allowable vibration levels for any installation and, if necessary, specify the installation of vibration isolation devices to meet those levels.

Air handling units may be suspended or floor mounted (see *Figure 31*). Steel springs are the most popular and versatile vibration isolators (see *Figure 32*). They can deflect a wide range of noisy vibrations.

Isolation hangers are used for pipe and suspended units. These hangers incorporate rubber, springs, or combination spring-and-rubber isolator elements. A rubber-in-shear isolator and a combination spring and rubber-in-shear isolator are shown in *Figure 33*. Specifications for isolation hangers used to suspend pipes must allow for temperature changes that will cause the pipes to expand and contract.

Rubber isolators are also available in mount or pad configurations and are usually made of neoprene (synthetic rubber) or molded rubber (see *Figure 34*). Fiberglass and cork isolators are also available for specific application needs. Rubber isolators provide high resistance to the transmission of high-frequency noise.

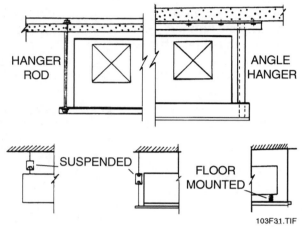

Figure 31 ◆ Air handling equipment (suspended and floor mounted).

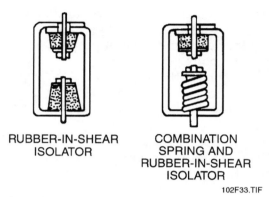

Figure 33 ◆ Isolation hangers.

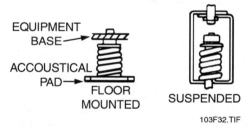

Figure 32 ◆ Steel springs.

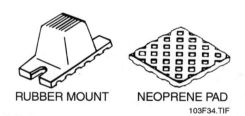

Figure 34 ◆ Rubber isolators.

Review Questions

Sections 6.0.0–9.0.0

1. The blind rivet consists of a hollow body that contains the rivet head attached to a _____.
   a. toggle bolt
   b. mandrel
   c. monel
   d. vibration isolator

2. Toggle bolts are strong because _____.
   a. the weight they hold is distributed over built-in wings
   b. they have a greater overall diameter than other fasteners
   c. they combine the best properties of screws and bolts
   d. they have the highest tensile strength

3. You must support rectangular risers with _____.
   a. vibration isolators
   b. temporary supports
   c. studs or pins
   d. angle irons or channels

4. Unless you use a _____ underneath round or flexible duct, the strapping material must never be less than 1 inch wide.
   a. neoprene pad
   b. rubber mount
   c. trapeze hanger
   d. sheet metal saddle

5. To reduce vibration, _____ are often used for pipe and suspended equipment.
   a. isolation hangers
   b. neoprene mounts
   c. trapeze hangers
   d. 1-inch rubber straps

Summary

Air distribution systems must be properly supported so that they can stand up to stress loads. These systems must also deliver heated or cooled air quietly and efficiently. A poorly designed or improperly installed air distribution system will be noisy and ineffective and can be dangerous because an improperly supported system can fall apart.

In this module, you learned how to identify and select fasteners used to fasten sheet metal parts. You also learned about the hangers and supports used to hold ductwork, fans, compressors, and diffusers in place. And you learned how to reduce or eliminate the noise that air distribution equipment can create.

As an apprentice you will not be responsible for the overall design of an air distribution system, but you should take every opportunity to learn about the concerns of designers and engineers who develop these systems. Learning all you can about your trade will make you a more valuable employee and will make your work more interesting for you.

Nick Phillips

Program Director, Retired, New Mexico State University
Manufacturing, Construction, and Maintenance Program
Carlsbad, New Mexico

University of Texas–El Paso, Part-Time Instructor
Associated General Contractors, New Mexico Building Branch

Nick Phillips earned a bachelor of science in marine engineering at the United States Merchant Marine Academy in 1956; a master of business administration from the University of Connecticut in 1971; and a doctorate in engineering from Kennedy-Western University, Los Angeles, in 1986. Recently, Nick was recognized with an Outstanding Professional Achievement Award at his 45-year college reunion. After years of work in the field, Nick now uses his expertise to contribute to the education of others by teaching at New Mexico State University and the University of Texas–El Paso.

How did you become interested in this industry?
In high school, my girlfriend's father was vice president of Turner Construction Company in New York. At the time, he was the project manager for the United Nations' building. One of my high school teachers was also an excellent mentor, who got me into the construction end of it. Another high school teacher recommended the U.S. Merchant Marine.

How did you decide on your current position?
I spent a year at sea on a merchant ship during my sophomore year of college as an engine cadet. I got turned on to running power plants and maintenance of plants. When I graduated, I was in the navy for 5 years and got to be chief engineer on a destroyer.

After that, I left the navy and got a job with General Dynamics Electric Boat on a shipyard that built submarines. I started out working on the wet dock on the waterfront. I stayed with them for 14 years and worked up through production to become the shipwright superintendent and did all the launching and dry dockings. I became production manager at Electric Boat and was responsible for 5,000 tradespeople and craft employees.

I was recruited and became shipyard manager at Marathon Le Tourneau. I managed fabrication, erection assembling, and outfitting of offshore oil platforms. I completed projects in Scotland, Holland, New Zealand, and India. I traveled all over for some 20 years.

I moved on to the field of education; I had done some part-time training, teaching courses here and there. I became an adjunct professor at University of Texas–El Paso. New Mexico State University was building a new training center, and they asked me to be the program manager. They also needed course work, so I put together construction, industrial, and mining skills training programs.

What do you think it takes to be a success in your trade?
I think, for me, it's been a focus on construction work. Be focused on what you are going to do—that leads to continuing education for yourself. All of my education went back to my fundamentals. I wouldn't be able to do my job if I hadn't kept up with advancements. That's where training and education come into play.

What are some things you do on the job?
I've worked on nuclear submarines, construction overhauls, nuclear refuelings, and offshore oil rigs. I've done fiberglass work with composites and construction of a special research submarine. I've built oceangoing fishing boats with fiberglass. A lot of it was electronics—I was responsible for three plants and outfittings. I've worked on engine overhauls. All of my work had the same theme of definition requirements.

It's a matter of what you have, what you want to do, and what you have to do to get there from here. They're simple questions. You go step by step.

What do you like most about your job?
Working with people. I like the challenge of putting a team together and doing a quality job on time and within budget.

What would you say to someone entering the trade today?
Keep up with the technology as you go through the stages of your career. You have to keep up with technology changes.

Trade Terms Introduced in This Module

Allen wrench: A hexagonal steel bar that is bent to form a right angle. Also called a *hex key wrench*.

Angle bracket: An L-shaped metal supporting member used to support vertical risers. Also called *angle iron*.

Blind rivet: A hollow rivet containing a rivet head and mandrel or stem that is used to set and fasten a workpiece from one side. Also called *pop rivets*.

Blind riveter: A hand or power tool designed to set and fasten blind rivets.

Case hardened: A term that describes metal made of an iron or steel alloy, the surface of which has been hardened by a special process that includes heat treatment.

Channel: A U-shaped piece of structural steel used as a supporting device.

Cotter pin: A metal pin with a loop on one end and two legs of slightly different lengths on the other end that is used for fastening.

Flange: An edge that projects from a pipe or a beam.

Lap-joined: A condition in which one piece is joined to another by partly covering one piece with another.

Mandrel: The stem on a blind rivet that snaps off during installation of the rivet.

Monel: An alloy of nickel, copper, iron, and manganese.

National Coarse: A thread measurement designation; fasteners designated National Coarse have a lower number of threads per inch than those designated National Fine.

National Fine: A thread measurement designation; fasteners designated National Fine have a higher number of threads per inch than those designated National Coarse.

National Fire Protection Association (NFPA): An association that develops and publishes standards about fire prevention.

Prems: An abbreviated term for preassembled screw and washer assemblies.

Risers: Ductwork that runs vertically in structures.

Shear load: The amount of weight or pressure that causes an exposed piece of metal to break or shear off.

Sheet metal saddle: A sling-like device that cradles insulated duct from underneath.

SMACNA: The Sheet Metal and Air Conditioning Contractors National Association.

Tensile load: The weight required to cause metal to stretch or compress.

Tolerance: The amount of deviation allowed in a specified size, dimension, or fitting.

Minimum Fasteners for Lap-Joined Straps

When straps are lap-joined for hanging rectangular metal duct, you must place the fasteners along the length of the strap in series, not side by side at the width of the strap. The minimum recommended sizes of fasteners used for lap joining are as follows:

1" × 22-, 20-, or 18-gauge	Two #10 screws or one ¼-inch diameter bolt
1" × 16-gauge	Two ¼-inch diameter bolts
1½" × 16-gauge	Two ⅜-inch diameter bolts

Maximum Loads for Single Metal Hangers

The maximum allowable loads for single metal hangers are as follows:

Size	Hanger Material	Maximum Load
1-inch	22-gauge strap	260 lbs.
1-inch	20-gauge strap	320 lbs.
1-inch	18-gauge strap	420 lbs.
1-inch	16-gauge strap	700 lbs.
1½-inch	16-gauge strap	1,100 lbs.
106-inch diameter	rod	80 lbs.
135-inch diameter	rod	120 lbs.
162-inch diameter	rod	160 lbs.
¼-inch diameter	rod	270 lbs.
⅜-inch diameter	rod	680 lbs.
½-inch diameter	rod	1,250 lbs.
⅝-inch diameter	rod	1 ton
¾-inch diameter	rod	1½ tons

Strap Sizes and Spacings

The following information is for round metal duct (conventional wall thickness with allowance for insulation).

Minimum metal hanger sizes recommended for round sheet metal duct with maximum spacing of 12 feet are as follows:

Duct Diameter	Strap Hanger(s)	Rod Hanger(s)	Wire Hanger(s)
Up through 24"	(1) 1" × 22-gauge	(1) ¼" diameter	(2) 10 gauge
25" through 36"	(1) 1" × 20-gauge	(1) ⅜ inch diameter	(2) 8 gauge
37" through 50"	(2) 1" × 20-gauge	(2) ⅜ inch diameter	No wires allowed
51" through 60"	(2) 1" × 18-gauge	(2) ⅜ inch diameter	No wires allowed
61" through 84"	(2) 1" × 16-gauge	(2) ⅜ inch diameter	No wires allowed

Additional Resources

This module is intended to present thorough resources for task training. The following reference works are suggested for further study. These are optional materials for continued education rather than task training.

HVAC Systems Design Handbook, 1998. Roger W. Haines. New York: McGraw-Hill.

Indoor Air Quality and HVAC Systems, 1993. David W. Bearg. Boca Raton, FL: Lewis Publishers.

One Good Turn: A Natural History of the Screwdriver and the Screw, 2000. Witold Rybczynski. New York: Charles Scribner's Sons.

Figure Credits

Erico Products, Inc.   103F16

The Rawlplug Co., Inc.   103F14

NCCER CRAFT TRAINING USER UPDATES

The NCCER makes every effort to keep these textbooks up-to-date and free of technical errors. We appreciate your help in this process. If you have an idea for improving this textbook, or if you find an error, a typographical mistake, or an inaccuracy in the NCCER's Craft Training textbooks, please write us, using this form or a photocopy. Be sure to include the exact module number, page number, a detailed description, and the correction, if applicable. Your input will be brought to the attention of the Technical Review Committee. Thank you for your assistance.

Instructors – If you found that additional materials were necessary in order to teach this module effectively, please let us know so that we may include them in the Equipment and Materials list in the Instructor's Guide.

Write: Curriculum Revision and Development Department
National Center for Construction Education and Research
P.O. Box 141104, Gainesville, FL 32614-1104

Fax: 352-334-0932

E-mail: curriculum@nccer.org

Craft _____ Module Name _____

Copyright Date _____ Module Number _____ Page Number(s) _____

Description _____

_____

_____

_____

_____

(Optional) Correction _____

_____

_____

(Optional) Your Name and Address _____

_____

_____

Installation of Air Distribution Accessories

COURSE MAP

This course map shows all of the modules in the first level of the Sheet Metal curriculum. The suggested training order begins at the bottom and proceeds up. Skill levels increase as you advance on the course map. The local Training Program Sponsor may adjust the training order.

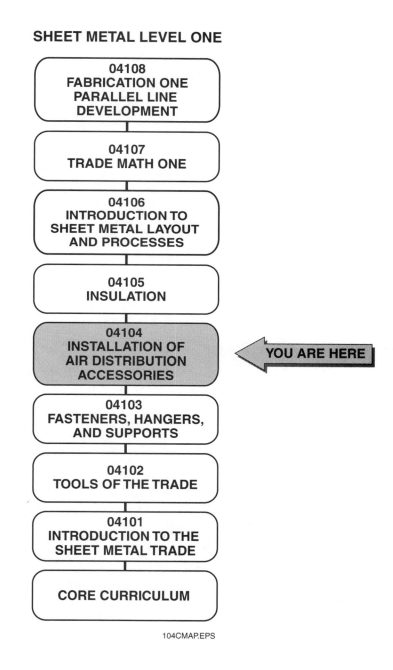

SHEET METAL LEVEL ONE

04108
FABRICATION ONE PARALLEL LINE DEVELOPMENT

04107
TRADE MATH ONE

04106
INTRODUCTION TO SHEET METAL LAYOUT AND PROCESSES

04105
INSULATION

04104
INSTALLATION OF AIR DISTRIBUTION ACCESSORIES ← YOU ARE HERE

04103
FASTENERS, HANGERS, AND SUPPORTS

04102
TOOLS OF THE TRADE

04101
INTRODUCTION TO THE SHEET METAL TRADE

CORE CURRICULUM

104CMAP.EPS

Copyright © 2001 National Center for Construction Education and Research, Gainesville, FL 32614-1104. All rights reserved. No part of this work may be reproduced in any form or by any means, including photocopying, without written permission of the publisher.

MODULE 04104 CONTENTS

Figures

Installation of Air Distribution Accessories

Objectives

When you finish this module, you will be able to do the following:

1. Explain the purpose of selected air distribution accessories.
2. Correctly install selected air distribution accessories.

Prerequisites

Before you begin this module, it is recommended that you successfully complete the following modules: Core Curriculum; Sheet Metal Level One, Modules 04101 through 04103.

Required Trainee Materials

1. Pencil and paper
2. Appropriate personal protective equipment

1.0.0 ◆ INTRODUCTION

In an effective air distribution system, **supply air** (indoor air blended with outside air) is filtered, then heated or cooled and delivered to various parts of a building. The system is also vented to make room for fresh supply air and to remove odors. The same system that delivers fresh heated or cooled air to a building can also carry fire or smoke, so safeguards must be installed in the ductwork.

Air distribution accessories handle many air-flow control tasks necessary in a heating, ventilating, and air conditioning (HVAC) system.

Each component in an air distribution system performs a specific task:

- Regulates the airflow in an HVAC system
- Allows access for service
- Provides safeguards against fire or smoke
- Provides zoning so that conditioned air is delivered to the parts of the building that need it
- Connects the various parts in the system
- Regulates the airflow in the occupied spaces in a building

In this module, you will learn how these air distribution accessories work, how to install them, and how to check your work to ensure that it is done properly.

2.0.0 ◆ LOUVERS

Louvers are vents that are installed in exterior wall openings. The louvers allow outside air to flow into a building and inside air to flow out. They are made up of a frame, blades (slats), and an interior or exterior screen. The blades are set at an angle to keep out rain or snow. The screens keep sand, leaves, insects, and small animals or birds from entering the building through the louver.

Louvers may be made of galvanized steel, extruded aluminum, or stainless steel and may have a painted or **anodized** (noncorrosive) finish. Most are mass-produced, which allows them to be sold for much less than they would cost if they were made by a custom sheet metal shop. However, sheet metal workers often fabricate very large or custom louvers.

DID YOU KNOW?
An Air Distribution System Saves Art

If you ever get a chance to visit the Sistine Chapel in Rome, you can see the famous paintings on its ceiling done by Michelangelo between 1508 and 1512. And if you know where to look, you may also see the air distribution system that is helping to preserve those paintings.

The paintings attract thousands of tourists who, unfortunately, also bring in a lot of dirt, heat, and humidity. These conditions threaten the paintings. And a recent cleaning made them even more vulnerable to changes in temperature and humidity.

The Carrier Company was asked to design and install a system that would preserve the paintings and allow tourists to keep visiting. The company combined off-the-shelf heating products with computer-based electronic sensors and controls to create a system that delivers temperate air and controlled humidity to the ceilings and walls. Powerful filters clean the air, removing even tiny particles. A higher-velocity airflow is directed toward the floor (where the tourists are). This airflow keeps dirt and humidity at floor level, away from the paintings. You will have to look carefully to see the system. It is almost invisible, concealed in 500-year-old walls, some of which are 10 feet thick.

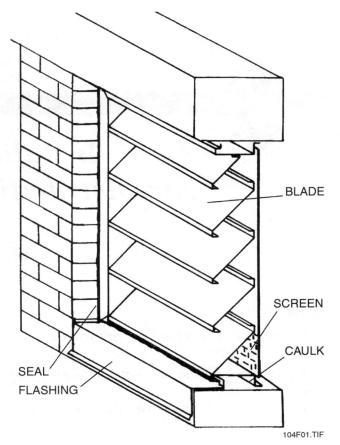

Figure 1 ◆ Stationary louver.

There are two basic types of louvers: stationary and operable. You must caulk and seal both types in accordance with the manufacturer's instructions. In the stationary louver, the blades are set permanently in a fixed position (see *Figure 1*). Note the locations of the **flashing,** interior screen, seal, and caulk. In the operable louver, the blades may be fully opened, fully closed, or set at an angle (see *Figure 2*). Attached to the blades are small arms that are, in turn, connected to a bar called the linkage. This assembly draws the blades open or closed.

For installations in areas that experience severe weather conditions, a weatherproof louver with specially designed blades is installed. This type of louver is designed to keep out wind-driven rain, snow, sand, and other debris.

For installations where the builder has provided a masonry sill, no sill flashing is required. However, flashing or caulking (or both) may be required at the head and **jambs** (sides).

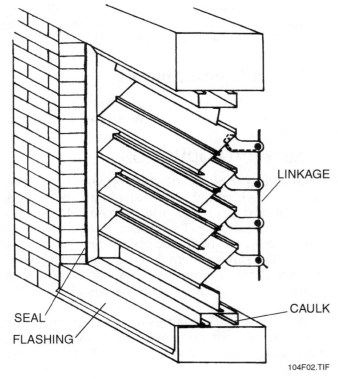

Figure 2 ◆ Operable louver.

Before Installing Louvers

When the louvers are delivered to the job site, you must handle and store them properly to prevent damage. Use the following checklist:

* Inspect the louvers to be sure they have not been damaged in shipping and that you have been sent the correct style, size, and color.
* Handle louvers carefully. Lift by the frame and not by the blade.
* Do not drop, drag, step on, or apply excessive force to a louver.
* Properly store the louvers in a clean, dry area until they are ready to be installed.

2.1.0 Installing Louvers

Before installing louvers, you must review the job specifications and the mechanical and architectural drawings. These documents will give you the installation locations and will show whether the architect or engineer has specified any details for installation. You must also read and follow the manufacturer's installation instructions. Note that the structural contractor will cut the opening in the wall for the louver. This opening should be ¼ inch to ½ inch larger than the overall size of the louver. Louvers are sold using the wall opening dimensions; the actual size of the manufactured louver is ¼ inch smaller. Be sure to check the manufacturer's sizing conventions.

The most important task in louver installation is to ensure that moisture cannot enter the building through the sides or blades of the louver. The manufacturer will provide installation instructions for the specific louvers on your project. Follow these general guidelines when installing louvers:

* Install louvers in the outside wall according to the manufacturer's instructions, with the blades set to direct water down and away from the building.
* Install flashing or caulking (or both if needed) at the head, sill, and jambs. In some cases, one subcontractor will complete all of the caulking work on the project. (Note that the ductwork may extend to the outside of the wall or it may be connected directly to the louver on the inside of the wall. Proper sealing of the edges with flashing, caulking, or both is required in either case.)

* When installing louvers on metal buildings, you must pay special attention to the flashing detail. The flashing at the head and sill of the louver must extend to the outside ribs of the building. Because the flashing material will be seen, you will usually be required to match the finish of the building panels. The manufacturer of the building panels may provide matching flashing.

2.1.1 Testing

To ensure that the louver is properly installed, use the following checklist:

* Does the installation follow the architectural or engineering details?
* Does the installation follow the manufacturer's specifications?
* Are the louver blades pointing down and away from the building?
* Has the proper flashing or caulking been installed to prevent moisture from penetrating around the edges of the louver?
* Do operable louvers open and close properly after installation?
* Is the screen installed correctly?
* Does the flashing material match the building panels? (*Note:* This applies only to metal buildings.)

Architectural Louvers

Sometimes an architect specifies a decorative louver. These louvers are installed in a prominent and visible spot on a building and are meant to be part of the building's design. Such louvers may be square, rectangular, round, oval, triangular, or crescent shaped. The architect may specify the shape and color of the louver frame and blades and even the color of the screen.

3.0.0 ◆ DAMPERS AND ACCESS DOORS

Like louvers, dampers are made up of a frame and movable blades. However, dampers are installed *within* the HVAC system where noted on the project drawings or in the project specifications. Dampers act like gates within the HVAC system. They regulate air distribution. Specially designed safety dampers control smoke and flames. You must install access doors wherever access to dampers or other components within the ductwork is needed. Access doors are discussed later in this section.

3.1.0 Manual Volume Dampers

Manual volume dampers (MVDs) may be round, oval, rectangular, or square. They may be made of galvanized steel, aluminum, or stainless steel. Depending on the overall size, an MVD may have a single blade or multiple blades.

Multiple-blade dampers are made in two basic types: opposed blade and parallel blade. In the **opposed-blade damper,** each blade moves in a direction opposite to the blade next to it (see *Figure 3*). This design allows for more precise airflow control than can be achieved with the **parallel-blade damper.**

104F03.EPS

Figure 3 ◆ Opposed-blade volume damper with damper quadrant.

The parallel-blade damper works like a venetian blind. All the blades move in the same direction at one time (see *Figure 4*). This type of damper is a good choice where two-position operation—fully opened or fully closed—is necessary.

104F04.EPS

Figure 4 ◆ Parallel-blade damper in wall.

3.1.1 Installing Manual Volume Dampers

Before installing MVDs, review the project specifications and the architectural or engineering drawings to determine the proper location. The specifications may state, "MVDs are required at each branch duct or at each reheat coil." Generally, you must locate MVDs in branch ducts as close to the main trunk duct as possible. Sometimes, a wall or another duct may block one side of the duct where you must install an MVD. In this case, you must always locate the shaft for the **damper quadrant** on the unblocked side. To install an MVD, follow these steps:

Step 1 Insert the damper into the duct so that you can view the operation of the blades.

Step 2 Install the screws in the frame *behind* the travel of the blade while it is opening or closing. The blade must travel freely from the open to the closed position and vice versa.

Step 3 Extend the shaft through the ductwork to mount the damper quadrant with either pop rivets or sheet metal screws.

CAUTION

During installation it is important not to block any blade on the damper. If one blade is blocked, all the blades will be blocked.

Step 4 Using a hacksaw, cut a slot in the end of the damper. The slot should be parallel to (facing the same direction as) the damper blade.

Step 5 Leave the damper in the open position.

3.1.2 Testing

To ensure that the damper is properly installed, use the following checklist:

- Can the damper rotate from fully open to fully closed without interference from mounting screws or rivets?

- Can the damper rotate from fully open to fully closed without interference from duct liner insulation?

- Does the slot in the damper shaft match the position of the damper blades?

- Is the damper in the open position with the damper handle locked?

3.2.0 Fire Dampers and Fire/Smoke Dampers

As you have learned, an HVAC system delivers clean, conditioned air to a structure and vents indoor air to the outside. However, unless specially designed dampers are installed, this air delivery system can also carry fire or smoke. These special dampers include fire dampers, combination fire/smoke dampers, and ceiling radiation dampers. Usually these dampers are located near fire-rated walls and fire-rated ceiling assemblies. All fire and smoke dampers must have an Underwriters Laboratories, Inc. (UL) label attached. This label certifies that the damper has been tested and approved for the specified use.

A *fire damper* closes automatically with a spring-loaded action (see *Figure 5*). By closing, it restricts the airflow that a fire needs to continue burning. It also restricts the passage of flames. The damper is controlled by a **fusible link**, which holds the damper open until the heat of a fire causes it to melt and close the damper. A fusible link is a metal chain link made of an alloy with a low melting point. The melting point is usually 160°F to 165°F minimum, with 212°F standard in many applications. The fire rating for fire dampers is specified in hours and may not necessarily match the fire rating of the wall or partition.

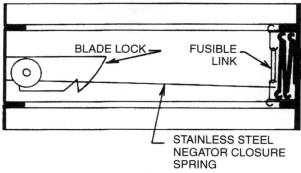

BLADE LOCK   FUSIBLE LINK

STAINLESS STEEL NEGATOR CLOSURE SPRING

104F05.TIF

Figure 5 ◆ Spring-loaded fire damper.

A fire damper must stay in the wall, even if ducts or ceiling components on either side of the wall fall down. Therefore, **breakaway connections** are placed between the duct sleeve containing the damper and the ductwork on either side. Retaining angles are attached to the sleeve or damper frame, not to the wall. The connectors shown in *Figure 6* are acceptable for fire damper installation. To properly seal the joints, you must follow the manufacturer's written instructions and the local code.

DID YOU KNOW?
The UL Mark

UL is a not-for-profit organization that tests and certifies a wide variety of products for public safety. Since its founding in 1894, it has certified nearly 16.1 billion products.

DID YOU KNOW?
The National Fire Protection Association

The National Fire Protection Association (NFPA) publishes standards for fire prevention in residential and commercial structures. The standards are revised annually. HVAC designers must have and use the latest edition of the standards.

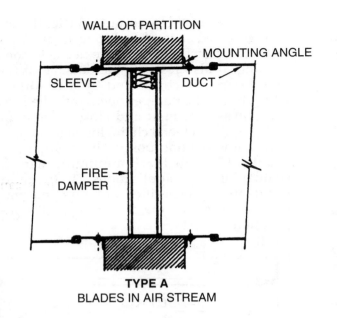

WALL OR PARTITION

MOUNTING ANGLE

SLEEVE

DUCT

FIRE DAMPER

TYPE A
BLADES IN AIR STREAM

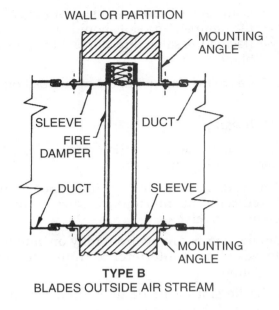

WALL OR PARTITION

MOUNTING ANGLE

SLEEVE

DUCT

FIRE DAMPER

DUCT

SLEEVE

MOUNTING ANGLE

TYPE B
BLADES OUTSIDE AIR STREAM

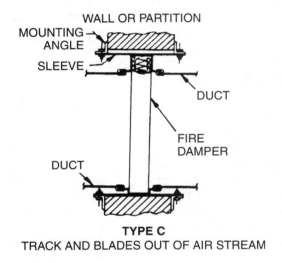

WALL OR PARTITION

MOUNTING ANGLE

SLEEVE

DUCT

FIRE DAMPER

DUCT

TYPE C
TRACK AND BLADES OUT OF AIR STREAM

104F06.EPS

Figure 6 ◆ Mounting angles for fire dampers.

A *fire/smoke damper* is controlled by a smoke detector and is designed to close automatically when smoke is present. This damper must be fail-safe; in other words, if it fails, it must fail in the closed position. This type of damper may accomplish other tasks in the duct system and still serve as an approved smoke damper.

Some HVAC installations require *combination fire/smoke dampers* (see *Figures 7* and *8*). These dampers combine fire and smoke detection capabilities. A *ceiling radiation damper* is designed for use in horizontal assemblies that are required to have a fire-resistance rating. It has a protective ceiling membrane that closes off a duct opening through the membrane in the event of a fire. This damper can detect heat radiating from the floor below.

104F07.EPS

Figure 7 ◆ Combination fire/smoke damper rough-in at wall opening.

Figure 8 ◆ Combination fire/smoke damper installed in wall.

104F08.EPS

3.2.1 Installing Fire Dampers and Fire/Smoke Dampers

The wall contractor usually provides the damper openings. Floor and wall openings must be sized according to the manufacturer's written instructions and local codes.

Before installing these dampers, review the project specifications and the architectural or engineering drawings to determine the proper location. In addition, you must read and follow the manufacturer's instructions for each type of damper. Because these instructions vary from manufacturer to manufacturer, no specific installation steps are presented here. Never assume that one manufacturer's instructions will apply to a damper made by another manufacturer.

3.2.2 Testing

Follow the manufacturer's instructions for testing the fire damper. You can test the closing ability of most fire dampers by removing the fusible link that holds the damper in the open position. The local building inspector will examine each damper installation. The building inspector will also review the manufacturer's installation instructions to verify that the installation has been done correctly.

3.3.0 Duct Access Doors

Once fire and smoke dampers have been installed, you will need a way to get to them to test the damper installation and to replace the fusible link when necessary. A duct access door must be installed in the duct at most fire damper and combination fire/damper locations. Duct access doors are available from a number of manufacturers in a variety of styles. Approved view ports (window-like panels) may be part of the door construction so that damper controls and fusible links can be inspected without opening the access door (see *Figure 9*). Framing, fastening, and hinge recommendations are shown in *Figure 10*.

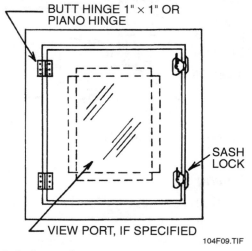

Figure 9 ◆ Access door.

104F09.TIF

3.3.1 Installing Access Doors

You must follow the manufacturer's installation instructions when installing access doors. Observe these general guidelines for installing access doors:

- Measure and cut the opening to the proper size.
- Use the hinge approved for the specific application.
- Make sure that the doors open fully and that they open out, not in.
- Ensure that nothing interferes with the door swing. Structural elements, pipe, electrical lines, and conduits cannot be in the way. Note that some of these elements may not yet be installed.
- Make sure the door fits into the opening snugly and that it is level and square with the duct.
- If the access door has a view port, make sure that it is aligned properly so that you can see the necessary parts of the damper through it.
- Lock the access door.

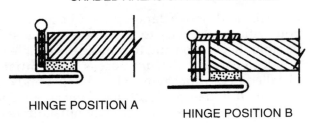

SHADED AREAS SHOW DUCT LINER

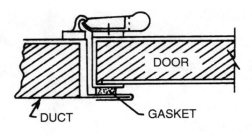

HINGE POSITION A

HINGE POSITION B

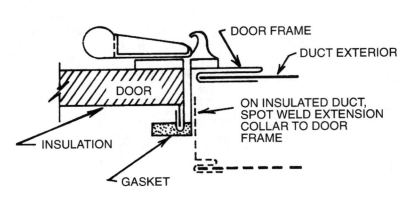

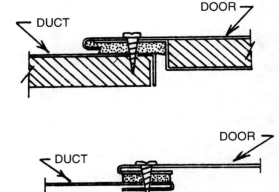

104F10.TIF

Figure 10 ◆ Access door standards.

3.3.2 Testing

To ensure that you have properly installed the access doors, use this checklist:

- Do the doors fit snugly and are they level and square?
- Do the doors swing out? Are they clear of any structural elements that are in place or that will be in place in the future?
- Is the access door locked?

3.4.0 Motorized Control Dampers

Motorized control dampers are used in HVAC systems to control, or regulate, the mixture of the air. They are usually located near the air handler in the mechanical room to modulate the return air, outside air, and exhaust air.

This type of damper may be round, oval, rectangular, or square and may be made of galvanized steel, aluminum, or stainless steel. Depending on the overall size, a motorized control damper may have a single blade or multiple blades. In the multiple-blade type, the blades may be either opposed or parallel. As you have learned, the opposed-blade damper provides better control to throttle the air as the damper is closed.

3.4.1 Installing Motorized Dampers

Before installing motorized dampers, review the project specifications and the architectural or engineering drawings to determine the proper location. Sometimes, a wall or another duct may block one side of the duct where you must install a motorized damper. In this case, you must always locate the shaft for the motor on the unblocked side. To install a motorized damper, follow these steps:

Step 1 Insert the damper into the duct so that you can view the operation of the blades.

Step 2 Install the screws into the frame behind the travel of the blade while it is opening or closing.

Step 3 Make sure the duct liner does not interfere with the blade rotation.

Step 4 Note that the motor may be mounted in the airstream or on the outside of the duct. If the motor is mounted on the outside of the duct, you must extend the motor's shaft through the ductwork. The opening for the shaft should be just large enough to allow the shaft to rotate.

Step 5 Install an access door so that you can install the damper linkage or the motor. This door will also allow for inspection of the damper.

3.4.2 Testing

To ensure that the damper is properly installed, use the following checklist:

- Do the damper blades open and close properly?
- Do the blades rotate freely without interference from mounting screws?
- Do the blades rotate freely without interference from the duct liner?

4.0.0 ◆ ZONING ACCESSORIES AND COILS

Some air distribution accessories provide separate zones in the HVAC air distribution system. These accessories include variable air volume boxes (VAVs), constant air volume boxes (CAVs), fan power terminal units (FPTUs), and inline duct fans.

VAVs are designed to save operating costs by varying the amount of air instead of varying the temperature. They save fan energy and reheat energy and allow for the use of smaller air handlers and ductwork. These units may be mounted on ceiling support members or suspended from the ceiling. A VAV box with a hot water reheat coil is shown in *Figure 11.* Some models are designed for use in fire-rated ceiling assemblies.

CAVs, as the name indicates, provide a constant volume of air within an air distribution system. They are less expensive to install than VAVs and are suitable for applications where variable air volume is not necessary.

FPTUs redistribute excess heat from interior zones in a building to perimeter zones where it is needed. They also can respond to a thermostat demand for heat when the central fan system is shut down.

Inline duct fans are designed to correct air distribution problems. For example, a building may have rooms that are too hot in the summer and too cold in the winter or rooms whose temperature varies greatly depending on the time of the day. The fans boost airflow so that a greater volume of heated or cooled air can reach the problem area and produce a comfortable temperature. These fans are designed to fit into rigid round or square duct as well as into flexible duct.

Each of these accessories has a top side, a bottom side, an inlet opening, and a duct outlet opening. Units with electric or hot water coils also include locations for the electrical or pipe connections. An installation project may have many similar pieces of equipment, but the connection locations for each unit may be on different sides. You must pay attention to details such as the location of the top side and the location of the connections to ensure proper installation and operation.

104F11.EPS

Figure 11 ◆ VAV box with hot water reheat coil.

How Does a VAV Work?

We will use an elementary school as our example. Before classes start, when the building is empty, not much cooling is needed. The main fans run more slowly, reducing the airflow through the building. As classrooms and offices fill up and the sun rises, the building becomes warmer and the system increases the airflow. However, some rooms in the building may remain unoccupied. The system closes off airflow to those unoccupied rooms. Note that the entire building is still being cooled; VAVs vary the amount of airflow, not the temperature. A wall-mounted thermostat determines how much the supply air valve should open to maintain a comfortable room temperature.

4.1.0 Installing Zoning Accessories

Before installing zoning accessories, review the project specifications and the architectural or engineering drawings to determine the proper location. You must also read and follow the manufacturer's instructions for each type of unit. These instructions specify the number and type of hangers to use. Because these instructions vary from manufacturer to manufacturer, no specific installation steps are presented here. Never assume that one manufacturer's instructions will apply to a unit made by another manufacturer.

Observe the following general guidelines for installation of these units:

- Ensure that nothing interferes with the duct or with the pipe or electrical connections. Structural elements, pipe, electrical lines, and conduits cannot be in the way. Note that some of these elements may not yet be installed.

- Allow enough room for access doors. The doors for electric reheat coils are very large and require additional space.

- Select and use properly sized hangers. Follow the manufacturer's recommendations for type and size of hanger and proper spacing.

- Ensure that hangers do not interfere with the unit's connection points.

- Ensure that hangers do not interfere with access doors.

- Install **vibration isolators** (cushioned supports) on motor-driven equipment to minimize noise.

- Ensure that the filters installed on the units draw return air from the **plenum** (the space between a suspended ceiling and the structure above).

4.1.1 Testing

To ensure that these units are properly installed, use the following checklist:

- Are the hangers sized correctly?

- Is there proper clearance of connections at all points?

- Is the equipment level?

- Is the installation in proper alignment with the airflow?

- Will there be enough room, now and in the future, for the access doors to open fully?

- Are the filters installed on the units correctly and are they drawing return air from the plenum?

Working With Other Trades

On any residential or commercial project you will encounter workers from many other trades. These workers include carpenters, plumbers, electricians, and drywall and flooring installers. The general contractor will schedule the work so that, for example, plumbers are not installing pipe at the same time the HVAC crew is installing ductwork. However, you must be aware of how the work of other trades may affect the work you are doing. For example, a plumber may have to run pipe around an obstruction. That pipe, in turn, may obstruct the work that you must do. Or you may have to plan your own installation to ensure that the ductwork is clear of structural elements that will be installed later. Careful review of the project plans and open communication will help avoid problems.

Riveting Ideas

Air Filter Arrows

You will find an arrow that shows the direction of airflow on all air filters. Be sure to install the filter with the arrow pointing in the direction that the air flows from the air handling equipment.

4.2.0 Reheat Coils

Reheat coils provide zone heating to different parts of a building. These coils can be electric, hot water, or steam.

4.2.1 Installing Reheat Coils

Before installing any type of reheat coil, you must determine the direction of the airflow as well as the location of the top, the bottom, and the connection side. It is very important to determine which side of the coil has the pipe or electrical connections. The project could have many heating coils that are similar except for the connections being on different sides. The project drawings may have this information. Or you may have to confirm this information with the mechanical or electrical contractor. You should also read and follow the manufacturer's instructions for proper installation. Because installation requirements may vary from manufacturer to manufacturer, no specific installation steps are provided here. To install reheat coils, follow these general guidelines:

- Install the reheat coil in the proper airflow direction.
- Install the reheat coil with the top side up.
- Install access doors on the upstream side of the water coil. Note that some engineers also require access doors on the downstream side. You will find this information in the project plans.
- Install access doors so that you can open them fully now and in the future. Structural elements, piping, electrical conduits, and structural hangers all can interfere with the opening of an access door. Note that some of these elements may not be installed when you install the reheat coil. Carefully review project plans to ensure that planned installations will not block the access doors.

4.2.2 Testing

To ensure that coils have been properly installed, use the following checklist:

- Is the coil located correctly in the direction of the airflow?
- Is the top side up?
- Can the door be opened fully, now and in the future, without interference from structural elements, pipes, electrical conduits, or hangers?
- Are the electrical or piping connections on the correct side and fully accessible?

Review Questions
Sections 2.0.0–4.0.0

1. The most important task in louver installation is _____.
   a. to handle the louvers by only the frames, not the blades
   b. to ensure that moisture cannot enter the building through the louver
   c. to install the screen in the proper direction to keep out insects, birds, and debris
   d. to install the louver with the proper hangers and seal it against moisture

2. When installing louvers on metal buildings, you are usually required to _____.
   a. install a lightning deflector attachment on each louver
   b. inset the louvers by ¼ inch on all sides
   c. match the flashing material to the exterior finish
   d. set the louver into a specially designed rubber gasket

3. You can achieve the best airflow control with a(n) _____.
   a. opposed-blade damper
   b. parallel-blade damper
   c. motorized damper
   d. manual volume damper

4. Fire dampers are controlled by a(n) _____.
   a. spring-loaded lock
   b. fusible link
   c. heat-sensing coil
   d. internal thermostat

5. When installing a VAV, you must _____.
   a. note on which side the connections are located
   b. first attach the electric coils to the unit
   c. use fire-rated hangers
   d. install hangers in front of the unit's connection points

5.0.0 ◆ TAKEOFFS

Takeoffs include tap-ins, hammerlocks, and spin-ins (see *Figure 12*). Tap-ins or hammerlocks are square or rectangular fittings that connect branch ducts to the main trunk duct. Spin-ins are round fittings, usually with dampers, that connect ceiling diffusers to the main duct.

104F12.EPS

Figure 12 ◆ Takeoffs.

CAUTION

You must remove the duct liner when installing a spin-in. If you don't, no air will flow through the branch line.

5.1.0 Installing Takeoffs

Installing takeoffs is a basic skill in the sheet metal trade. Learning how to install them properly is an opportunity for you to use your craft skills early in your apprenticeship. You must cut the opening so that the fitting fits into the duct snugly and smoothly. There must be no holes at the corners. Use a drill to make a pilot hole and then cut the opening with aviation snips.

A tap-in may be installed as an *inside knockover* or an *outside knockover*. These terms refer to the direction in which you hammer the tabs. To ensure an airtight, professional installation, you must hammer the tabs smoothly and tightly to the duct.

You must install tap-ins with a transition type takeoff, or clinch tee, with the tapered end upstream of the airflow (see *Figure 13*). You may be required to install **extractors** at tap-ins with the hinged end upstream of the airflow. The extractor arm must extend out of the duct on the downstream side of the airflow.

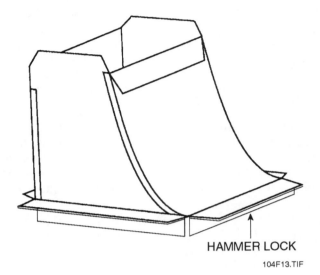

HAMMER LOCK

104F13.TIF

Figure 13 ◆ Clinch tee.

After installing the spin-in, you must ensure that the damper is open and locked in position. When installing spin-ins with scoops, you must ensure that the scoop is installed on the downstream side of the airflow. A scoop looks exactly like its name would suggest. It is a scoop-shaped piece of metal attached to the spin-in. When properly installed, it directs the airflow down the branch line from the main line.

5.1.1 Testing

To ensure that tap-ins and spin-ins are properly installed, use the following checklist:

- Is the hole cut to the proper size?
- Are the corners neat and free of holes?
- Can you set the fitting easily and snugly into the duct?
- Are the tabs hammered over neatly, smoothly, and tight to the duct?
- Is the fitting installed with the proper airflow direction?
- Is the spin-in damper open and locked in position?
- Has the duct liner been removed?

6.0.0 ◆ FLEXIBLE DUCT

Flexible duct is round duct that may or may not be insulated. A wire coil that runs around the inside of the duct gives flexible duct some stiffness and makes it easier to handle. Flexible duct is used as a connection between the rigid duct and heating/cooling equipment and ceiling diffusers. Standard practice permits the installation of flexible duct and connectors only for indoor comfort HVAC systems.

> **CAUTION**
>
> Never locate flexible duct near furnaces, boilers, steam or hot water piping, or any equipment that generates heat at temperatures above the recommended flexible duct temperature.
>
> Avoid running flexible duct across sharp corners or places where it may touch metal fixtures, pipes, or conduits. Otherwise the duct can be damaged.

6.1.0 Installing Flexible Duct

Before installing flexible duct, review the project plans for proper placement. To install flexible duct, follow these steps:

Step 1 Measure to determine the length of duct required. Be sure to allow the correct amount for any turns.

Step 2 Cut completely around and through the duct with a sharp utility knife.

Step 3 Trim the interior wire with lineman pliers (side cutters).

Step 4 Pull back the insulation (if any) from the core and slide at least 1 inch of the core over the collar, pipe, or fitting (see *Figure 14*). Note that sheet metal collars must be at least 2 inches long.

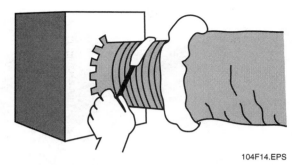

104F14.EPS

Figure 14 ◆ Pull back vapor barrier jacket and insulation.

Step 5 Tape with at least two wraps of approved duct tape. Note that the tape must be **plenum-rated** if the ceiling space is to be used as a return air plenum. You may use an approved clamp in place of or with the tape (see *Figure 15*).

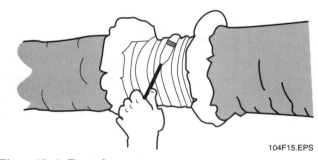

104F15.EPS

Figure 15 ◆ Duct clamps.

Step 6 Fully extend the duct for installation. Do not compress the duct. Radius bends at the duct centerline should not be less than the diameter of the duct (see *Figure 16*).

Step 7 Support the duct at the manufacturer's recommended intervals, but at least every 4 feet. The maximum permissible sag is ½ inch per foot of spacing between supports. For long horizontal runs that have sharp bends, use additional supports before and after the bend.

 *Lineman Pliers*

Lineman pliers (or side cutters) have wide jaws that allow you to cut heavy-gauge wire and to hold work in place. When cutting wire, cut at a right angle to the wire. Always point the loose end of the wire down so that it will fall away from you.

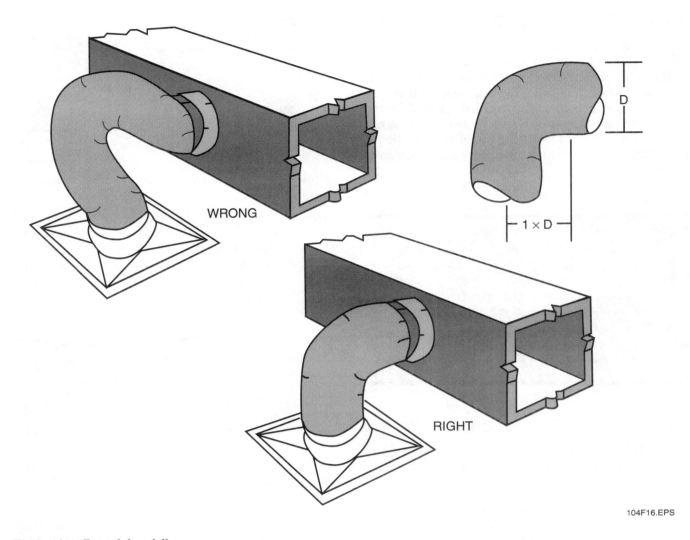

104F16.EPS

Figure 16 ◆ Extend duct fully.

Step 8 Splice flexible duct together with a sheet metal sleeve at least 4 inches long. Tape splices with at least two wraps of approved duct tape (see *Figure 17*).

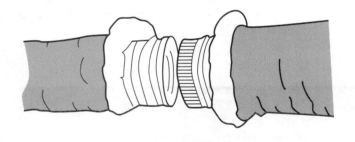

104F17.EPS

Figure 17 ◆ Splicing.

Step 9 Place a hanger at connections to rigid ducting, splice connections, or equipment supports. Hangers or saddles used to support flexible duct must be at least 1½ inches wide (see *Figure 18*). Other types of approved supports—for horizontal duct on ceiling joists, for angled duct, and for vertical duct—are shown in *Figure 19*.

Step 10 Repair any tears or damage to the **vapor barrier jacket** with approved duct tape or according to the manufacturer's instructions. If the internal core is penetrated, replace flexible duct or splice and seal it as in Steps 4 and 5.

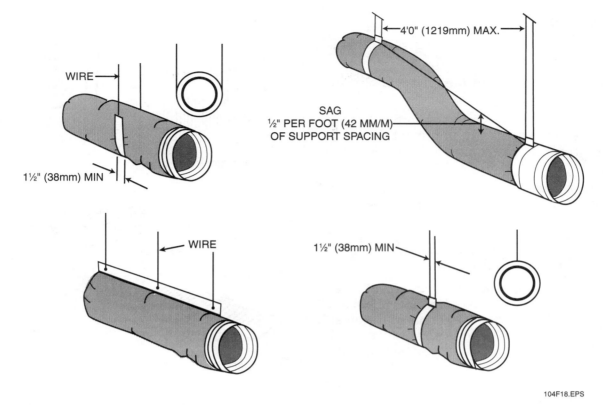

104F18.EPS

Figure 18 ◆ Flexible duct supports.

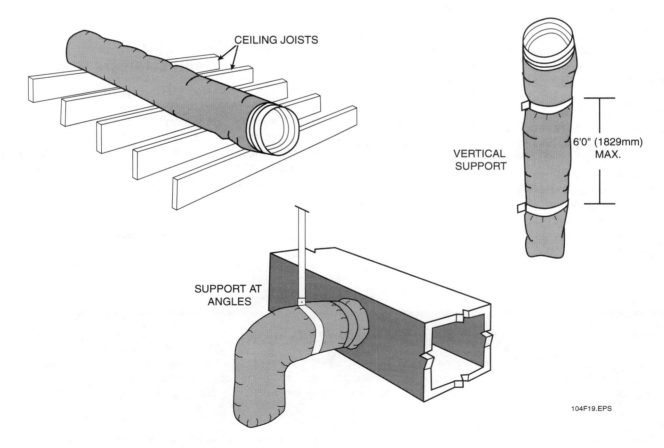

104F19.EPS

Figure 19 ◆ Other types of approved supports for flexible duct.

6.1.1 Testing

To ensure that flexible duct is properly installed, use the following checklist:

- Do the hangers support the duct without cutting into it, especially at the bends?

- Have tears or damage to the vapor barrier jacket been repaired with approved duct tape or according to the manufacturer's instructions?

- Have you checked to ensure that the duct does not sag more than ½ inch between supports?

7.0.0 ◆ REGISTERS, GRILLES, AND DIFFUSERS

Imagine that the room in which you are now sitting had no ventilation. Small amounts of outside air could leak in and small amounts of inside air could leak out, but eventually, the room's air quality would decrease. If you cooked in the room, the air quality would decrease even faster. Proper airflow—intake and exhaust—is required in an HVAC system. This airflow is achieved with registers, grilles, and diffusers.

Registers, grilles, and diffusers are the most visible part of an HVAC installation (see *Figure 20*). The customer can easily see them and will judge your skills by how neatly you install these components. You can imagine a customer saying, "If the parts I *can* see are crooked or poorly installed, what about the parts I *can't* see?" Be sure to carry out your pride of craftsmanship to the finishing details of each job.

Registers, grilles, and diffusers are used as air inlets and outlets on walls or ceilings. Registers and grilles have opposed-blade dampers that control the volume of air. Diffusers are most often used as ceiling outlets for supply air; however, special diffusers can be used as wall outlets. Diffusers consist of vanes (blades) that discharge supply air in various directions. The vanes mix supply air with air that is already in the room. Vanes may be fixed or movable.

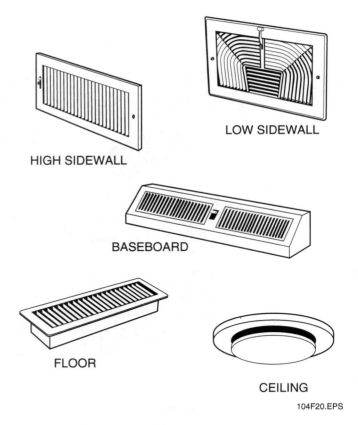

HIGH SIDEWALL

LOW SIDEWALL

BASEBOARD

FLOOR

CEILING

104F20.EPS

Figure 20 ◆ Registers, grilles, and diffusers.

7.1.0 Installing Registers, Grilles, and Diffusers

Before installing registers, grilles, or diffusers, review the project specifications for proper placement and any architectural or engineering details. Because these units must be installed flush with the finished walls, you must measure carefully to ensure that the ductwork does not extend beyond the finished surfaces. Follow these guidelines to install registers, grilles, and diffusers:

- For walls and ceilings made of drywall, complete the duct rough-in before the drywall is installed. Extend the duct beyond the framing studs to ⅛ inch less than the drywall width.

Measure Twice, Cut Once

When measuring and cutting, a professional measures twice—once to record the measurement and again to verify that the measurement is correct. It takes a little extra time, but it's worth it. It ensures that you won't waste time fixing cuts that are too long or waste materials because of cuts that are too short.

- Make sure the duct rough-in is level and square with the building.
- The duct or sleeve must have a flange (see *Figure 21*). The flange will hold the sheet metal screws used to fasten registers, grilles, and diffusers to the wall or ceiling. The flange must be wide enough to hold the screws, but not so wide that it can be seen from the finished side. If the flange is too wide, you will have to cut it. Cutting a flange against a wall or ceiling is very difficult.
- Install a wider flange on the raw end of the duct and against the studs to ensure a flush fitting and a solid surface for fastening the screws.
- Attach registers, grilles, and diffusers to the wall or ceiling with sheet metal screws. (The manufacturer supplies the screws for each unit.)

- Install the registers, grilles, and diffusers level and square with the building and flush with the finished wall or ceiling.

Special attention is required when installing diffusers in a **rigid ceiling** (a drywall ceiling with limited or no access). You must follow the manufacturer's instructions for this type of installation. Note the following general guidelines:

- The ceiling opening is usually larger than the duct connection.
- The duct connection may be above the ceiling.
- You may have to support the diffuser separately from the duct connection if the duct connection cannot support the weight of the diffuser.
- You must support ceiling diffusers with ceiling radiation dampers from the structure.

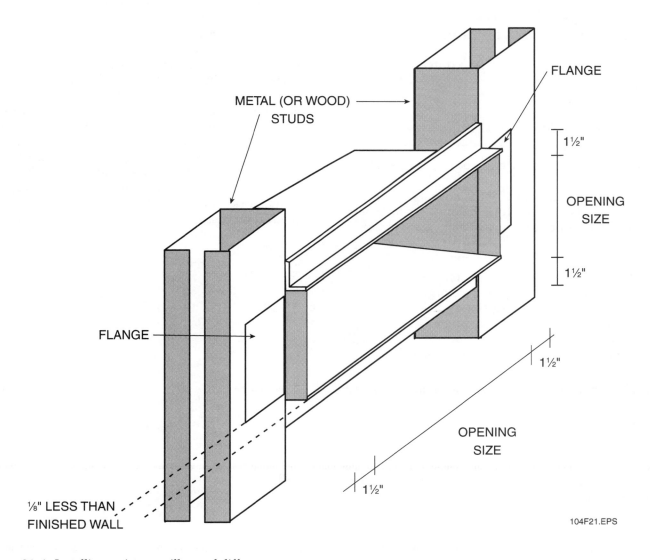

Figure 21 ◆ Installing registers, grilles, and diffusers.

7.1.1 Testing

To ensure that registers, grilles, and diffusers are properly installed, use the following checklist:

- Is the rough-in of the duct level and square with the building?
- Is the duct or sleeve flush with the *finished* wall?
- Does the duct have a flange for installing registers and diffusers with exposed sheet metal screws? Is the flange the correct width?
- At drywall construction, is the flange fastened to the studs and extended the width of the drywall sheet? (This helps prevent the duct from buckling in or bowing out).
- Is the extra weight of the ceiling diffuser separately supported and not dependent for support on the duct alone?
- Is the opening in a rigid ceiling made according to the manufacturer's instructions?

Review Questions

Sections 5.0.0–7.0.0

1. When installing tap-ins and spin-ins, you must cut the opening so that _____.
   a. the fitting can extend above the opening by $\frac{1}{8}$ inch
   b. there are no holes at the corners
   c. there is no need for tabs or other fasteners
   d. the damper can stay in a closed position

2. You must never locate flexible duct near _____.
   a. ceilings that have not been plenum-rated
   b. equipment that generates high heat levels
   c. the main plumbing stack
   d. window and door openings

3. When installing flexible duct, you must _____.
   a. support the duct with approved duct tape
   b. ensure that there is no more than a 1-inch sag
   c. use hangers that are no more than 1 inch wide
   d. fully extend the duct

4. You must support flexible duct at an interval no greater than _____.
   a. 4 feet
   b. 5 feet
   c. 6 feet
   d. 7 feet

5. When installing registers, you must _____.
   a. attach them flush with the finished walls
   b. extend them slightly beyond the finished wall to fit into a frame
   c. attach them to the finished wall with color-matched plastic clips
   d. set the blades into a locked and open position

Summary

Each component in an air distribution system performs a specific task: regulating the air distribution, allowing access for service, safeguarding against fire or smoke, providing zoning, connecting the various parts in the system, and regulating the airflow. In this module, you learned about air distribution accessories and how they work within the system. A variety of these accessories is available, and installation instructions will vary from manufacturer to manufacturer. So it is important to always read, understand, and follow the manufacturer's installation instructions. Those instructions and the local codes will guide you in making a proper installation. Once you have completed installing air distribution accessories, you must test your installation to ensure that you have done the work correctly. Whether the accessories you install are out of sight within the ductwork or in view in the occupied spaces of a building, you must perform your work carefully so that it reflects your pride of craftsmanship.

Larry Marye

President
Action Air Inc.
Denver, Colorado

Larry was born and raised in Denver, Colorado. After high school, he completed a four-year apprenticeship while attending night school two evenings a week at Sheet Metal Union Local #9. Larry is part of a family of tradesmen. His uncle was a sheet metal worker, and his brother is an air balancer. Even his sons are involved in the trade—one is a field superintendent and the other is a foreman. Larry has come a long way from his first job as a grocery store caddy; he is now president of Action Air Inc.

How did you become interested in this industry?
My uncle was a sheet metal worker and owned his own business. He started his company in 1952, and I worked for him from 1961 until 1977, when he retired.

How did you become president of Action Air Inc.?
After my uncle retired and sold his business, I joined Action Air Inc. I worked for nine years in the field, first as an estimator and then as a project manager. In the mid-1980s, I was named vice president of Action Air Inc., and today I'm president.

What are some things you do on the job?
I oversee more than 50 employees, so I do everything from estimating to project management to human resources. We serve approximately 100 commercial clients each year, from small tenant finishes to multistory offices and water treatment plants. I manage jobs through every stage, from the estimate through completion and warranty.

What do you think it takes to be a success in your trade?
You need to have an interest in the field, and you need to work hard. If you do, you can go as far as you want. You can be anything from an apprentice to president. There are no limits to this trade.

What do you like most about your job?
There is variety in the work we do. Every day there is something different to do—with every job and every client, there is something new. There is never a routine, which keeps it interesting.

What would you say to someone entering the trade today?
I would tell that person to work hard, to learn as much as you can on the job and at school, and to take every class that is available to you. You can learn something new every day, no matter how long you work in this field, because the industry is constantly changing.

Trade Terms Introduced in This Module

Anodize: To give metal a hard, noncorrosive finish through electrolyte action.

Breakaway connection: A structural connection designed to break free under certain stress or load conditions caused by fire.

Damper quadrant: A handle located outside the duct that is used to move the damper blade. It also shows the location of the blade.

Extractor: A device used to straighten out airflow behind a register.

Flashing: A thin material placed in mortar joints in masonry to prevent water penetration or to provide water drainage. Flashing is often found over exterior door and window openings and around chimneys, roof vents, and skylights.

Fusible link: A metal chain link made of an alloy with a low melting point. If there is a fire, the chain breaks and the damper closes.

Jamb: The vertical framing at either side of a doorframe, window frame, or door lining.

Louvers: Vents installed in exterior wall openings, allowing outside air to flow into a building and inside air to flow out.

Opposed-blade damper: A type of damper in which each blade moves in a direction opposite to the blade next to it.

Parallel-blade damper: A type of damper in which all of the blades open and close in one direction at the same time.

Plenum: In suspended ceiling construction, the space between the suspended ceiling and the main structure above.

Plenum-rated: A term that refers to the suitability of an air distribution accessory for use in a plenum.

Rigid ceiling: A drywall ceiling with limited or no access.

Supply air: Indoor air that is blended with outside air, filtered, and delivered to the enclosed spaces of a building as heated or cooled air.

Vapor barrier jacket: A membrane designed to prevent moisture from penetrating the insulation in insulated duct or pipe.

Vibration isolator: A resilient support for machinery, piping, or ductwork. It reduces the amount of vibration and noise transmitted to a building's occupied areas.

Additional Resources

This module is intended to present thorough resources for task training. The following reference works are suggested for further study. These are optional materials for continued education rather than for task training.

Air Distribution Basics for Residential and Small Commercial Buildings, 2000. Hank Rutkowski. Arlington, VA: Air Conditioning Contractors of America.

Air Distribution in Rooms: Ventilation for Health and Sustainable Environment, 2000. Hazim B. Awbi, editor. New York, NY: Elsevier Science.

Figure Credits

Larry Marye of Action Air, Inc.	104F03, 104F04, 104F07, 104F08, 104F11
Sheet Metal Connectors, Inc.	104F12
Vent Products Co., Inc.	104F05

NCCER CRAFT TRAINING USER UPDATES

The NCCER makes every effort to keep these textbooks up-to-date and free of technical errors. We appreciate your help in this process. If you have an idea for improving this textbook, or if you find an error, a typographical mistake, or an inaccuracy in the NCCER's Craft Training textbooks, please write us, using this form or a photocopy. Be sure to include the exact module number, page number, a detailed description, and the correction, if applicable. Your input will be brought to the attention of the Technical Review Committee. Thank you for your assistance.

Instructors – If you found that additional materials were necessary in order to teach this module effectively, please let us know so that we may include them in the Equipment and Materials list in the Instructor's Guide.

Write: Curriculum Revision and Development Department
National Center for Construction Education and Research
P.O. Box 141104, Gainesville, FL 32614-1104

Fax: 352-334-0932

E-mail: curriculum@nccer.org

Craft _____ Module Name _____

Copyright Date _____ Module Number _____ Page Number(s) _____

Description _____

_____

_____

_____

(Optional) Correction _____

_____

_____

(Optional) Your Name and Address _____

_____

_____

Ancient Roman soldiers went into battle equipped by the finest metal workers of the day.

Photo - Terry Nix, www.niximperial.com

THE METAL WORKING TRADE

METALWORKING IS ONE OF THE MOST ANCIENT OF CRAFTS. EXAMPLES OF METALWORKING IN ART, TOOLS, BATTLE ARMOR, AND ARCHITECTURE DATE BACK MORE THAN 5000 YEARS.

The roof of the famous Chateau Laurier in Ottawa, Canada, built in the early 1900's, is made entirely of copper. *Photo - Copper Development Association*

In ancient times, the domes of many government buildings and churches were fabricated by metal workers. Modern metal workers help to restore these ancient works of art.

Photo - Vulcan Supply Corp.

In the Middle Ages, metal workers were kept busy fabricating suits of armor and shields for knights.

Photo - Christian Fletcher

SHEET METAL TOOLS

TODAY'S SHEET METAL WORKER MUST LEARN TO USE A VARIETY OF TOOLS, RANGING FROM SIMPLE HAND TOOLS TO COMPUTER-GUIDED LASER INSTRUMENTS.

① Hand snips are often used for simple layout and on-the-job adjustment work.
Photo - Topaz Publications, Inc.

② A nibbler is like a pair of electric shears. It is used to cut shapes and trim material.
Photo - TRUMPF Portable Power Tools

③ A seam locker is used to join two pieces of metal.
Photo - TRUMPF Portable Power Tools

④ A metal brake like this one is often used for on-site work.
Photo - Tapco Integrated Tool Systems

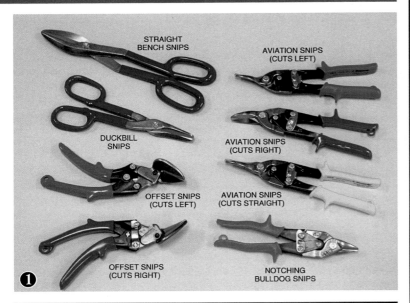

STRAIGHT BENCH SNIPS

DUCKBILL SNIPS

OFFSET SNIPS (CUTS LEFT)

OFFSET SNIPS (CUTS RIGHT)

AVIATION SNIPS (CUTS LEFT)

AVIATION SNIPS (CUTS RIGHT)

AVIATION SNIPS (CUTS STRAIGHT)

NOTCHING BULLDOG SNIPS

①

②

③

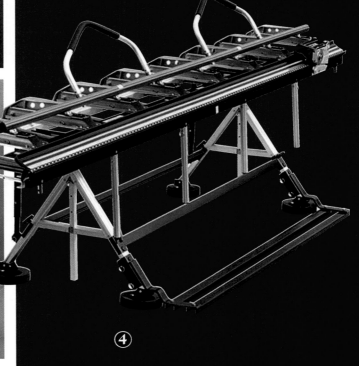

④

SOPHISTICATED TECHNOLOGIES LIKE LASERS AND PLASMA CUTTING TOOLS HAVE BECOME COMMONPLACE IN FABRICATION SHOPS AND MANUFACTURING PLANTS.

⑤ A plasma cutting torch is used for precision cutting work.
Photo - Hypertherm, Inc.

⑥ These heavy-duty shears make fast work of cutting steel plate.
Photo - TRUMPF Portable Power Tools

⑦ A box and pan brake uses centuries-old technology to leverage human strength.
Photo - National Sheet Metal Machines, Inc.

⑧ This automated laser cutting machine is driven directly from a computer-aided design (CAD) system.
Photo - TRUMPF Inc.

⑤

⑥

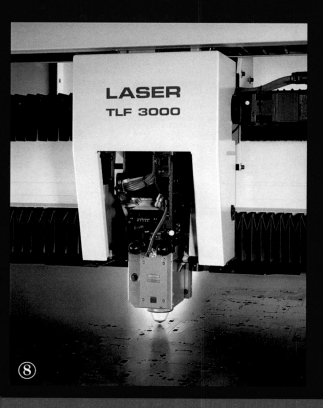
LASER
TLF 3000
⑧

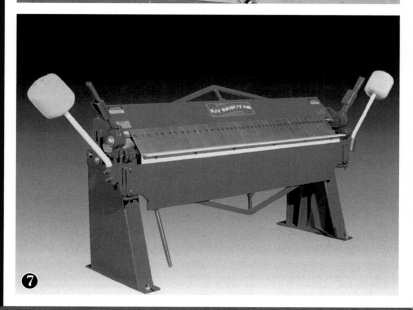
❼

OPPORTUNITIES

THE OPPORTUNITIES FOR SHEET METAL WORKERS RANGE FROM THE PURELY FUNCTIONAL TO THE ARTISTIC.

THE METAL
WORKING TRADE

This prototype of a Mars Landing Module was built from sheet metal. *Photo - The Mars Society*

Many sheet metal workers are employed by mechanical contractors to fabricate and install air conditioning ductwork. *Photo - McGill AirFlow LLC*

Some manufacturers specialize in creative metal work like this exotic room divider. *Photo - Precision Custom Metals, Inc.*

Great attention to detail is needed when crafting artistic metal work. *Photo - Vulcan Supply Corp.*

Insulation

COURSE MAP

This course map shows all of the modules in the first level of the Sheet Metal curriculum. The suggested training order begins at the bottom and proceeds up. Skill levels increase as you advance on the course map. The local Training Program Sponsor may adjust the training order.

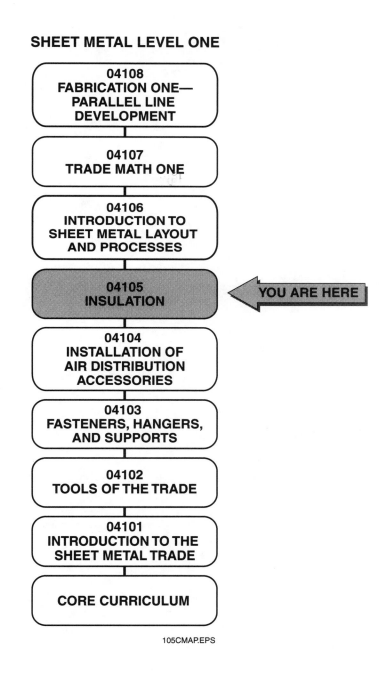

SHEET METAL LEVEL ONE

04108
FABRICATION ONE—
PARALLEL LINE
DEVELOPMENT

04107
TRADE MATH ONE

04106
INTRODUCTION TO
SHEET METAL LAYOUT
AND PROCESSES

04105
INSULATION ⟵ YOU ARE HERE

04104
INSTALLATION OF
AIR DISTRIBUTION
ACCESSORIES

04103
FASTENERS, HANGERS,
AND SUPPORTS

04102
TOOLS OF THE TRADE

04101
INTRODUCTION TO THE
SHEET METAL TRADE

CORE CURRICULUM

105CMAP.EPS

Copyright © 2001 National Center for Construction Education and Research, Gainesville, FL 32614-1104. All rights reserved. No part of this work may be reproduced in any form or by any means, including photocopying, without written permission of the publisher.

MODULE 04105 CONTENTS

Figures

Tables

Insulation

Objectives

When you finish this module, you will be able to do the following:

1. Explain the principles of thermal insulation.
2. Explain the principles of acoustic insulation.
3. Install liner materials on selected duct sections.
4. Install duct wrap on selected duct sections.

Prerequisites

Before you begin this module, it is recommended that you successfully complete the following modules: Core Curriculum; Sheet Metal Level One, Modules 04101 through 04104.

Required Trainee Materials

1. Pencil and paper
2. Appropriate personal protective equipment

1.0.0 ◆ INTRODUCTION

Insulation is an important part of the sheet metal trade. As a sheet metal worker, you will install the systems that raise or lower the temperature of air and water in buildings. To control heat loss or heat gain, you may also insulate the duct and pipe installed in these systems. You will line duct in the shop or wrap duct, pipe, and hangers in the field. If you work for a full-service mechanical contractor, you may also insulate hot or cold water pipes.

In this module, you will learn how to install fibrous glass duct liner, fiberglass blanket insula-

tion, fiberglass pipe insulation, and flexible foam insulation. You will also learn how to properly and safely apply insulation adhesives.

2.0.0 ◆ INSULATION PROPERTIES

The conditioned air and water that make your living and working spaces comfortable may travel quite a distance from the air conditioning equipment to get to you. But the farther from the equipment you are, the greater the chance of heat transfer. Heat naturally moves toward colder areas, so we need to insulate to slow or minimize this heat transfer.

Insulation is also required for cold air and water systems. However, in addition to insulation, these cold systems also require a **vapor barrier** over porous insulation to prevent condensation. Why is a vapor barrier required? Because the insulation is porous, it will allow a certain amount of heat transfer. When the warm, moist **ambient air** comes into contact with the colder temperature of a pipe covered with porous insulation, it will hit its **dew point** and condensation will form. If the porous insulation is not protected with a vapor barrier, the condensation will wet it. And wet insulation is as effective as no insulation at all.

Insulation also provides **sound attenuation,** which means it reduces noise generated in a heating, ventilating, and air conditioning (HVAC) system. Sound attenuation is an important feature of insulation because it keeps unwanted noise out of the occupied spaces in a building.

There are also other characteristics and benefits of insulation. These are covered later in this module in the sections that discuss the principles of thermal insulation and acoustic insulation.

2.1.0 Insulation Materials and Types

Insulation is made of a variety of porous materials such as glass, rock or slag wool, calcium silicate, bonded perlite, vermiculite, and ceramics. It may also be made of closed-cell materials such as cork, foam rubber, polystyrene, and polyurethane. There is also reflective insulation, which has a smooth metallic or metallized surface.

Insulation may be flexible, semi-rigid, rigid, or formed in place. Flexible and semi-rigid insulation comes in blanket or batt form and is available in sheets or rolls. A covering or facing material may be fastened to one or both sides. This facing may serve as a reinforcing vapor barrier, reflective surface, or surface finish.

Rigid insulation is available in blocks, boards, or sheets. Rigid insulation for pipes or curved surfaces is supplied in half sections designed to fit standard pipe sizes.

Insulation that is formed in place is available as a liquid or expandable pellets. This type of insulation is poured or sprayed in place, where it hardens to form rigid or semi-rigid foam insulation. Fibrous materials mixed with binders may also be sprayed in place.

3.0.0 ◆ PRINCIPLES OF THERMAL INSULATION

Thermal insulation is designed to slow the flow of heat energy. It is commonly used to control heat transfer from ductwork to the surrounding area in temperatures ranging from 0°F through 3,000°F and higher. Thermal insulation has the following characteristics:

- Conserves energy by reducing heat loss or heat gain through ducts, pipes, and buildings.
- Controls surface temperatures of equipment for safety and personal comfort.

DID YOU KNOW?
Dew Point

The dew point is the temperature at which air becomes saturated with moisture. As warm air cools to the temperature of the ambient air, the relative humidity approaches 100 percent. At this point, the air is saturated—it can't hold any more moisture. The extra moisture forms tiny drops of water called condensation. This is why you can see your breath on a cold day and why windows often have moisture on them in the winter. The dew point is proportional to the amount of moisture in the air: The higher the moisture content in the air, the higher the dew point temperature.

DID YOU KNOW?
R-Values

The thermal resistance value, or R-value, is a measurement of the ability of insulation to retard the flow of heat. The American Society of Heating, Refrigerating, and Air-Conditioning Engineers (ASHRAE) has developed a standard that sets minimum recommended R-values for both commercial and residential construction. The standard, which has been published by ASHRAE, is called ASHRAE/IES 90.1-1989 *Energy Efficient Design of New Buildings Except Low-Rise Residential Buildings*.

Choosing the Right Insulation

Choosing the right insulation depends on a variety of factors, including the type of system to be insulated, the materials available, and the project budget. You should also consider the operating temperature of the system. Generally, operating temperatures fall into three ranges:

- *Low*, ranging from –100°F to 60°F. Examples include refrigeration, cold/chilled water, rain leaders, roof drains, and commercial heating and cooling systems.
- *Medium*, ranging from 61°F to 600°F. Examples include hot water and low-pressure steam, power or process piping, and ovens and stacks.
- *High*, ranging from 601°F to 1,500°F. Examples include power generators, high-pressure steam, turbines, kilns, smelters, exhaust systems, and power piping.

You must also consider whether the system is outside, inside, or both. If the system must function outside, the insulation needs to be protected from weather. Finally, consider whether the ambient temperature fluctuates or is constant.

- Allows for temperature control of a piece of equipment or a building.
- Prevents vapor condensation at surfaces that have a temperature below the dew point of the surrounding environment.
- Helps to control hazardous fire conditions that can be created by grease-laden air in a kitchen exhaust system.

Depending on the type, thermal insulation may also have some of the following characteristics:

- Adds structural strength to a wall or ceiling.
- Provides support for a surface finish.
- Prevents condensation.
- Reduces damage to equipment or buildings if they are exposed to fire or freezing temperatures.
- Reduces noise and vibration.

4.0.0 ◆ PRINCIPLES OF ACOUSTIC INSULATION

An HVAC system not only transmits air, but can also transmit noise. There are two types of potential noise in an HVAC system: system-generated noise (for example, noise produced by HVAC equipment, air flowing through the system, and equipment vibration) and occupant-generated noise (people talking, televisions and radios playing, and so on).

The fan, or blower, is the main source of system-generated noise in an HVAC system. Part of the horsepower supplied to the fan radiates out as sound. The more powerful the fan, the noisier it will be. Manufacturers provide a rating, called *sound power level*, that tells you how much noise a fan will produce.

As air flows through the ductwork, it produces noise when it changes direction, when it flows through a damper, or when there is a change in the duct size. Under certain conditions, air can also produce noise as it flows through straight sections of duct.

Some motors in an HVAC system transmit vibrations and low-frequency noise to the structure to which they are attached. Antivibration mountings, therefore, are usually needed between such motors and the structure. These mountings, which may be made of springs or rubber, help to absorb the vibration and reduce the noise level.

Sheet metal ductwork can act as a speaker tube. For example, if one duct serves two rooms, sound can pass from one room through the duct into the other room. So without proper sound attenuation, this occupant-generated noise, called cross-talk, can get into the ductwork as easily as system-generated noise can get out. The direction of the airflow has little to do with the direction of the noise transmitted. Sound can be transmitted both upstream and downstream from the source.

DID YOU KNOW?

Air Noise

The amount of noise that flowing air makes depends on air velocity (speed) and the size of the space through which the air flows. The next time you are riding in a car on the highway, roll down your window. You will hear the sound of wind rushing past the car. Roll your window halfway up and you will notice that the wind sounds louder. Roll the window up almost all the way, leaving a small space for the air to enter the car. Notice that the sound has changed again and now sounds higher as air whistles through the small space. In an HVAC system, air will produce sound in the same way. The more the airflow is restricted, the higher the sound will be.

HVAC System Layout

In an HVAC system, it is important to avoid abrupt changes in the size or direction of the ducts. Duct components that will cause turbulence, such as dampers, should not be placed close to bends in the system. Dampers should be placed as far as possible from diffusers and from rooms that will be occupied. It is better to install two dampers that are 20 percent closed than one damper that is 40 percent closed. Why? Two dampers that only slightly restrict the airflow will make less noise than one damper that highly restricts airflow.

1. In addition to insulation, cold air and water systems also require a _____ over porous insulation.
    a. condenser cover
    b. vapor barrier
    c. sound attenuator
    d. fiberglass blanket

2. When air has become completely saturated with moisture, it is said to be at the _____.
    a. dew point
    b. vapor barrier point
    c. ambient temperature
    d. convection temperature

3. Thermal insulation is designed to _____.
    a. transfer heat by convection
    b. transfer heat by conduction
    c. slow the flow of heat energy
    d. increase the flow of heat energy

4. The term *R-value* is a shorter way of saying _____.
    a. attenuation resistance value
    b. vapor resistance value
    c. sound resistance value
    d. thermal resistance value

5. The acoustic rating that manufacturers provide for the fan or blower in an HVAC system is called the _____.
    a. sound vibration level
    b. sound power level
    c. straight-flow sound level
    d. turbulence vibration level

5.0.0 ◆ FIBROUS GLASS DUCT LINER

Fibrous glass duct liner is made of glass fibers bonded with a thermosetting (heat-setting) resin. Two forms are available: flexible blankets supplied in rolls (see *Figure 1*) and rigid boards supplied as sheets (see *Figure 2*).

Fibrous glass duct liner is designed to do the following:

-   Lessen noise generated by the HVAC system and by building occupants
-   Reduce heat loss or gain through sheet metal duct surfaces

-   Prevent water vapor condensation on the inside and outside of the duct

Fibrous glass duct liner is not suitable for all applications. Its use is *not* recommended for the following applications:

-   With equipment that does not include automatic temperature controls
-   In any application where an operating temperature of 250°F may be exceeded
-   In kitchens or fume exhaust ducts
-   In ducts carrying solids or corrosive gases
-   With coal- or wood-fueled equipment
-   In any application where the duct may come in contact with water (such as cooling coils, humidifiers, or evaporative coolers) unless the duct is protected from the water source
-   Inside fire damper sleeves
-   Near high-temperature heating coils unless the duct is protected from heat radiation
-   In systems supplying operating rooms, delivery rooms, recovery rooms, nurseries, isolation rooms, and intensive care units

105F01.EPS

Figure 1 ◆ Flexible fibrous glass duct liner.

105F02.EPS

Figure 2 ◆ Rigid fibrous glass duct liner.

5.1.0 Property Requirements

The **American Society for Testing and Materials (ASTM)** tests many materials used in the sheet metal trade and other industries. It sets standards, called property requirements, that these materials must meet. Manufacturers must make their products in accordance with ASTM requirements in order to use the ASTM seal. The ASTM has established property requirements (ASTM C 1071) for fibrous glass duct liner in the following areas:

- *Acoustical performance*—a standard for how well sound is attenuated.
- *Corrosiveness*—a standard for limiting corrosion where duct liner contacts sheet metal.
- *Moisture vapor absorption*—a standard to limit moisture absorption.
- *Fungi resistance*—a standard to limit the growth of fungi and bacteria.
- *Temperature resistance*—a standard to prevent burning, glowing, smoking, smoldering, or delamination of the liner material.
- *Erosion resistance*—a standard to prevent the insulation from breaking away, flaking off, or delaminating.
- *Odor emission*—a standard to prevent the transmission of objectionable odors from the insulation.
- *Flame and smoke rating*—a standard that defines how quickly flames and smoke will spread when the materials are ignited.
- *Thermal conductivity*—a standard that defines the rate at which heat is conducted.

5.2.0 Cutting

Fibrous glass duct liner may be cut using one of the following methods:

- By hand, using a utility knife or insulation knife (see *Figure 3*). Knives that are specially designed to cut duct liner are available from several manufacturers.
- By machine, using automatic coil line equipment (see *Figure 4*). Many different types of coil line equipment exist. You must read, understand, and follow the manufacturer's cutting recommendations for the specific equipment you are using.
- By computer, which can be programmed to cut rectangular shapes for straight duct sections or special shapes for fittings.

When using mechanical or computer-operated equipment, you must follow the manufacturer's operating instructions and safety guidelines.

DID YOU KNOW?

ASTM

ASTM develops and publishes standards for a wide range of materials, products, systems, and services. Volunteer committees made up of industry professionals and experts develop and review the standards on a regular basis. Some of the areas covered include iron and steel, medical devices, electrical insulation, paints, plastics, rubber, and textiles. These standards promote public health and safety and commerce.

105F03.EPS

Figure 3 ◆ Cutting fibrous duct liner by hand.

105F04.EPS

Figure 4 ◆ Cutting fibrous duct liner on an automatic coil line.

5.3.0 Adhesives and Mechanical Fasteners

Fibrous glass duct liners are fastened inside sheet metal ductwork with special adhesives, which must meet the property requirements of ASTM C 916. These adhesives are also used to repair minor damage to the liner surface and to coat exposed edges of the liner.

These adhesives are either **solvent** based or water based and are classified by ASTM according to their flammability when wet and when dry. Vapors from solvent-based adhesives can be dangerous. However, solvent-based adhesives generally become tacky and bond more quickly than water-based adhesives. You can apply adhesives by roller coating, spraying, or brushing.

 WARNING!
Vapors from some solvent-based adhesives may be explosive. Never apply solvent-based adhesives near open flames, welding operations, or other potential ignition sources. You must always follow the manufacturer's recommendations regarding fire hazards, proper ventilation, and storage.

Mechanical fasteners are required in addition to adhesives when installing fibrous duct glass liners. Three types of fastener are commonly used:

- *Mechanically secured*—these are hardened steel fasteners that are driven into the duct (see *Figure 5*).

- *Weld-secured*—these fasteners either have integral (see *Figure 6*) or press-on (see *Figure 7*) heads. The welding equipment used to secure these fasteners must be carefully adjusted to get a solid weld without burning through the liner material.

- *Adhesive secured*—these fasteners have a large base to hold the adhesive (see *Figure 8*). However, some adhesives lose their gripping power as they age, so this type of fastener may not be appropriate for all applications. Follow the manufacturer's recommendations.

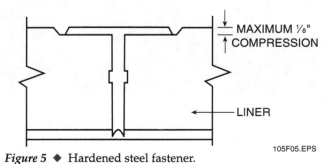

Figure 5 ◆ Hardened steel fastener.

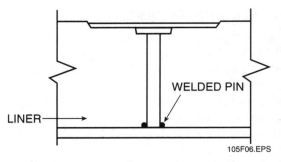

Figure 6 ◆ Weld-secured fastener with integral head.

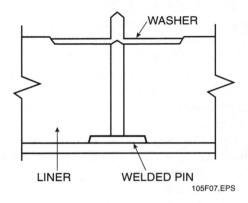

Figure 7 ◆ Weld-secured fastener with press-on head.

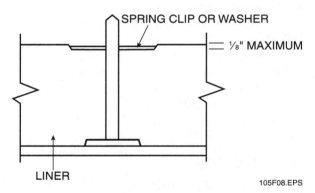

Figure 8 ◆ Adhesive-secured fastener.

Fastener heads should have a minimum area of .75 inches and a minimum thickness of .01 inches. They should also have either cupped or beveled heads. Fastener heads must not compress the insulation more than ⅛ inch.

Correct spacing of mechanical fasteners is very important. Mechanical fasteners must have the following characteristics:

- Be as corrosion resistant as G60 galvanized steel when installed. (G60 means there are 60 ounces of zinc coating used for every 100 square feet of steel.)

- Indefinitely sustain a 50-pound tensile dead load test perpendicular to the duct wall.

- Not affect the fire hazard classification of the duct liner and adhesive.

- Not damage the duct liner when applied as recommended.
- Not cause leakage in the duct.
- Be able to be installed perpendicular to the duct surface.
- Project only nominally into the airflow.
- Be the correct length for the specified duct liner thickness.
- Not compress the duct liner more than ⅛ inch based on nominal insulation thickness.

In addition, mechanical fasteners must be located and spaced regardless of airflow direction as shown in *Figure 9*. As you can see, the expected velocity of air moving through the duct affects the spacing of mechanical fasteners.

5.3.1 Metal Nosing

When air velocity exceeds 4,000 feet per minute (fpm), metal nosing—either channel nosing (see *Figure 10*) or zee nosing (see *Figure 11*)—must be mechanically secured on the edges of the duct liner facing the air stream. Metal nosing is also required in the following areas:

- Over transverse liner edges facing the air stream at **fan discharge.**
- At any interval of lined duct preceded by unlined duct.

Dimension		Velocity, fpm (m/sec) 0–2500 (0–12.7)	Velocity, fpm (m/sec) 2501–6000 (12.7–30.5)
A	From corners of duct	4" (100mm)	4" (100mm)
B	From transverse end of duct liner	3" (75mm)	3" (75mm)
C	Across duct width, OC, minimum 1 per side	12" (300mm)	6" (150mm)
D	Along duct length, OC, minimum 1 per side	18" (450mm)	16" (400mm)

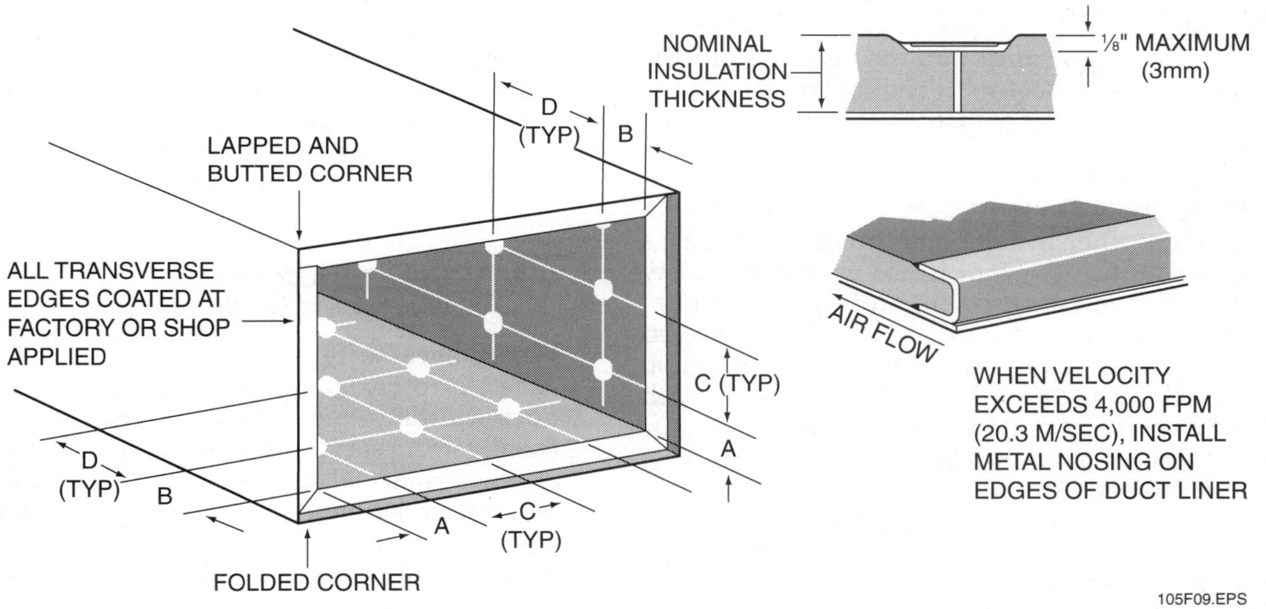

Figure 9 ◆ Mechanical fastener spacing.

Riveting Ideas

Fastening Fibrous Duct Liner

On fittings with tight radiuses, the duct liner may separate from the sheet metal before the adhesive has had time to bond. To solve this problem, you must apply additional mechanical fasteners to ensure that the duct liner remains in contact with the sheet metal until the adhesive dries.

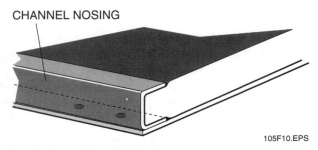

CHANNEL NOSING

105F10.EPS

Figure 10 ◆ Channel nosing.

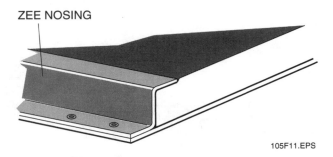

ZEE NOSING

105F11.EPS

Figure 11 ◆ Zee nosing.

5.4.0 Installing Duct Liner

Store all materials and fabricated duct sections in a safe, dry place until you are ready to do the installation. Protect materials from dust, dirt, moisture, and damage before and during installation. You must replace any wet or contaminated duct liner.

Wear the appropriate personal protective equipment when installing fibrous duct liner. This equipment includes, but is not limited to, safety glasses, gloves, a hard hat, and eye protection. You should also wear a loose-fitting, long-sleeved shirt and long pants. In addition, the National Institute for Occupational Safety and Health (NIOSH) recommends that when the level of dust is not known you should wear a NIOSH-rated and -approved respirator.

Before installation, make sure that the duct liner can be installed in accordance with project drawings, performance guidelines and limitations, and the standards for installation published by the **North American Insulation Manufacturers Association (NAIMA)**. The following are general installation guidelines:

- Cover 100 percent of the interior metal surfaces of the duct sections.
- Neatly butt all joints.
- Make sure there are no interruptions or gaps at the joints.
- Install duct liner with the surface treatment exposed to the air stream.

- Fasten duct liner to the duct with a minimum of 90 percent coverage of the surface with adhesive. The adhesive must comply with ASTM C 916.
- Apply an approved adhesive coating to all transverse edges that are not to be covered with sheet metal nosing.
- Confirm that longitudinal joints occur at the corners of the duct.
- Remember, if longitudinal joints are exposed, you must coat these joints with an adhesive designed for duct liner application that meets the ASTM C 916 standard.
- Ensure that, in addition to the adhesive coating, you secure longitudinal joints with mechanical fasteners.
- Secure duct liner with additional mechanical fasteners, as described in this module, that conform to the standard published by NAIMA.
- Where air velocity exceeds 4,000 fpm, install metal nosing on the upstream edges of lined duct sections, as described in this module.
- When installing flexible duct liner, use one of two methods on the corners: fold and compress it at the corners of rectangular duct sections or cut and fit it to ensure a lapped, compressed corner joint (see *Figure 12*).
- When installing rigid duct liner, cut and fit it to ensure taut, overlapped corner joints. The top pieces of rigid duct must be supported by the side pieces of rigid duct (see *Figure 13*).

5.4.1 Installing Accessories Inside Lined Duct

Where accessories—such as dampers, turning vanes, or other devices—are placed inside lined duct or fittings, the installation must not damage the air stream surface. The use of metal hat sections or other build-outs is optional. If you use a build-out, you must mechanically secure it to the duct wall. All inside spaces of hat sections or other build-outs must be insulated as shown in *Figure 14*.

DID YOU KNOW?

NAIMA

NAIMA serves all segments of the construction industry. NAIMA promotes energy efficiency and environmental preservation through the use of insulation products and encourages their safe production and use.

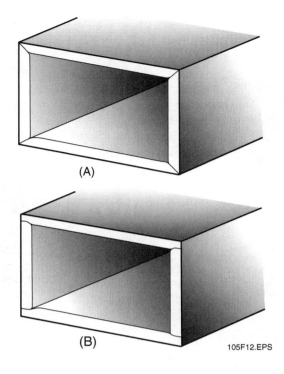

(A)

(B)

105F12.EPS

Figure 12 ◆ Flexible duct liner. (A) Corners folded. (B) Corners lapped.

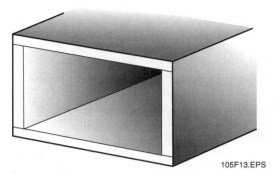

105F13.EPS

Figure 13 ◆ Rigid duct liner with corners lapped and side pieces supporting top pieces.

If air velocity ranges between 4,001 and 6,000 fpm (20.3 to 30.5 minutes per second), metal nosing must be applied to the upstream exposed edges of the duct liner. As noted in an earlier section of this module, metal nosing is also required in the following areas:

• Over transverse liner edges facing the air stream at fan discharge
• At any interval of lined duct preceded by unlined duct

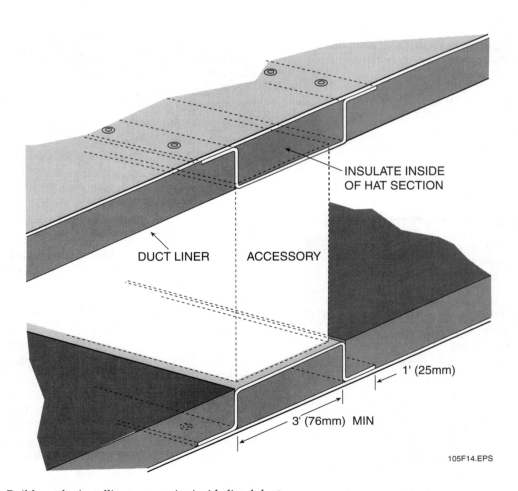

INSULATE INSIDE OF HAT SECTION

DUCT LINER   ACCESSORY

1' (25mm)

3' (76mm) MIN

105F14.EPS

Figure 14 ◆ Build-out for installing accessories inside lined duct.

5.4.2 Installing Liner at Fire-Rated Assemblies

Duct liner must be interrupted at fire-rated assemblies, such as fire dampers, to avoid interfering with the damper's operation and to meet the minimum clearance specified for the assembly. In *Figure 15*, the damper sleeve is installed through the firewall. (The damper manufacturer will provide specifications for securing the sleeve assembly to the wall.) The duct is attached to the sleeve assembly with *S* connectors. Exposed sleeve surfaces must be insulated with duct wrap, and metal nosing is required on upstream exposed edges of the duct liner.

5.4.3 Two-Layer Installation

NAIMA does not recommend installing two layers of fibrous duct liner. However, if the job specifications require the use of two layers, these steps must be followed:

Step 1 Adhere the first layer of duct liner to the sheet metal.

Step 2 Adhere the top layer of duct liner to the bottom layer using a minimum of 90 percent adhesive coverage.

Step 3 Use mechanical fasteners of the proper length for the double layer of duct liner.

Step 4 Ensure that leading edges of double-layer duct linings are firmly fastened to prevent separation of the two layers.

When air velocity exceeds 4,000 fpm, nosing must also be installed in two-layer liner installations (see *Figure 16*).

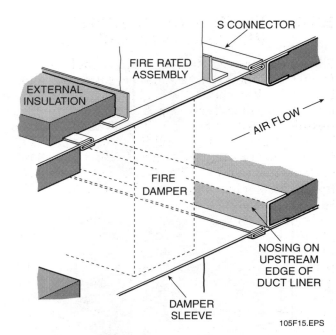

Figure 15 ◆ Interruption of duct liner at a fire-rated assembly.

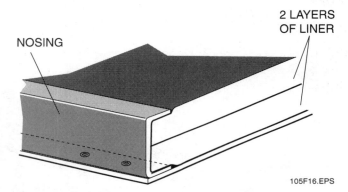

Figure 16 ◆ Nosing on two-layer duct installation.

Riveting Ideas
Housekeeping Tips

To prevent fiberglass fibers from transferring to your other clothes, wash work clothing separately, then rinse your washing machine thoroughly before using it again. If you have a lot of glass fibers on your clothes, soak them first, then wash them.

Keep your work area clean. Avoid unnecessary handling of scrap fibers by keeping waste disposal equipment as close to the work area as possible.

Never use a compressed air line to clean up the work area. Using this tool stirs up fibers and produces airborne dust. It is best to use a filtered vacuum.

5.5.0 Inspecting

After the lined duct system is completely installed, conduct a final inspection. This inspection should include the following:

- Check all registers, grilles, and **diffusers** to make sure that they are clean and free of construction debris.
- Using the manufacturer's instructions, check all filters.
- Cover air supply openings with temporary filters before starting up the system to catch any loose material that may still be in the ductwork.
- Turn the HVAC system on and allow it to run until steady operation is reached.
- Remove the temporary filters and any loose material caught by the filters.

6.0.0 ◆ FIBERGLASS BLANKET INSULATION (WRAP)

Fiberglass blanket insulation is available in two forms: flexible blankets sold in rolls and rigid boards sold as sheets. Fiberglass blanket insulation is also called duct wrap, flexible insulation, or flexible blanket insulation. It is used to insulate HVAC duct systems in buildings and to insulate the exterior of **plenums,** fittings and valves, and surfaces that require temperature control. You will install blanket insulation mainly above ceilings or behind finished walls.

This type of insulation is made of fine, inorganic glass fibers that are bonded with a heat-setting resin. It is sold in large rolls that are tightly compressed in a plastic bag, so it may not appear to be as thick as the package indicates. However, the insulation will return to the stated thickness when you remove it from the bag and unroll it. It comes in ¾-pound, 1-pound, and 1½-pound densities (sometimes called Type 75, Type 100, and Type 150). Density is measured in cubic feet. For example, a density of 1 pound means that 1 cubic foot of insulation weighs 1 pound. Thickness ranges from 1 to 3 inches with 1½ inches by ¾-pound density as a common selection. The roll length depends on the thickness. The most common lengths are 100 feet for a 1½-inch thickness and 75 feet for a 2-inch thickness. The standard width is 48 inches.

Manufacturers also apply a facing material on one side of the insulation blanket. This facing material is designed to meet heat, sound, condensation, and fire-resistance requirements. Facings include **Foil Scrim Kraft (FSK),** vinyl, and **All Service Jacket (ASJ).** They usually have a 2-inch staple flap along the edge to assist in installation (see *Figure 17*).

In a typical commercial HVAC system, you will insulate the ducts after the ductwork is installed, tested, and inspected, and before the ceiling grid is in place. Generally, you will insulate the trunk line or main line of duct first and then move on to the **runouts** or branches. A simplified drawing of a typical duct system is shown in *Figure 18*. Parts of some duct systems may be lined internally with insulation. Lined duct may or may not require external insulation.

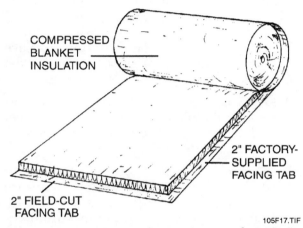

Figure 17 ◆ Fiberglass blanket insulation with staple flaps.

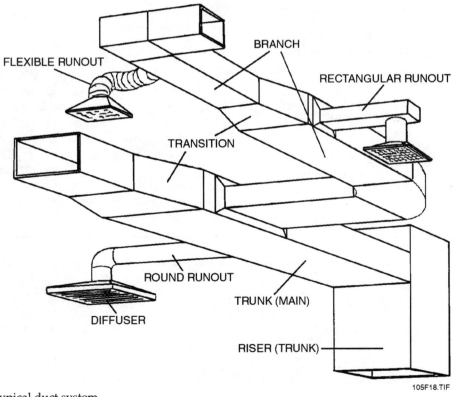

Figure 18 ◆ A typical duct system.

6.1.0 Measuring and Cutting

To measure and cut fiberglass blanket insulation, you will need a tape measure, a utility knife and blades, a straightedge, and a large piece of heavy cardboard. Because fiberglass may irritate your eyes and skin, wear safety glasses, gloves, long pants, a long-sleeved shirt, and a hat. In addition, NIOSH recommends that when the level of dust is not known that a NIOSH-rated and -approved respirator be worn.

The following instructions contain information for rectangular, round, and oval duct. To measure and cut fiberglass blanket insulation, follow these steps:

Step 1 Choose an area in which to measure and cut the insulation. It should be out of the way of foot traffic and near where you will install the insulation. You will most likely cut the insulation on the floor, so place heavy cardboard or plywood under the insulation to prevent floor damage.

Step 2 Open one end of the plastic bag and remove the blanket. Roll out several feet with the facing side down. Save the plastic bag to dispose of scraps.

Step 3 Measure the distance around the straight section of rectangular duct. If you are using a 1½-inch thick blanket, add an 8-inch stretchout to this measurement. This new figure is the length of insulation you will cut to wrap around the duct. The additional 8 inches will allow for the thickness of the insulation at each corner of the duct plus a 2-inch facing (staple flap) tab. If the insulation is 2 inches thick, add a 10-inch stretchout to the length. An example of how to measure a 1½-inch thick blanket to fit a 12" × 6" rectangular duct is shown in *Figure 19*.

For round or oval duct, first measure the circumference. If the insulating material is 1½ inches thick, add 10 inches to the circumference to find the proper length to cut. If the insulation is 2 inches thick, add 12 inches to the circumference.

Step 4 Check the end of the roll to ensure that it is straight and square. Some ends may become damaged or separated in packing. Use your utility knife and straightedge to cut off any damaged portion.

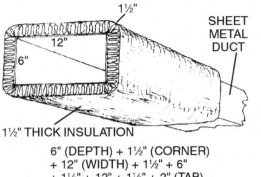

1½"
12"
6"
SHEET METAL DUCT
1½" THICK INSULATION

6" (DEPTH) + 1½" (CORNER)
+ 12" (WIDTH) + 1½" + 6"
+ 1½" + 12" + 1½" + 2" (TAB)
= 44" TOTAL LENGTH TO BE CUT
OF 1½" THICK BLANKET INSULATION

105F19.TIF

Figure 19 ◆ How to measure duct insulation.

 DID YOU KNOW?
How Fiberglass Insulation Works

Heat naturally moves toward cold by conduction or convection. For example, a stainless steel pan is an excellent conductor. It allows heat to travel freely from its source (a stove-top burner) to the food in the pan.

The glass fibers in fiberglass insulation, on the other hand, are poor conductors, so fiberglass insulation is an excellent material for controlling heat loss. Fiberglass insulation is made up of fine strands of glass randomly held together in a mat. Tiny pockets of air lie between each of the fibers. Heat can travel through these air pockets by convection. But because the glass fibers are randomly placed, no direct path exists. The longer it takes the heat to travel through the mat, the more effective the insulation is at controlling heat loss. This is why you must not overly compress the insulation blanket—you will shorten the convection path and reduce the insulation's effectiveness.

 *Riveting Ideas*

Roof Openings

During construction, some parts of a building may still be unfinished when you install the insulation. For example, openings may have been left in the roof for equipment installation. You must be alert to any roof openings over the ducts you install. Because these areas are exposed to the weather, you should not install insulation until the roof openings are closed.

Step 5 Measure and mark both edges of the unrolled insulation (see *Figure 20*).

Step 6 Align your straightedge with the marks and cut from the far edge to the near edge. Make a clean cut through *both* fiberglass and facing (see *Figure 21*).

Step 7 Create a facing tab. Move the straightedge 2 inches in from your cut. Cut through the fiberglass but *not* through the facing material. Remove the 2-inch-wide strip of fiberglass. Use your knife to scrape the fiberglass loose from the facing (see *Figure 22*).

Step 8 Place scraps in the plastic bag for proper disposal. The piece is now ready for installation.

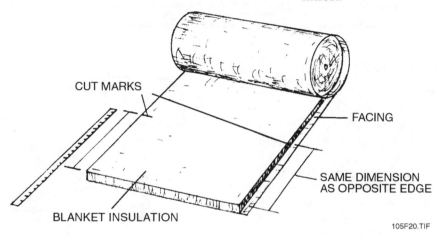

CUT MARKS

FACING

SAME DIMENSION AS OPPOSITE EDGE

BLANKET INSULATION

105F20.TIF

Figure 20 ◆ Measuring and marking the cut.

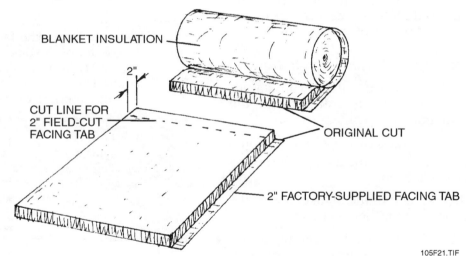

BLANKET INSULATION

2"

CUT LINE FOR 2" FIELD-CUT FACING TAB

ORIGINAL CUT

2" FACTORY-SUPPLIED FACING TAB

105F21.TIF

Figure 21 ◆ Fiberglass blanket after cutting.

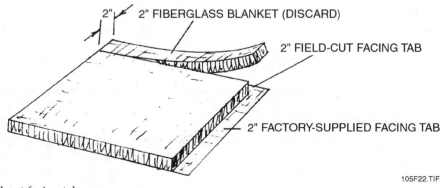

2" 2" FIBERGLASS BLANKET (DISCARD)

2" FIELD-CUT FACING TAB

2" FACTORY-SUPPLIED FACING TAB

105F22.TIF

Figure 22 ◆ Field-cut facing tab.

Riveting Ideas

You can use math to determine how much insulation to cut for a round or oval duct. Say that the insulation you will wrap around the round or oval duct is 1½ inches thick. When you wrap the insulation around the pipe, you will increase the pipe's circumference by 3 inches (1½ inches on each side of the pipe). When you multiply 3 inches by 3.14 (pi), you will get approximately 10 inches (with a little compression). So that is the length of insulation you should cut. You can apply the same principle for any thickness of insulation. If, for example, the insulation is 2 inches thick, you would multiply 4 inches × 3.14. So the length of the insulation you would cut is 12 inches (with a little compression).

6.2.0 Installing Fiberglass Blanket Insulation

There are several acceptable methods for attaching fiberglass blanket insulation to pipes or ductwork. These methods include the butt joint with stapled tab method, the adhesive method, and the stitch method. Another method, the wire method, may be required for some installations. For this method, you tie wire around the insulation blanket on 8-inch centers. However, this method is not recommended because the wire may puncture the vapor barrier and crush the insulation. You should follow local practice or use the method required in the job specifications.

6.2.1 Butt Joint With Stapled Tab Method

For this method you will use flare-head staples and an outward-clinch staple gun to fasten the ends of the insulation. Follow these steps:

Step 1 Place the cut piece of insulation over the top of the duct with the facing tab toward you (see *Figure 23*).

Step 2 Hold the top end of the blanket and reach under the duct for the other end.

Step 3 Pull the end of the blanket snugly around the duct. Do not compress the blanket more than 50 percent at the corners. Check for proper fit.

Step 4 Hold the facing tab down snugly on the blanket underneath. Staple in the middle of the facing tab. Check the underside of the duct to ensure the insulation is snug.

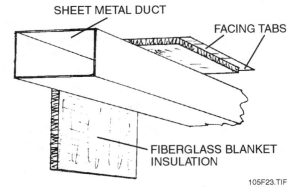

Figure 23 ◆ Applying the insulation to the duct.

Step 5 Staple every 2 to 4 inches as required to securely fasten the facing tab. Staple from the center of the piece out to the edges (see *Figure 24*). You must install the staples with a flared head or outward clinch so that they do not penetrate the facing (see *Figure 25*).

CAUTION

The corners of projections are sharp. You must avoid puncturing the facing on these corners. If you puncture the facing, you must apply a patch made of insulation and facing over the puncture and seal it.

Step 6 Install the next piece of insulation in the same way, butting it snugly against the first piece. After fastening the insulation with staples, pull the facing tab over the first piece of insulation and staple this tab around the duct. The staple ends should not penetrate through the facing.

Riveting Ideas

Efficient Cutting

If the duct requires several pieces of the same size, you can cut these pieces at one time. Make sure that you do not overly compress the insulation when cutting more than one piece at a time. Compressing the fibers reduces the effectiveness of the insulation.

When installing blanket insulation around duct hangers, split the butt end of the blanket at the hanger to allow the two split pieces to be pulled over the duct. Secure with staples. Seal the facing split with manufacturer-approved tape (see *Figure 26*).

Ductwork may have projections that stand out 1½ to 2 inches from the surface of the duct. These projections include standing seams, reinforcement flanges, and ribs (see *Figure 27*).

Install the insulation blanket so that it blouses over the duct and is taut but not compressed at these projections.

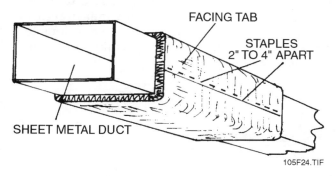

Figure 24 ◆ Insulation with staples.

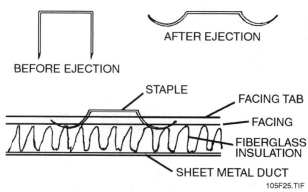

Figure 25 ◆ Proper staple application.

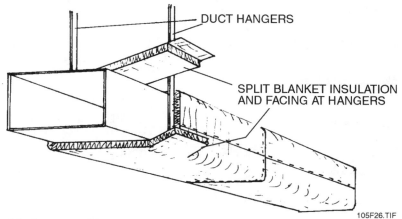

Figure 26 ◆ Installing the blanket around hangers.

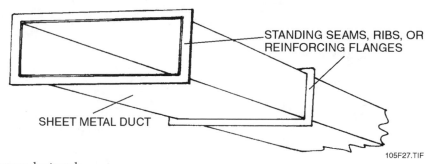

Figure 27 ◆ Projections on ductwork.

You can use tape tabs to hold down the nonflap side of the insulation against the ductwork. This will enable you to use both hands to control the flapped edged of the insulation and the staple gun.

Step 7 Continue installing sections of blanket until you reach a branch connection, a reducer connection, or a tee. Do not cut a circular or rectangular piece from the blanket. Instead, split the blanket around the branch to allow it to flare out (see *Figure 28*).

Install the blanket around fittings (offsets, elbows, transitions, reducers, and so on) by working from the largest duct to the smaller runouts. Wrap the insulation around the largest section of duct first, split it at the corners, tuck it, and secure it by pulling snugly on the smaller sections (see *Figure 29*).

Install blanket insulation on the branch lines and runouts beginning at the trunk line. The insulation must snugly butt or overlap the trunk line insulation. Split the facing tab at the corners to allow the tab to flare over the trunk line insulation. Staple the facing tab to the trunk line insulation (see *Figure 30*).

Overlap any pre-installed flexible duct insulation. Continue the insulation to the diffuser. Cut, fit, and seal the insulation to the back of the diffuser. Seal all insulation ends at **fire dampers,** connections, and so forth with manufacturer-approved tape. Make sure the tape overlaps to a metal surface. Rub the tape firmly to ensure a complete seal.

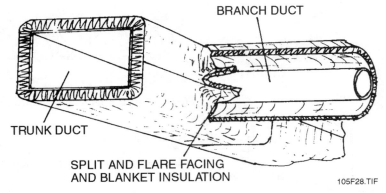

Figure 28 ◆ Splitting the blanket around a branch.

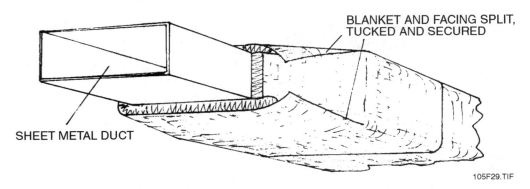

Figure 29 ◆ The blanket facing is split, tucked, and secured.

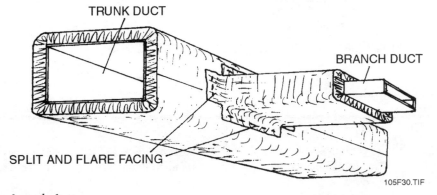

Figure 30 ◆ Insulating a branch duct.

6.2.2 Adhesive Method

Job specifications may require you to cement the blanket insulation to the duct with a solvent-based adhesive. Follow these steps:

Step 1 Read the safety precautions on the adhesive label. They may require you to wear a respirator, to work in a well-ventilated area, or both.

Step 2 Make sure no one in your work area is using equipment that produces sparks or flames. Solvent-based adhesives are flammable when wet.

Step 3 Cover finished floors to protect the finish from adhesive drips and splatters.

Step 4 Brush a coat of adhesive on the top edge of the duct.

Step 5 Place the blanket insulation on the top edge of the duct and press into place.

Step 6 Brush on strips of adhesive spaced about 6 inches apart around the sides and bottom of the duct (see *Figure 31*).

Step 7 Pull the blanket snugly around the duct and press into place.

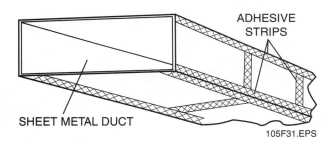

ADHESIVE STRIPS

SHEET METAL DUCT

105F31.EPS

Figure 31 ◆ Brushed-on adhesive strips.

6.2.3 Stitch Method

With this method, you will measure the duct as described earlier in this section, but you must add an extra 2 inches to the measurement. Follow these steps:

Step 1 Pull the insulation blanket snugly around the duct.

Step 2 Fold the two horizontal edges outward and staple along the edge every 2 to 4 inches (see *Figure 32*).

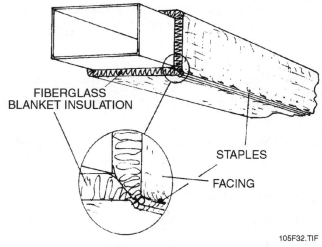

FIBERGLASS BLANKET INSULATION

STAPLES

FACING

105F32.TIF

Figure 32 ◆ The stitch method.

6.3.0 Sealing

You must seal the seams, joints, or facing tabs on blanket insulation with manufacturer-approved tape or adhesive. Some applications require that you also apply vapor barrier **mastic** to joints, seams, and staple penetrations. Review the job specifications for sealing requirements and recommended materials.

6.3.1 Insulation Tape

To use insulation tape, follow these steps:

Step 1 Measure and cut the amount of tape needed.

Step 2 Peel the protective paper contact strip from the tape.

Step 3 Press the tape down over the staples and the facing joint. Seal any punctures or tears in the facing with tape.

Step 4 Seal the facing to metal surfaces at termination points, such as air handling units, diffuser backs, and fire dampers. Rub the tape firmly to ensure a complete seal.

Riveting Ideas

Insulation Tape

Manufacturers supply tape that has been specially designed for use with insulation and that meets the temperature requirements of the installation. The adhesive part of the tape is covered with a protective paper contact strip. Always read the manufacturer's specifications for any application restrictions (such as temperature).

6.3.2 Adhesive

To use adhesive, follow these steps:

Step 1 Read the label for the manufacturer's instructions regarding application, drying time, and safety precautions. Wear recommended appropriate personal protective equipment.

Step 2 Brush the adhesive under the facing tab.

Step 3 Rub the tabs firmly to ensure a complete seal.

Step 4 Staple the blanket insulation or apply a quick-drying contact adhesive.

6.3.3 Vapor Barrier Mastic

To use vapor barrier mastic, follow these steps:

Step 1 Read and follow the manufacturer's instructions and safety precautions. Wear recommended appropriate personal protective equipment.

Step 2 Protect finished floors and equipment from drops and splatters of mastic.

Step 3 If the manufacturer specifies glass-fiber mesh as reinforcement, fasten the mesh in place by stapling or gluing according to the manufacturer's instructions.

Step 4 Brush or trowel the mastic over the seams and staples. Apply the mastic to the hardest-to-reach areas first and work from the furthest point to the nearest. Do this to avoid reaching over wet mastic. Cover the mesh completely with the mastic.

Step 5 Seal all penetrations of the facing (such as duct hangers) tightly.

6.4.0 Mechanical Fasteners

You will use mechanical fasteners on the bottom surface of large ducts to keep fiberglass blanket insulation from sagging. Fasteners include self-adhesive stickpins, cemented stickpins, weld pins, and cupped-head weld pins. Some of these fasteners are shown in *Figure 33*.

Install cupped-head weld pins as you apply the insulation to the duct or after you have applied several pieces. When using cupped-head weld pins, follow these steps:

Step 1 Press the pins through the insulation and facing.

Step 2 Seal over the head with vapor barrier mastic or tape to ensure a complete vapor seal.

Install cemented stickpins and weld pins before you apply the insulation to the duct. You will first cement the pins to the duct. Use a heavy-bodied, general-purpose adhesive. You can apply it using a putty knife (if the adhesive comes in a can) or a caulking gun (if the adhesive comes in a tube). Follow these steps:

Step 1 Cut a piece of cardboard about 18" × 18".

Step 2 Stick several fastening pins into the cardboard with the anchor bases up (see *Figure 34*).

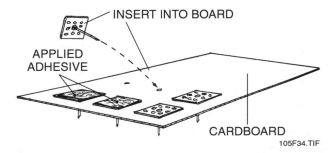

Figure 34 ◆ Fasteners set in cardboard.

Step 3 Apply adhesive to the entire base of each fastener. Cover each base with an even coat that is about ³⁄₁₆ of an inch thick.

Step 4 Place the fastener on the duct surface and press firmly into position (see *Figures 35 and 36*).

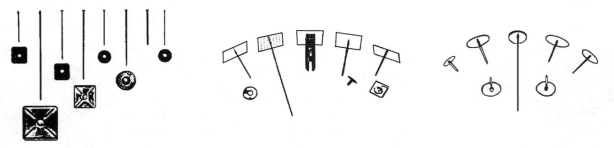

WELD PINS   CUPPED-HEAD WELD PINS   CEMENTED STICKPINS

105F33.TIF

Figure 33 ◆ Mechanical fasteners.

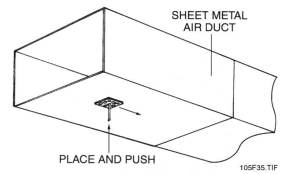

Figure 35 ◆ Fastener applied to sheet metal duct.

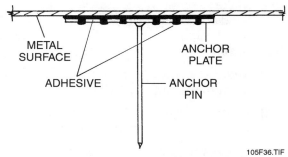

Figure 36 ◆ Close-up view of cemented fastener.

Wiggle the fastener on the surface slightly to set the adhesive. Some adhesive will press out through the holes in the base. Next, apply the insulation. Follow these steps:

Step 1 Press the pins into place. They should penetrate both the insulation and the facing.

Step 2 Place a self-locking washer or clip on the pin. Place the washer snug against the insulation. Do not press the washer completely to the duct surface.

Step 3 Cut the protruding pin flush, with the washer using end-cutting nippers.

Step 4 Place vapor barrier mastic or tape over the washer to ensure a complete vapor seal.

Job specifications may require you to install these fasteners on the bottom surface of all ducts more than 24 inches wide. Generally, a row of fasteners spaced every 18 inches in the middle of a duct that is 24 to 36 inches wide is adequate (see *Figure 37*).

If the duct is more than 36 inches wide, two or more rows of fasteners are required. Note that if you use adhesive to cement the insulation blanket to the duct, mechanical fasteners usually are not required. You should always check the job specifications.

6.5.0 Factory-Applied Adhesives

Some types of insulation are manufactured with a factory-applied adhesive. It has excellent gripping power and is easy to apply. The adhesive covers the entire sealing area, even the edges, uniformly.

One type of factory-applied adhesive is applied to insulation covered with a facing material, or **jacket** (see *Figure 38*). The adhesive is applied to a lap on the jacket and then covered with a protective paper contact strip. You must not remove this strip until you have positioned the insulation properly because the adhesive bonds on contact. This type of adhesive is also called a **self-sealing lap.**

To install insulation with a self-sealing lap, follow these steps:

Step 1 Make sure that the surfaces to be bonded are clean and dry, and that the temperature is above 50°F.

Step 2 Keep the jacket lap in the overlap position until you have fitted the insulation on the pipe or duct.

Step 3 Pull the jacket for a snug, not tight, fit.

Step 4 Make sure the jacket is in its final position before removing the contact strip.

Step 5 Remove the strip and press the jacket overlaps closed. Rub the seal briskly to ensure a proper seal. You can rub the seal with a knife handle, but it is best to use a plastic rubbing tool supplied by the manufacturer for this purpose.

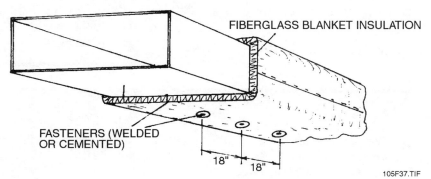

Figure 37 ◆ Fastener placement.

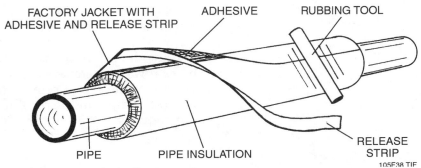

FACTORY JACKET WITH
ADHESIVE AND RELEASE STRIP   ADHESIVE   RUBBING TOOL

RELEASE
STRIP

PIPE   PIPE INSULATION

105F38.TIF

Figure 38 ◆ Insulation with factory-applied adhesive.

6.6.0 Field-Applied Adhesives

Field-applied adhesives also have excellent gripping power. More steps are involved in their application. The uniformity of the adhesive coverage depends on the skill of the installer. Because some field-applied adhesives contain solvents, you must wear respiratory protection and work in a well-ventilated area.

You will apply a liquid adhesive to seal laps or to bond fibrous insulation to sheet metal. Liquid adhesives are solvent-based and may be flammable when wet. However, most have a low **flame spread rating** and **smoke developed rating** when dry. You can apply the adhesive by spraying or brushing it on (see *Figure 39*). To apply solvent-based adhesives, follow these steps:

Step 1 Make sure the work area is properly ventilated, and wear approved respiratory protective equipment. Follow the manufacturer's recommended safety precautions.

Step 2 Make sure there is no danger of sparks or open flame in the work area.

Step 3 Spray or brush a light coat of adhesive on the lap surface, covering the surface completely to the edges.

Step 4 Allow the adhesive to dry until it becomes tacky to the touch.

Step 5 Install the insulation and rub the seal briskly. You can rub the seal with a knife handle, but it is best to use a plastic rubbing tool provided by the manufacturer for this purpose.

To use solvent-based adhesives, follow these steps:

Step 1 Make sure the work area is properly ventilated and wear approved respiratory protective equipment. Follow the manufacturer's recommended safety precautions.

Step 2 Make sure there is no danger of sparks or open flame in the work area.

Step 3 Protect finished floors, surfaces, and equipment from drips and splatters.

Step 4 Brush a heavy coat of adhesive on the surface to which you will apply the insulation.

Step 5 Press the insulation on the adhesive while the adhesive is still wet.

WARNING!

Solvent-based adhesives can be flammable and toxic. You must read and follow the manufacturer's safety and application instructions. Never remove the manufacturer's label from the container. Never apply a solvent-based adhesive in the presence of sparks or open flame. Always apply the adhesive in a well-ventilated area. If necessary, wear respiratory protection. When finished, store the brushes inside the container and close the container tightly.

CAUTION

Some solvent-based adhesives may not be compatible with plastic insulation and plastic insulation jackets. You must read the label carefully before using a solvent-based adhesive with plastic materials.

Volatile Organic Compound Emissions

Many manufacturers are producing safer adhesives in response to concerns about **volatile organic compound** (VOC) emissions. Check the solvent label and always use the safest adhesive that will suit the application.

Doing a High-Quality Job

As you have learned, pride of craftsmanship is an important quality. It separates the ordinary worker from the true professional. The following job-site guidelines will help you do a professional insulation job:

- Work safely. You may have to work from a ladder or scaffold. Set the ladder or scaffold on a hard, level surface. Inspect the scaffold for signs of weak joints before using it. If the scaffold is on wheels, make sure they are locked in place. Never exceed the recommended weight limit for a ladder or scaffold.
- Before beginning the installation, review the job specifications and check to make sure that you have the right size, type, and amount of insulation for the job.
- Don't open boxes or bags of insulation until you are ready to measure, cut, and install it. Open only one container at a time.
- Store the insulation in a clean, dry area to prevent it from becoming damaged or wet. Place the insulation and installation materials on pallets or boards to keep them off the floor. This is especially important in a building under construction where floors can become wet or damp.
- Be aware of others in your work area. If you are on a ladder or scaffold, secure tools and materials so that they can't fall to the floor. Never use flammable materials in the presence of sparks or flames.
- Clean up your work area. At the end of your work period, remove materials from passageways. Stack cartons neatly. Secure ladders and equipment. Pick up packaging, scraps, and other debris and place these items in cartons for proper disposal.

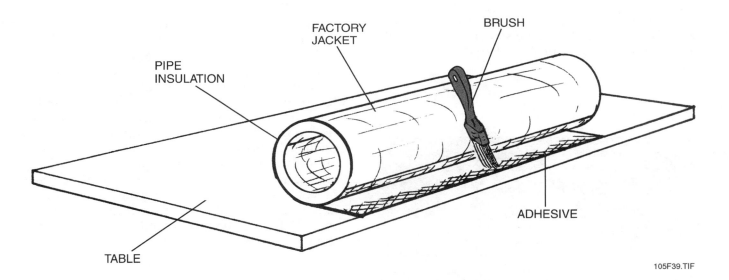

Figure 39 ◆ Field-applied adhesive.

Self-Sealing Laps and Temperature

Self-sealing laps generally work best at room temperature or at least at temperatures no lower than 50°F. The adhesive may become loose if exposed to temperatures over 150°F. Note that recommendations will vary somewhat from manufacturer to manufacturer and from product to product. You must always read and follow the manufacturer's recommendations for installation temperatures.

7.0.0 ◆ FIBERGLASS PIPE INSULATION

Fiberglass pipe insulation is made of glass fibers that are molded into a shape that fits around a pipe. It comes in standard 3-foot-long sections. The standard thickness ranges from ½ inch to 3 inches. To achieve more thickness, you can place thicker pieces over thinner pieces. This is called nesting or **sleeving.** Many manufacturers can provide fiberglass pipe insulation in a specific thickness on request.

Pipe insulation sizes are stated with the pipe size first, then the insulation thickness. For example, 2" × 1" pipe insulation is 1-inch-thick insulation that will fit a 2-inch pipe (inside dimension). The inside dimension of the insulation (the part that fits around the pipe) measures approximately 2⅜ inches.

Insulation sizes required for iron pipe are different from insulation sizes required for copper pipe (see *Table 1*). Note that some iron pipe insulation sizes will also fit a different size copper pipe. For example, ½-inch iron pipe insulation will also fit a ¾-inch copper pipe.

Fiberglass pipe insulation is specified for many types of pipe systems, including plumbing pipes, hot water heating pipes, steam pipes, chilled water pipes, and other pipe systems that operate at temperatures from below 0°F up to 850°F.

Fiberglass pipe insulation comes from the factory with a jacket wrapped around the pipe. This laminated cover consists of a layer of aluminum foil and strands of fiberglass thread for reinforcement. It usually has a white finish. The most widely used jacket is the All Service Jacket, or ASJ. The ASJ usually has a self-sealing lap—a factory-applied adhesive on the overlap of the jacket covered with a contact paper strip. The ASJ may be the final finish on the pipe insulation and may be painted or left plain. Additional jackets or coatings can be applied for appearance or to meet environmental requirements. The ASJ is not a weather barrier, and it cannot be installed outdoors without additional weather protection.

When fiberglass pipe insulation is installed on pipe systems operating at temperatures lower than the ambient temperature, the ASJ serves as a vapor barrier. The self-sealing lap also prevents moisture from entering the insulation. You must make sure that the ASJ is completely sealed to prevent moisture from entering the fiberglass. You must seal all staples as well as any cuts in the ASJ with vapor barrier mastic.

7.1.0 Measuring and Cutting

Use a sharp utility knife to cut fiberglass pipe insulation, and use scissors to cut the ASJ. You will have little cutting to do along straight, uninterrupted stretches of pipe. However, you will have to cut or trim the insulation around fittings. It is important to do this properly to avoid wasting insulation. Measure up to the fitting and cut the insulation section to fit. Use the remaining section of insulation on the other side of the fitting. Always place the cut ends toward the fitting (see *Figure 40*). You will also cut segments of insulation to insulate the fittings, or you can use **preformed fitting covers** such as Zeston®. If you use preformed fitting covers, you must butt the pipe insulation to the cover. This is done to support the covers.

Iron Pipe Size	Iron Pipe Insulation Size	Copper Pipe Size	Copper Pipe Insulation Size
½	½	½	⅝
¾	¾	¾	⅞ or ½ IPS*
1	1	1	1⅛ or ¾ IPS
1¼	1¼	1¼	1⅜ or 1 IPS
1½	1½	1½	1⅝ or 1¼ IPS
2	2	2	2⅛
2½	2½	2½	2⅝
3	3	3	3⅛
4	4	4	4⅛
5	5	5	5⅛
6	6	6	6⅛

*IPS indicates an iron pipe size insulation that may also be used.

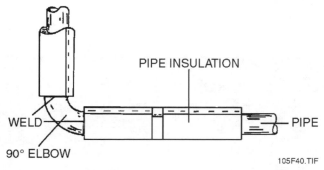

Figure 40 ◆ Place cut ends toward the fitting.

7.2.0 Installing Fiberglass Pipe Insulation

Fiberglass pipe insulation comes from the manufacturer pre-slit along its standard 3-foot length. To install it, follow these steps:

Step 1 Spread the 3-foot section along the slit and snap it onto straight sections of pipe.

Step 2 Hold the seams closed.

Step 3 Remove the protective paper contact strip and press the self-sealing lap to the jacket face (see *Figure 41*). Self-sealing laps work best at room temperatures, or at least at temperatures over 50°F. For cold applications, you must staple the laps with flared staples.

Figure 41 ◆ Fiberglass pipe insulation with self-sealing lap.

Step 4 Smooth the self-sealing lap down tight. There should be no wrinkles or puckers.

Step 5 Rub briskly to ensure good adhesion. If you don't seal the lap properly, open places called **fish-mouths** will appear along the seal.

Step 6 Place the paper contact strips and any scrap in cartons and dispose of properly.

CAUTION

Fiberglass pipe insulation is semi-rigid. You must not use it where it may be subject to weight loads or where it could be compressed, such as by foot traffic in ground-level pipe racks.

7.3.0 Sealing

You must seal the ends of each 3-foot section and the ends of any cuts you have made. To do this, you will use a **butt strip** (see *Figure 42*). This is a strip of the ASJ that comes with each section of insulation. Follow these steps:

Step 1 Place the butt strip snugly around the pipe where cut ends of insulation butt against one another. Do not pull the strip so tightly that it wrinkles or puckers.

Step 2 Make sure the exposed end of the butt strip is even with the jacket lap.

Step 3 If the job specifications require jacket stapling, staple the end of the butt strip. Place staples on 4-inch centers in a straight line about ¼ inch from the edge of the lap.

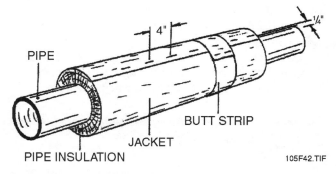

Figure 42 ◆ Butt strip wrapped around ASJ.

Riveting Ideas — *Protecting the Vapor Barrier*

The vapor barrier can be cut during installation and cuts reduce its effectiveness. In response to this problem, some manufacturers have developed a product that has a special wick. The wick pulls the moisture away from the pipe and allows it to evaporate along a perforated strip. The perforated strip looks like a row of holes. You must not cover these holes.

7.3.1 Vapor Barrier Adhesive

Installations on cold pipe systems may require you to seal the jacket laps with a vapor barrier adhesive. After you have cut and fit the insulation to the pipe, brush this adhesive on the laps. Allow the adhesive to become tacky and then lay the lap down and rub it briskly to ensure a complete seal.

Riveting Ideas

Using a Staple Gun

You must use your outward-clinch staple gun properly to avoid breaking, wrinkling, or deforming the insulation jacket. Hold the staple gun in loose contact with the jacket. Let the gun do the work. Do not jam it into the jacket. Keep your staple gun in good condition and replace the head if it does not flare the staples properly.

Job specifications may also require you to staple the laps. You must apply vapor barrier mastic over the staples to prevent any moisture from entering the insulation at the staple penetration points. You must also vapor seal any punctures or cuts in the vapor barrier jacket.

7.4.0 Installing Without a Jacket

Occasionally, job specifications require you to install fiberglass pipe insulation without the ASJ. You will attach this type of insulation with tape, wire, or bands. If the pipe is concealed in the walls or ceiling of the building, no other finish is required. Otherwise, you may install a jacket over the plain fiberglass for a better appearance.

CAUTION

When using wire to secure unjacketed insulation, be careful not to cut the fiberglass insulation by pulling the wire too tightly.

8.0.0 ◆ FLEXIBLE FOAM INSULATION

Flexible foam insulation—for example, Armaflex® or Rubatex®—is used most widely for cold applications at temperatures as low as –40°F. Rubatex® is a closed-cell (nonporous) product, so a separate vapor barrier is not needed. Flexible foam insulation may also be used in hot applications at temperatures as high as 220°F.

The technical name for flexible foam insulation is flexible **elastomeric cellular thermal insulation.** An elastomeric material is one that can expand and contract without rupturing. After expanding or contracting in response to stress or temperature changes, this material can rapidly return to its original dimensions. The major types of flexible foam insulation are rubber, polyethylene, and polyolefin.

Manufactured in tube, sheet, and roll form, flexible foam insulation is available for iron pipe sizes (IPS) ranging from ⅜ inch to 4 inches (outside diameter). Standard tube insulation wall thicknesses are ⅜ inch, ½ inch, ¾ inch, and 1 inch.

You can sleeve (or nest) different sizes if you need more thickness. The standard tube insulation length is 6 feet, but manufacturers do offer smaller sizes. Sheets and rolls are available in thicknesses of ⅛ inch, ¼ inch, ⅜ inch, ½ inch, ¾ inch, and 1½ inches. The standard sheet size is 3' × 4'.

8.1.0 Installing Flexible Foam Insulation

Manufacturers generally supply tube insulation without a slit along the length. You can slide the tube onto straight lengths of pipe or make a slit down the center and snap the tube onto the pipe. You must join the sides of the slit with a suitable adhesive. Follow the manufacturer's recommendations for the recommended adhesive and application procedures.

DID YOU KNOW?

Hot and Cold Applications

Some piping systems are described as either hot or cold applications. Piping systems that deliver chilled water or air are cold applications. Systems that deliver heated water or air are hot applications.

You must always vapor seal cold applications. Here is why. Chilled water systems operate at temperatures ranging from 42°F to 52°F—temperatures that are lower than the temperature of the ambient air. As you have learned, warm air naturally moves toward colder air. This causes condensation, which decreases the insulation's effectiveness.

Vapor barriers are not required on hot applications because hot applications function at temperatures above the ambient temperature. However, you must insulate to control heat loss. Some insulation adhesives will not work as effectively at higher temperatures. You must check the manufacturer's specifications to determine which adhesives will be most effective in a hot application.

Use a sharp knife to make smooth, clean cuts on flexible foam insulation. To cut butt ends or to make angled cuts, use a finely serrated bread knife.

8.1.1 Slip-On Method

For this method, you will slide the tube insulation on the pipe as the piping is installed (see *Figure 43*). The installation is easy; however, you must coordinate your schedule with the pipe installer's schedule. Also, the insulation must be applied before the pipe is tested, which can cause problems for the pipe installer. For these reasons, this method is not widely used. However, it is still useful to learn how to do it. Follow these steps:

Step 1 Make sure that you have the right amount, size, and thickness of tube insulation for the task.

Step 2 Check to see if any of the pipes to be insulated pass through floors or walls. You will need the help of a co-worker to insulate these pipes.

Step 3 Measure and cut the right amount of insulation to cover a straight stretch of pipe up to a fitting. It is best to always cut sections slightly longer than needed to ensure a snug fit.

Step 4 Slide the insulation over the open end of the pipe and push—don't pull—it to the fitting at the opposite end. Never stretch the insulation by pulling on it.

Step 5 Cover all open ends of pipe with manufacturer-approved tape to keep dust or dirt from getting into the pipe during installation.

Step 6 Spread the butt ends apart and brush a coat of adhesive on each end. Hold the ends apart until the adhesive has dried completely. It will not be tacky to the touch.

Step 7 Join the ends by pressing them firmly together.

You may push the insulation around 45-degree elbows (see *Figure 44*). Never push the insulation around 90-degree elbows (see *Figure 45*).

When you use the slip-on method, you will install covers over the soldered fittings after all of the pipes have been insulated and tested. Note that you may have to solder the fitting before installing the cover. In this case, you must push the insulation on the pipe away from the fitting. To hold it in place, apply clamps to the pipe—not to the insulation. Remove the clamps after the solder has cooled.

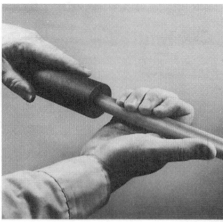
105F43.EPS

Figure 43 ◆ Slip-on insulation.

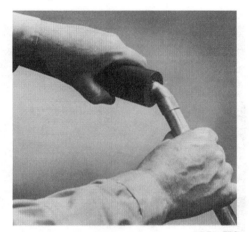
105F44.EPS

Figure 44 ◆ Insulating at a 45-degree angle.

105F45.EPS

Figure 45 ◆ Insulating at a 90-degree angle.

CAUTION

Never push insulation around 90-degree elbows. Doing so could cause the insulation to compress and lose its effectiveness. This is especially true for cold applications.

Riveting Ideas

Installation Tips

Always install flexible foam tube insulation on pipes that are clean, dry, and at room temperature.

Never crowd pipes insulated with flexible foam insulation. Always space the piping to allow for free air circulation, which helps prevent condensation.

To install a fitting cover over a soldered fitting, follow these steps:

Step 1 Carefully slit the fitting cover (see *Figure 46*).

Step 2 Snap the cover into place over the fitting (see *Figure 47*).

Step 3 Brush a coat of adhesive on all joint surfaces (see *Figure 48*).

Step 4 Allow the adhesive to dry until it is not tacky to the touch. This will take from 3 to 10 minutes depending on the temperature and level of humidity.

Step 5 Press the joints firmly together (see *Figure 49*).

105F46.EPS

Figure 46 ◆ Slit fitting cover.

105F48.EPS

Figure 48 ◆ Applying adhesive.

105F47.EPS

Figure 47 ◆ Fitting cover installed.

105F49.EPS

Figure 49 ◆ Joints connected.

Riveting Ideas

Straight Cutting

Tube insulation has the manufacturer's trademark printed down one side. You can use this printing as a guide for cutting a straight line.

When you use the slip-on method, you will also install covers over any screwed fittings after all of the pipes have been insulated and tested. To do this, you must make sleeve-type fitting covers from tube insulation. The inside diameter of the insulation should overlap the insulation on the adjacent straight pipe by at least 1 inch. See *Table 2* for an example of one manufacturer's sleeving sizes.

CAUTION

Insulation sleeving sizes differ from manufacturer to manufacturer. Never use one manufacturer's sleeving size chart to work with another manufacturer's insulation.

To insulate screwed fittings, follow these steps (use these steps for heavy bronze fittings also):

Step 1 Slide the insulation over the straight length of pipe, butting it tightly against the fitting (see *Figure 50*).

Step 2 Slit the fitting cover and snap it into position over the fitting (see *Figure 51*).

Step 3 Brush adhesive along the sides of the slit.

Step 4 Allow the adhesive to dry until it is no longer tacky to the touch.

Step 5 Press the sides firmly together.

Step 6 Cement the 1-inch overlap between the fitting cover and the pipe insulation. To do this, you must force the brush between the two surfaces.

Step 7 Check the fit (see *Figure 52*).

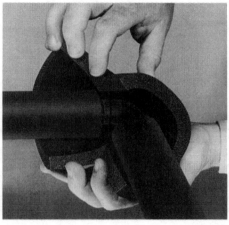
105F51.EPS

Figure 51 ◆ Snap insulation into place.

105F50.EPS

Figure 50 ◆ Butt insulation against the fitting.

105F52.EPS

Figure 52 ◆ Insulated fitting.

Riveting Ideas

Turn Tubes for a Neat Job

Tube insulation has the manufacturer's trademark information printed down one side. If you will not be painting the insulation, turn the printed side toward the ceiling for a neater appearance. Insulation is painted to protect it from the elements. Insulation used on rooftop applications, for example, is painted to protect it from the sun and weather.

Table 2 Nominal Sleeving Sizes in Inches

	Copper Tubing			Nominal Sleeving Sizes		
Insulation Sizes	Nominal Size	O.D. Size	Nominal IPS	⅜" Wall	½" Wall	¾" Wall
⅜ I.D.	¼	⅜	—	1⅛ I.D.	1⅜ I.D.	1⅝ I.D.
½ I.D.	⅜	½	¼	1⅜ I.D.	1⅜ I.D.	1½ IPS
⅝ I.D.	½	⅝	⅜	1⅜ I.D.	1⅝ I.D.	2⅛ I.D.
¾ I.D.	⅝	¾	—	1⅝ I.D.	1½ IPS	2 IPS
⅞ I.D.	¾	⅞	½	1⅝ I.D.	1½ IPS	2 IPS
¾ IPS	—	—	¾	1½ IPS	2⅛ I.D.	2½ IPS
1⅛ I.D.	1	1⅛	—	1½ IPS	2⅛ I.D.	2½ IPS
1⅜ I.D.	1¼	1⅜	1	2⅛ I.D.	2 IPS	3⅛ I.D.
1⅝ I.D.	1½	1⅝	1¼	2 IPS	2½ IPS	3⅝ I.D.
1½ IPS	—	—	1½	2½ IPS	3⅛ I.D.	3⅝ I.D.
2⅛ I.D.	2	2⅛	—	2½ IPS	3⅝ I.D.	4⅛ I.D.
2 IPS	—	—	2	3⅝ I.D.	3⅝ I.D.	4⅛ I.D.
2⅝ I.D.	2½	2⅝	—	3⅝ I.D.	4⅛ I.D.	4 IPS
2½ IPS	—	—	2½	—	4⅛ I.D.	4 IPS
3⅛ I.D.	3	3⅛	—	—	4 IPS	5 IPS
3⅝ I.D.	3½	3⅝	3	—	5 IPS	5 IPS
4⅛ I.D.	4	4⅛	3½	—	5 IPS	Sheet
4 IPS	—	—	4	—	Sheet	Sheet
5 IPS	—	—	5	—	Sheet	Sheet

(I.D. = inside diameter; O.D. = outside diameter; IPS = iron pipe size; Sheet = available in sheet form.)

8.1.2 Slit-Snap Method

This method involves slitting the tube insulation along its length, snapping it onto straight lengths of pipe, and sealing the slit with an adhesive. You will use this method after all of the pipes have been installed and tested. Note that pre-slit insulation is available from the manufacturer on request. Follow these steps:

Step 1 Slit the insulation along its length (see *Figure 53*).

Step 2 Spread the sides of the insulation and snap it around the pipe (see *Figure 54*).

Step 3 Spread the sides of the insulation and brush on a light coat of adhesive (see *Figure 55*). You can also apply the adhesive to the slit sides before placing the insulation on the pipe.

Step 4 Slide the insulation down onto the pipe so that the adhesive-coated sides are held apart until the adhesive dries.

Step 5 Allow the adhesive to dry until it is no longer tacky to the touch (see *Figure 56*).

Step 6 Make sure the insulation is in the right position.

Step 7 Press the sides of the insulation firmly together (see *Figure 57*). Note that the butt ends of the insulation must also be sealed.

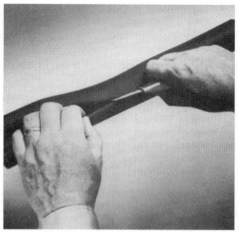

Figure 53 ◆ Slitting insulation.

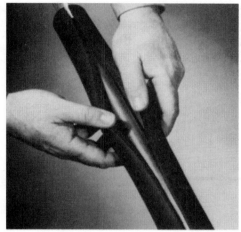

Figure 54 ◆ Placing the insulation.

Figure 55 ◆ Applying the adhesive.

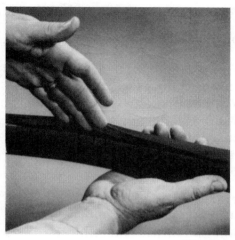

Figure 56 ◆ Checking the adhesive.

Figure 57 ◆ Pressing the insulation closed.

Riveting Ideas *Keeping a Sharp Blade*

Tube insulation quickly wears down the blade of your utility knife. Keep a sharpening stone handy and sharpen often, generally after every third cut. It takes less time to quickly hone the blade than it does to change a dull blade for a sharp one after three cuts. A sharp knife not only allows you to cut quickly, but also helps you to cut in a straight line. A dull blade can catch in the material and slip off the cutting line.

Review Questions

Sections 5.0.0–8.0.0

1. You must install metal nosing on the edges of fibrous duct liner facing the air stream when air velocity is _____.
   a. less than 4,000 fpm
   b. greater than 4,000 fpm
   c. between 2,000 and 3,000 fpm
   d. between 500 and 1,000 fpm

2. Fiberglass blanket insulation may be faced with FSK or ASJ. These initials stand for _____.
   a. Foil Shield Kit and Aluminum Standard Jacket
   b. Flexible Shield Kraft and All Service Jacket
   c. Foil Scrim Kraft and All Service Jacket
   d. Fiberglass Standard Kit and Ambient Service Jacket

3. Self-sealing laps generally work best at _____.
   a. room temperature
   b. temperatures between 25°F and 35°F
   c. temperatures greater than 150°F
   d. temperatures between 35°F and 40°F

4. When fiberglass pipe insulation is marked 2" × 1", it means that the _____.
   a. insulation is 2 inches thick and the pipe dimension is 1 inch
   b. pipe dimension is 2 inches and the insulation is 1 inch thick
   c. insulation will fit a pipe with a 2-inch outside dimension
   d. insulation will fit a pipe with a 1-inch inside dimension

5. When installing flexible foam tube insulation using the slip-on method, you must _____ it onto the pipe.
   a. pull
   b. push
   c. start by pushing, then pull
   d. twist or screw

Summary

Insulation is an important part of the sheet metal trade. Properly insulated systems provide comfort, safety, and energy savings. Insulation also prevents unwanted noise from moving through the system.

As you work with insulation, you will find that manufacturers design and make different types and thicknesses of insulation to suit a wide variety of applications. Manufacturers also make a wide variety of adhesives and fasteners designed for use with specific types of insulation. You must learn about these different types of insulation and how to install, fasten, and vapor seal them when necessary.

Learning about the different types of insulation and how to install them properly is only one part of your job. To do a professional installation job, you must review the job specifications; check that you have all the tools and materials required; store your work materials in a clean, dry place during the installation process; and, finally, inspect your work to make sure that you have done it properly. You must also be aware that some of the tools and materials used to install insulation can be dangerous if improperly handled, so you must read, understand, and follow the manufacturer's safety recommendations.

This module also introduced you to organizations that affect how insulation is manufactured, rated, and installed. You must learn about these organizations and keep up with current standards, especially those affecting proper installation and safety.

Glenn Schwenneker

Team Leader, Encompass Mechanical Services
Special Projects Group
Orlando, Florida

Glenn grew up in Orlando, Florida. After completing high school, he stayed in Orlando and went to work for Disney World. In 1983, he went to work for Encompass Mechanical Services, and has been with them ever since. He is a certified State Mechanical Contractor, an NCCER Master Trainer, and one of his company's valued team leaders.

How did you become interested in this industry?
My uncle, who worked in the trade for more than 30 years, got me involved. I was working for Disney and he suggested that I learn a trade. At the time, there was no formal apprenticeship program at Encompass Mechanical Services. But I completed on-the-job training—I learned daily—and I took a ton of classes through the local Central Florida Association of Builders and Contractors.

What path did you take to your current position?
I've been with Encompass Mechanical Services since I was 19 years old. I was hired as a pre-apprentice and worked in the apprenticeship program for about three years. Then I started my own project and was classified as a junior mechanic. I was named a Class A mechanic and spent the next four years in the field before coming into the office as a project manager. To know what it takes to do the job of an estimator, you need to have done the work in the past. I enjoyed the work and I was good at leading people, so it was a natural progression to team leader.

I recently received my State Mechanical Contractor Certification. After completing an eight-week course at a local construction school, I applied with the state to take the exam. The 19-hour exam is administered in four segments over a two-day period. The first day covers business and finance, and the second day covers technical matters. I was awarded my certification in August 2001.

What do you like most about your job?
My people. I get a lot of satisfaction from the people I work with. They're my friends, and they also consider me their friend. We have a lot of camaraderie and teamwork.

What do you think it takes to be a success in your trade?
It takes dedication, hard work, and commitment—a lot of motivation, daily and hourly. You do this through mentoring and treating people right. People who work for me have various levels of skill. I teach others what I know—people learn through experience—and I try to be understanding. It takes a combination of good leadership, mentoring, and discipline.

What are some things you do on the job?
As a project manager, you are in charge of your own budget, sales, and estimating. As a team leader, you are in charge of yourself as well as of other project managers and all of their responsibilities. I oversee 30 field employees and nearly $10 million in revenue for my team and myself. What I do ranges from managing safety responsibilities for the company to managing the apprenticeship program for 50 in-house apprentices. I received my Master Trainer Certification from NCCER to train our own instructors, to monitor the program, and to ensure the quality of the program.

What would you say to someone entering the trade today?
Work hard. Learn everything that you can possibly learn. Motivate yourself, search for and seek out windows of opportunity, and throw yourself through them. Don't wait for someone else to make you successful. Do it yourself.

Trade Terms Introduced in This Module

All Service Jacket (ASJ): A facing material that is applied to insulation by the manufacturer.

Ambient air: The surrounding air.

American Society for Testing and Materials (ASTM): An organization that develops and publishes standards for a wide variety of materials, products, systems, and services.

Butt strip: A strip of insulation jacket material used to seal the butt ends of pipe insulation.

Dew point: The temperature at which a vapor begins to condense.

Diffuser: An air distribution outlet that mixes air already in the room with incoming air.

Elastomeric cellular thermal insulation: The technical name for flexible foam insulation. Elastomeric materials stretch in response to stress or temperature changes and quickly return to their original dimensions.

Fan discharge: The area directly in front of the fan in which the airstream is moving.

Fire damper: In a duct system, a device designed to close an open duct in the event of a fire. Also called *fire control damper*.

Fish-mouths: On fiberglass pipe insulation, gaps that occur along the self-sealing laps indicating that a proper bond was not made.

Flame spread rating: A rating applied to a product to determine how quickly flames spread when the product is ignited.

Foil Scrim Kraft (FSK): A facing material applied to insulation to provide vapor protection.

Jacket: A facing material that covers insulation.

Mastic: A protective coating applied by trowel or spray on the surface of thermal insulation to prevent its deterioration and to weatherproof it.

North American Insulation Manufacturers Association (NAIMA): A trade association of North American manufacturers of fiberglass, rock wool, and slag wool insulation products.

Plenum: In a suspended ceiling, the space between the suspended ceiling and the main structure above.

Preformed fitting cover: An insulation cover made by a manufacturer to fit standard fittings.

Runout: In a duct system, the branch of pipe or duct that runs out from the main or trunk line.

Self-sealing lap: A tab or edge on facing material coated with an adhesive covered with a paper contact strip.

Sleeving: The act of nesting several pieces of insulation together to build up to a desired thickness.

Smoke developed rating: A rating applied to a product to determine the amount and density of smoke that develops when the product is ignited.

Solvent: A volatile liquid used to dissolve a solid so that it can be brushed on; examples include paint and liquid adhesives.

Sound attenuation: The reduction in the level of sound that is transmitted from one point to another.

Vapor barrier: A barrier, such as a mastic, placed between insulation and the surrounding air to control condensation.

Volatile organic compound (VOC): Any organic compound produced naturally or synthetically that has a high evaporation rate.

Additional Resources

This module is intended to present thorough resources for task training. The following reference works are suggested for further study. These are optional materials for continued education rather than for task training.

Fibrous Glass Duct Liner Standard: Design, Fabrication, and Installation Guidelines, 1998. NAIMA. Alexandria, VA: North American Insulation Manufacturers Association.

Insulation Handbook, 2000. Richard T. Bynum, Jr. New York, NY: McGraw-Hill.

Thermal Insulation Building Guide, 1990. Edin F. Strother and William C. Turner. Melbourne, FL: Krieger Publishing.

Thermal and Moisture Protection Manual, 1998. Christine Beall. New York, NY: McGraw-Hill.

Acknowledgments

The material on fibrous glass duct liner in this module has been adapted with the permission of the North American Insulation Manufacturers Association (NAIMA), which holds the copyright on Fibrous Glass Duct Liner Standard, Design, Fabrication, and Installation Guidelines. For more information about NAIMA and its publications, contact NAIMA, 44 Canal Center Plaza, Suite 310, Alexandria, VA 22314.

NAIMA assumes no responsibility and accepts no liability for the application of principles or techniques contained in the material on fibrous glass duct liner. NAIMA makes no warranty of any kind, express or implied or regarding merchantability or fitness for any particular purpose in connection with the information supplied.

Authorities considering adoption of NAIMA standards should review all federal, state, local, and contractual regulations applicable to specific installations. These materials are not intended to address issues relating to thermal or acoustical insulation within and furnished as integral parts of HVAC equipment such as air handling units, coils, air cleaners, silencers, humidifiers, and terminal devices. Manufacturers of such equipment are responsible for design, specification, and installation of appropriate insulation components in their products so that thermal, acoustical, and indoor air quality requirements are met.

Figure Credits

NAIMA	105F01, 105F02, 105F03, 105F04, 105F09, 105F10, 105F11, 105F12, 105F13, 105F14, 105F15, 105F16
National Insulation Association	105F34, 105F35, 105F36, 105F38, 105F39

NCCER CRAFT TRAINING USER UPDATES

The NCCER makes every effort to keep these textbooks up-to-date and free of technical errors. We appreciate your help in this process. If you have an idea for improving this textbook, or if you find an error, a typographical mistake, or an inaccuracy in the NCCER's Craft Training textbooks, please write us, using this form or a photocopy. Be sure to include the exact module number, page number, a detailed description, and the correction, if applicable. Your input will be brought to the attention of the Technical Review Committee. Thank you for your assistance.

Instructors – If you found that additional materials were necessary in order to teach this module effectively, please let us know so that we may include them in the Equipment and Materials list in the Instructor's Guide.

Write: Curriculum Revision and Development Department
National Center for Construction Education and Research
P.O. Box 141104, Gainesville, FL 32614-1104

Fax: 352-334-0932

E-mail: curriculum@nccer.org

Craft _____   Module Name _____

Copyright Date _____   Module Number _____   Page Number(s) _____

Description _____

_____

_____

_____

_____

(Optional) Correction _____

_____

_____

(Optional) Your Name and Address _____

_____

_____

Introduction to Sheet Metal Layout and Processes

COURSE MAP

This course map shows all of the modules in the first level of the Sheet Metal curriculum. The suggested training order begins at the bottom and proceeds up. Skill levels increase as you advance on the course map. The local Training Program Sponsor may adjust the training order.

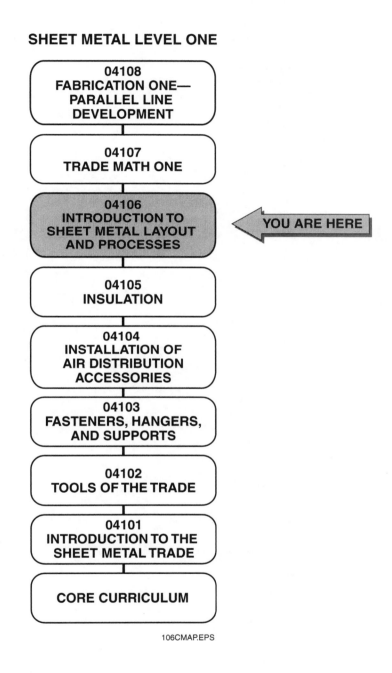

SHEET METAL LEVEL ONE

04108
FABRICATION ONE—
PARALLEL LINE
DEVELOPMENT

04107
TRADE MATH ONE

04106
INTRODUCTION TO
SHEET METAL LAYOUT
AND PROCESSES

YOU ARE HERE

04105
INSULATION

04104
INSTALLATION OF
AIR DISTRIBUTION
ACCESSORIES

04103
FASTENERS, HANGERS,
AND SUPPORTS

04102
TOOLS OF THE TRADE

04101
INTRODUCTION TO THE
SHEET METAL TRADE

CORE CURRICULUM

106CMAP.EPS

Copyright © 2001 National Center for Construction Education and Research, Gainesville, FL 32614-1104. All rights reserved. No part of this work may be reproduced in any form or by any means, including photocopying, without written permission of the publisher.

MODULE 04106 CONTENTS

Figures

Introduction to Sheet Metal Layout and Processes

Objectives

When you finish this module, you will be able to do the following:

1. Define basic trade terms pertaining to sheet metal layout.
2. Demonstrate skill and competence in the selection and use of layout and marking tools.
3. Identify and explain the three development methods for laying out sheet metal patterns.
4. Demonstrate skill in the selection and use of hand snips, hacksaws, and squaring shears for cutting out sheet metal parts and patterns.
5. Demonstrate the ability to select and use forming tools.
6. Demonstrate skill and competence in the construction of seams and edges.

Prerequisites

Before you begin this module, it is recommended that you successfully complete the following modules: Core Curriculum; Sheet Metal Level One, Modules 04101 through 04105.

Required Trainee Materials

1. Pencil and paper
2. Appropriate personal protective equipment

1.0.0 ◆ INTRODUCTION

In this module you will learn the trade terms used in layout work, and you will be introduced to the three methods of developing and laying out sheet metal *patterns*. You will also learn how to select and use the right layout and marking tools, hand tools, and machine tools. You will

learn how to square up a piece of metal, how to transfer patterns, and how to cut, form, and assemble parts.

Before attempting to do layouts on sheet metal, you must have a solid knowledge of math and geometry. You will use these skills every day in your work, especially when you need to develop a nonstandard pattern or when your shop has no master patterns or *templates*.

2.0.0 ◆ LAYOUT TERMINOLOGY

You must first learn the language of layout—the trade terms associated with the layout process. Study these terms. You may recognize some of them from previous math and blueprint modules you studied in the Core Curriculum. As you will see, some of these terms have slightly different meanings when applied to sheet metal work.

Angle: An intersection of any two straight lines, or rays, that connect at a point. Angles are always measured in degrees, from 1 degree to 360 degrees. In layout, the term also refers to angular fittings, branches, or sections of round or rectangular duct.

Axis: An imaginary line around which an object rotates; for example, the earth rotates on its axis. In geometry, it also means a straight line around which a three-dimensional object is symmetrical.

Centerlines: Lines used to show the centers, or axes, of parts or circles shown on a layout. A centerline is also used to show the axis of a path of motion.

Cheek: The flat side of any rectangular curved elbow or fitting, as opposed to the curved sides. Each rectangular curved fitting generally has two cheeks.

Constructions: Two-dimensional representations or drawings of three-dimensional objects.

Curved lines: Lines with a constantly changing direction. This change can be a regular, mathematical change, or it can be random and irregular.

Development: The act of creating a sheet metal pattern.

Dimension lines: Lines on plans or patterns that indicate size (width and height). Dimension lines have solid arrowheads at each end.

Elevation: Sometimes called the side view. It shows the flat, vertical view of any object as seen face-on.

Extension lines: These are lines that extend from a plan or pattern to the dimension lines to indicate where the dimension begins and ends.

Fitting: Any irregularly shaped sheet metal object for which a pattern must be developed—for example, elbows, **offsets,** and transitions. Straight pieces of pipe or duct generally are not considered to be fittings. Also, the term *fitting* generally refers to a completely fabricated unit rather than to any individual parts of that unit. As you will see, many fittings consist of more than one piece, and each piece has its own layout pattern.

Gore: A section of a round sheet metal elbow, which is basically a straight section cut at an angle at one or both ends. A gore fits together with other gores to make a complete *gored elbow.*

Heel: The long side or longest curved surface on any rectangular curved elbow or fitting. It is on the opposite side of the throat. (Compare this definition with the definition for *throat.*) The heel is also called the *outside radius* of a curved fitting. On drawings it is indicated by the capital letter *R.*

Horizontal lines: Straight lines that are parallel to the horizon.

Layout: The process of measuring and marking lines on metal that are to be cut, drilled, or bent.

Miter line: The line of intersection for two pipes or other fittings joined together at any angle. The term *miter* refers to any angle associated with a fitting. Note that no matter how two pipes are joined, the miter line will never be a perfect circle.

Oblique lines: Lines drawn at any angle found between vertical and horizontal.

Parallel lines: In geometry, these are straight lines equally spaced apart that never meet or intersect and continue infinitely on the same *plane.* In layout, these are straight lines equally spaced apart that never meet or intersect, but that are finite (they come to an end within the pattern).

Pattern: The flat outline of a fitting or object to be fabricated. The pattern always includes all allowances for seams, edges, and notches. After you lay out the pattern, you cut it out of the sheet and then form it into the fitting.

Perpendicular line: A line that is at a right angle to another line or a plane.

Plane: A surface having two dimensions (length and width) that may be horizontal, vertical, or oblique (at an angle).

Plan view: A drawing of an object or room as it would appear if you could see it from directly overhead. In drafting, this is also called the *top view.* On blueprints, any floor plan is a *plan view.*

Profile: In curved pipe layout, the shape of half of a fitting at any given point, shown as a plan view. The profile shows only half of the plan view, as the other half is a duplicate.

Radius: In geometry, this is the distance between the center of a circle and any point on its circumference. In layout, the term *radius* also indicates the distance from a center position to the *throat* or *heel* of any curved fitting.

Stock: The sheet of metal on which you lay out your patterns; this term also describes the supply of metal sheets in the shop.

Stretchout: This term is somewhat similar to the term *pattern,* in that it describes what a three-dimensional object looks like when stretched out flat. However, it also refers to the measurement around or across the flattened object. The stretchout of a pipe or round duct is the circumference. The stretchout of a rectangular duct is the perimeter.

Tee: A configuration consisting of two intersecting pipes that form a T shape. A tee can be one fitting, but it is formed by one pipe section connecting with another pipe section. Note that any tee has three openings—two to the sides and one at the bottom or top.

Template: A master pattern usually made of metal that sheet metal mechanics use to trace the shape of a given fitting or object onto sheets of metal. Most master patterns are for standard fittings with outlines that are easily traced.

Throat: The short side or the shortest curved surface on any rectangular curved elbow or fitting. It is on the opposite side of the heel. (Compare this definition with the definition for *heel.*) The throat is also called the *inside radius* of a curved fitting. On drawings it is indicated by the lowercase letter *r.*

True length: This term describes a line whose true length is not distorted by perspective.

Vertical lines: Straight lines that are perpendicular (at right angles) to the horizon. In layout, as you face the stock, horizontal lines run from left to right and vertical lines run from bottom to top. In layout, you always draw vertical lines from bottom to top and never from top to bottom.

3.0.0 ◆ VISUALIZING LAYOUTS

Layout is the process of **scribing** (drawing) patterns on metal sheets that will be used to fabricate fittings used in the sheet metal trade. The scribed lines show where the metal is to be cut, drilled, or bent.

Layout is basically making a flat pattern for something that will be formed into a metal fitting that has height, width, and depth. Your ability to visualize—to see—a three-dimensional object simply by looking at a two-dimensional drawing is very important. Recognizing the relationship between the flat layout and the completed object will help you avoid making mistakes as you scribe your layouts. With practice you will be able to visualize how an object would flatten into a layout and how a layout would form a three-dimensional object.

You will use plan views and elevations for the fittings you will lay out on sheet metal. To get a simple idea of what these terms mean, do the following:

- Stand a closed, empty cereal box on end and look down at it. The only part of the box you can see is the top. This is a plan view of the box. You can't see the other sides of the box because they are in different planes that are out of your line of vision.

- Look at the box face-on. The only part of the box you can see now is the front. This is the elevation view of the box. You can't see the other sides of the box because they are in different planes that are out of your line of vision.

- Cut along one fold of the box, unfold the box entirely, and lay it out flat. You can now see all sides of the box because all the sides are lying in one plane (see *Figure 1*). This view is what a pattern looks like.

4.0.0 ◆ LAYOUT RULES

The following rules apply to all sheet metal layout work. Following them will enable you to work quickly and with minimum waste.

Before you do anything, check the sheet metal. Make sure it is the proper gauge and that the edges are square.

Square up the edges. If the sheet is not perfectly square, you can still make accurate layouts by

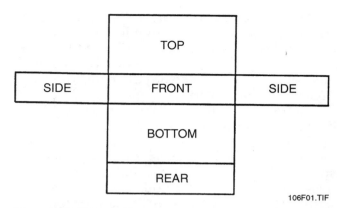

Figure 1 ◆ Flattened box.

squaring the edges. To square up the left-hand edge, align your framing square with the bottom edge of the sheet and scribe a vertical line about ¼ inch in from the left-hand edge. To square up the bottom edge, align your framing square with the left-hand edge and scribe a horizontal line about ¼ inch up from the bottom. Once you have squared up the edges, be sure to take all of your measurements from the lines and not from the edges. Always measure from the left-hand side of the metal toward the right and from the bottom toward the top.

Always start your layout in the lower left-hand corner of the sheet. Doing this will allow you to make the most of every sheet and reduce waste. Once you have done your first layout on the lower left, you can place other layouts in the upper and right sides of the sheet.

Lay out and mark measurements using the edge of a steel rule and a scratch awl. To lay out a given dimension, place the rule with the desired dimension at the scribed mark in alignment with the pattern edge. Then scribe the line from the end of the steel rule to this mark using a scratch awl.

Always measure two points before scribing your lines. Do not trust your square to be true from a one-point measurement only. Let's say you want to scribe a horizontal line that is 3 inches up from the bottom of a squared metal sheet. You could just measure up 3 inches on the left-hand side, make a mark, and then scribe your line. But without another reference mark to line up your square, it is likely that your scribed line will be off the mark by the time you finish scribing it. To keep this from happening, make a second mark that is 3 inches up from the bottom line and to the right of the first mark you made. Now you have a reference point with which to line up your square. Connect the points to make a horizontal line that is 3 inches up from the bottom line for its entire length.

Scribe in one direction before scribing in another direction. If you start with the horizontal lines, scribe all of them before scribing the vertical lines (and vice versa). This method is easier and more efficient than constantly changing direction from horizontal to vertical.

Always scribe all horizontal and vertical lines before marking angled lines. Don't take shortcuts by marking angled lines before you've completed the horizontals and verticals. Never assume that you will remember where the horizontal and vertical lines should be if you haven't carefully scribed them in. Never start cutting or forming metal using an incomplete layout.

Prick-punch (mark) all brake lines and forming lines. Prick-punch your patterns lightly to avoid making unnecessary marks. Place the point of the punch at the intersection of two lines, tilt it at an angle to sight the work spot, then lift it to the vertical position and tap it with a hammer. Make these marks about ¼ inch from either end of all bend lines before bending the pattern. Prick-punching is important for several reasons:

- It helps identify bend lines that must be formed from the unmarked side of the sheet.

- It keeps you from bending a line that should not be bent.

- You will be able to mark other patterns from the first pattern.

- Without prick marks, relying on indications such as notches will cause you to make mistakes.

- Prick marks will help you locate centers for arcs and holes that are to be drilled.

Become familiar with the basic shapes of standard patterns so that you can visualize fabricated fittings. For example, box patterns may be made in many different sizes and with a variety of seams and edges—but they all have the same basic shape. You should always be able to tell that you're laying out a box and not a pipe, for example, just by looking at the pattern.

Check and confirm the overall dimensions on each side of the pattern after your layout is complete. All parallel lines of the same length must measure the same, and they must be the same distance apart from each other on both ends. The easiest way to check this is to measure each pair of lines on both sides of the pattern. A variance of ¹⁄₁₆ of an inch or greater tells you there's an error in your layout.

Use a scratch awl with a narrow, sharp point and scribe lines using only one stroke. Don't move the scratch awl back and forth—or you could end up scribing more than one line. You must angle the point against the rule to avoid distorting your line with the thick part of the awl.

Use a 9H drafting pencil for certain metals. Use this pencil on stainless steel, alloys, or copper to prevent marring or weakening these surfaces.

4.1.0 Marking and Prick-Punching Fittings

Two or more identical patterns might be required for a fitting. The first pattern is always used to mark the other patterns needed. Although patterns may be identical, the direction in which they are to be formed can be different. For example, one pattern may be formed as a right-hand piece or as a left-hand piece. Be sure to note such directions clearly with a felt-tipped marker.

Do not punch or drill any holes required in the pattern until you have scribed all the pattern marks. Make all prick-punch markings and all scribe lines on the inside of the pattern so that the fabricated fitting appears neat and clean on the outside.

Fabricating each of your layouts in proper order is very important. If you don't follow each pattern's metal-forming sequence in order, it may be impossible to fabricate the fitting. You might have to lay out a whole new pattern, which is wasteful and expensive.

Until you gain enough experience, you must write each step in the sequence with a felt-tipped marker directly on the pattern. You must always write the sequence on the pattern if someone else is to do the fabricating. In any case, always follow the procedures established for your shop.

Reference Points

How far apart should you make reference points and how many should you make?
It depends on the size of the fitting you are laying out. You don't want to make so many reference points that you waste time. A rule of thumb: the longer the line you must scribe, the more reference points you will need. So, for example, if the line to be scribed is longer than the blade of your square, you will probably need to add reference points to keep the line true.

5.0.0 ◆ LAYOUT TOOLS: A REVIEW

This section provides a brief review of the layout tools you learned about in the Sheet Metal Level One Module, *Tools of the Trade*. The tools you'll use most often are the following:

- A metal *straightedge* to lay out straight lines on flat metal surfaces.
- A flexible *steel rule* to measure straight lines and to mark irregular curves. You can set the flexible steel rule on edge and bend it through the two points you need to connect. While you hold the position, another worker can help you by scribing the curve from the edge of the bent rule.
- A *circumference rule* to measure lengths and to see, at a glance, the circumference of any given cylinder. The reverse side of a circumference rule often has tables indicating sizes, measurements, and capacities.
- A *combination square* to scribe lines at 45-degree angles (see *Figure 2*). The variable head protractor attached to the square allows lines to be scribed at most other angles as well.
- A *scratch awl* to mark guidelines on the metal.
- An adjustable *sheet metal scriber* to scratch a line parallel to and equally distant from the straight edge of a square metal sheet.
- *Pencils* to sketch a line before scribing it if you are unsure of your line placement. Remove any extra pencil markings before starting to fabricate your layout.
- *Felt-tipped markers* to mark notes (especially shop or job notes) on the layouts. Examples of notes include information about whether a surface is *inside* or *outside*, or whether a line is to be *bent up* or *bent down* and by how many degrees. You must also mark which number fitting each layout is for, especially on jobs for which many fittings are required. For large jobs, a sheet

metal mechanic will also number the blueprints, matching the numbers on the blueprints to the fittings for that job.

- *Punches* to mark measuring points or to make indentations where holes are to be drilled. You will need a prick-punch (which has a tapered point ground to an angle of about 30 degrees) and a center punch (which has a tapered point ground to an angle of about 90 degrees).
- A *trammel* to lay out large circles or areas having a large radius (*Figure 3*). You can also use the trammel to measure or copy extended distances.
- *Dividers* to lay out areas or circles and to step off equal distances. You can adjust wing dividers to accurately make very fine adjustments (see *Figure 4*).

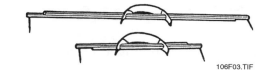

106F03.TIF

Figure 3 ◆ Trammel points.

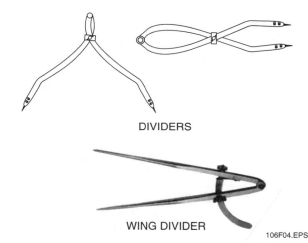

DIVIDERS

WING DIVIDER

106F04.EPS

Figure 4 ◆ Dividers.

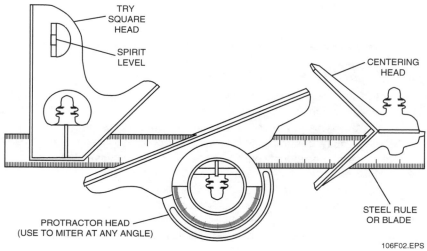

TRY SQUARE HEAD

SPIRIT LEVEL

CENTERING HEAD

PROTRACTOR HEAD (USE TO MITER AT ANY ANGLE)

STEEL RULE OR BLADE

106F02.EPS

Figure 2 ◆ Combination square.

Review Questions

Sections 2.0.0–5.0.0

1. The long side or longest curved surface on any rectangular curved elbow or fitting is called the _____.
   a. throat
   b. gore
   c. cheek
   d. heel

2. The short side or the shortest curved surface on any rectangular curved elbow or fitting is called the _____.
   a. throat
   b. gore
   c. cheek
   d. heel

3. The first thing you must do before beginning a layout is _____.
   a. file all of the edges of the metal using a flat file
   b. reserve the lower left-hand corner for layout notes and other instructions
   c. check that the metal is the correct gauge and has square edges
   d. set out all of your tools in order and sharpen any tools that are dull

4. If you start scribing a layout using horizontal lines, it is best to _____.
   a. number all of the angled lines before scribing the vertical lines
   b. use a brightly colored felt-tipped marker to highlight the vertical lines
   c. number all of the vertical lines before scribing them
   d. finish scribing all the horizontal lines before scribing the vertical lines

5. To measure straight lines and to mark irregular curves, it is best to use a(n) _____.
   a. wing divider
   b. adjustable scriber
   c. flexible steel rule
   d. trammel

6.0.0 ◆ LAYOUT METHODS

Sheet metal layout work is done by one of three methods:

- Parallel line development
- Radial line development
- Triangulation

The most basic layout is done using parallel line development, which is the method you are most likely to use as a first-year sheet metal apprentice.

6.1.0 Parallel Line Development

You will use parallel line development to develop a pattern for any fitting in which the opposite lines are parallel to each other. Examples of fittings you can make using this method are shown in *Figure 5*. Even fittings that require triangulation also involve some principles of parallel line development. You will also use this method to develop patterns for miters to join moldings and pipes at any angle and against any other form or surface.

6.1.1 Layout Examples

In this first example you will see the steps for laying out a rectangular duct with a double angle mitered in one end (see *Figure 6*). Note that the figure is simplified and does not include seam allowances.

Using Dividers and Trammels

To set dividers for establishing a distance, put the point of one leg on the 1-inch mark of a steel rule and the other point on the desired distance. Remember, because you started on the 1-inch mark, you will have to add 1 inch to locate the second point. In scribing arcs or circles, you must prick-punch the center pivot point. Hold the sheet steady by putting pressure on it with the palm of your free hand to prevent movement of the sheet metal while you scribe these lines.

Trammel points are handled in a similar way. You prick-punch and hold one point while you adjust the other point for radius distance and then use it to scribe an arc or a circle.

SHEET METAL LEVEL ONE — TRAINEE MODULE 04106

Work Efficiently

Your employer has made agreements with customers to deliver fittings in a timely, cost-effective manner. Competition; the cost of labor, benefits, and materials; and the need to comply with government regulations all add to your employer's costs. Because poor work habits waste time and materials, they also add to your employer's costs. Work efficiently to conserve time and resources. You'll help your company to be more profitable, and that, in turn, can result in better benefits and pay for you.

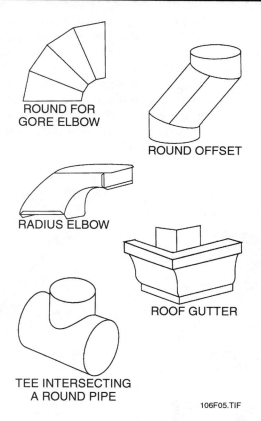

Figure 5 ◆ Fittings made using parallel line development.

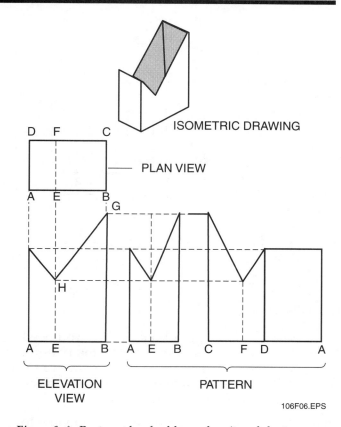

Figure 6 ◆ Rectangular double-angle mitered duct.

To lay out the duct shown in the figure, follow these steps:

Step 1 Draw the plan view and the elevation view. (Remember that the plan view is seen from above and the elevation view is seen face-on.) The (partially) dashed measuring lines (DA and CB) on the elevation are taken from the corners of the plan view. You must add one additional measuring line (EH) to locate the **apex** (peak) of the angles.

Step 2 Transfer the elevation measuring lines to the pattern. As you can see, the pattern is the duct stretched out flat.

Step 3 Draw solid lines to connect the resulting points to complete the stretchout.

Compare the stretchout of the pattern to the drawing of the duct. Can you visualize the duct flattening out into the pattern? Can you visualize the pattern being formed into the duct?

In this second example, you will see the steps for laying out a mitered pipe. Laying out a pipe involves a slightly different approach. There are no convenient corners from which to make measuring lines. Therefore, you must locate the lines on the elevation in a way that makes the lines easy to locate on the stretchout of the pattern. The steps for laying out a mitered pipe (see *Figure 7*) are as follows:

Step 1 Divide one-half of the plan view into six equal spaces on the circumference. This enables you to locate the lines in equal spaces on the pattern. (Line number 7

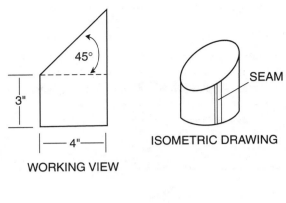

WORKING VIEW

ISOMETRIC DRAWING

SEAM

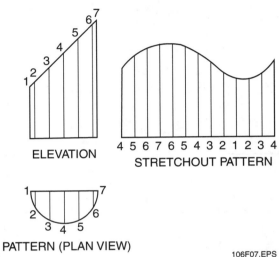

ELEVATION

STRETCHOUT PATTERN

4 5 6 7 6 5 4 3 2 1 2 3 4

PATTERN (PLAN VIEW)

106F07.EPS

Figure 7 ◆ Mitered pipe.

shows the height of the fitting.) You need at least six spaces to develop the pattern. On larger fittings, the more spaces into which you divide the plan view, the more accurate the fitting will be.

Step 2 Project the lines up from the plan view to the elevation. Notice that the lines on the elevation do not appear to be equally spaced, but they are. Because the elevation is a view of the pipe surface curving away from you, it cannot show any true distances between the projected vertical lines.

Step 3 Draw the stretchout of the pattern and divide it into the same number of equal spaces as shown on the plan view. Start with point number 4 so that the seam will be on the side.

Step 4 Transfer the lengths of the measuring lines to the pattern. You can do this by projecting the lines as shown in the figure, or by setting your dividers to the vertical lengths on the elevation and marking each measuring point (one by one) on the corresponding lines on the pattern.

Step 5 Draw the curve of the miter through the measuring points. You can draw this curve freehand, with a template curve, or with a flexible steel rule.

Compare the drawing of the pipe to the stretchout of the pattern. Can you visualize the pipe flattened out into the pattern? Can you visualize the pattern being formed into the pipe?

6.2.0 Radial Line Development

You will use the radial line development method for fittings in which all sides meet at an apex, or common center point. Examples of shapes include cones, funnels, and pyramids. Examples of fittings made using radial line development are shown in *Figure 8*. This method employs many of the procedures used in both triangulation and parallel line development, but it is used less frequently than those methods.

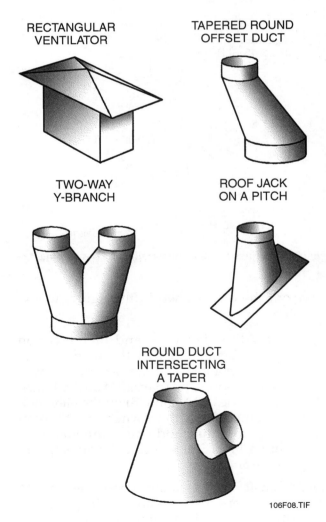

RECTANGULAR VENTILATOR

TAPERED ROUND OFFSET DUCT

TWO-WAY Y-BRANCH

ROOF JACK ON A PITCH

ROUND DUCT INTERSECTING A TAPER

106F08.TIF

Figure 8 ◆ Examples of fittings made using radial line development.

The following two principles must be kept in mind when using radial line development:

- All lines of the fitting must radiate at an equal angle from a common center, but this center need not be located on the fitting itself.
- The taper of those lines must not be too steep. When using radial line development, first draw the elevation view and then extend the side lines of the view up until they meet at a peak. If the taper is too steep, this peak will be several feet above the fitting. The radius needed to swing such a stretchout arc would be too long for your tools to establish.

Because of these principles, you can use radial line development only for limited applications. Thus, it is used less frequently.

One use for radial line development is on a round taper pattern, as long as the fitting is equally tapered on all sides. (A round taper pattern can also be done by triangulation, but radial line development is faster when the slant lines all come to a center and all slants are equal.)

The round taper pattern shown in *Figure 9* is essentially the same as a cone pattern, except that it has a sawed-off top.

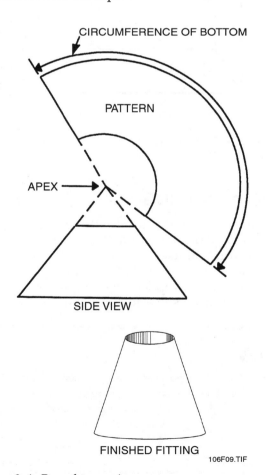

Figure 9 ◆ Round taper view.

To lay out this pattern, follow these steps:

Step 1 Draw the elevation, or side view, of the fitting.

Step 2 Extend the tapered lines of the sides of the fitting upward until they meet, establishing the peak or apex. (In the figure, the broken lines are the extended lines.)

Step 3 Using the apex as a center point, project the distance on your dividers from this center to the bottom corner of the side view.

Step 4 Draw the stretchout arc. The distance of this arc equals the circumference of the circle formed by the bottom of the fitting.

Step 5 Draw lines from the apex to the ends of the stretchout arc.

Step 6 To complete the pattern, measure and draw the top arc from the vertical dimension shown on the side view.

6.3.0 Triangulation

The triangulation method involves dividing a surface into triangles. This process makes it possible to transfer the shape to a new position or to duplicate it a number of times. You will learn how to use the triangulation method later in your apprentice training. The following section, which discusses planes and true lengths, is included here to introduce you to some of the concepts related to this method. Your instructor will decide whether to cover this material now.

6.3.1 Planes and True Lengths

When you use triangulation, you will work with planes and true lengths. A plane is a surface with two dimensions—length and width. There are three types of planes:

- A *horizontal* plane is a surface that is level with the horizon.
- A *vertical* plane is a surface at a right angle or perpendicular to the horizontal plane.
- An *oblique* (slanted) plane is a surface at any angle found between the horizontal and vertical planes.

Some lines in planes are true lengths—lines whose true length is not distorted by perspective. When you look at plan and elevation views, you can see which lines on those views are true lengths and which are not. How can you tell which is which? Any lines that are perpendicular to your line of vision are true lengths. Any lines that are at an angle to your line of vision are not true lengths.

Here is an easy way to understand this concept. When you look at an elevation drawing of any object, it is the same as viewing the object face-on. The object's vertical lines run perpendicular to your line of vision, so they are true lengths.

When you look at a plan view of an object, it is the same as viewing the object from above. Horizontal lines that lie in the same plane on a plan view also run perpendicular to your line of vision, so they are also true lengths.

Now let's apply what you've learned. Look at *Figure 10*. It shows three views of one object: (1) a pictorial view, (2) an elevation view, and (3) a plan view. The pictorial view shows that this object looks like a pyramid with its top sawed off. (If this were a duct fitting, it would be called a transition.) The elevation view shows that the top and bottom surfaces of this object are perfectly flat.

Now look at the plan view. Compare it with the elevation view. You will see that lines GFEJ outline the top surface of this object and lines DCBA outline the bottom surface. The top surface and the bottom surface are horizontal planes and the lines in them are perpendicular to your line of vision. Thus, all those lines are true lengths.

Lines DG, FC, EB, and AJ are *not* true lengths. You can see that these lines are drawn in perspective, which distorts their true length. Remember, too, that you are looking at them as though you were seeing them from above. Thus, those lines are not perpendicular to your line of vision. You can determine the true lengths of these lines only by using geometry. With an understanding of plan and elevation views, planes, and geometry, you will be able to find the true lengths for all slanted surfaces and develop a pattern using triangulation.

You will use the triangulation method to make fittings with sides that are not parallel and do not all slant at the same angle or meet at a common point. Examples of fittings made using triangulation are shown in *Figure 11*.

You will learn more about triangulation concepts as you progress in your training. They may seem a little confusing now, but as you become more experienced these concepts will become easier to understand and apply.

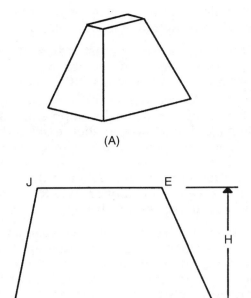

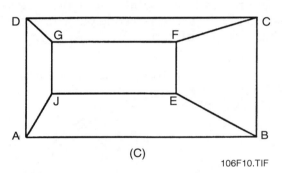

Figure 10 ◆ Finding true lengths. (A) Pictorial view. (B) Elevation view. (C) Plan view.

106F10.TIF

7.0.0 ◆ CUTTING

The most commonly used cutting tools in sheet metal are hand snips, hacksaws, and squaring shears. You will use hand snips in the field when machines are not available or not practical. In the shop, when the application calls for it, you will use the squaring shear to cut metal sheets.

True Lengths and Floor Plans

Some lines in a plan view that may look horizontal are not. For example, lines that show handrails for stairs on a floor plan may look flat on the plan view, but they actually exist in a slanted plane. Therefore, they are at an angle to your line of vision and are not true lengths. When looking at floor plans, you must keep in mind both your line of vision and the planes in which the lines actually exist.

ROUND TO SQUARE

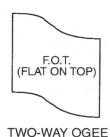
F.O.T.
(FLAT ON TOP)

TWO-WAY OGEE

F.O.T.

TRANSITION ELBOW

TRANSITION

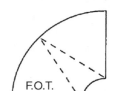
ROOF JACK
ON A PITCH

Y-BRANCH

106F11.TIF

Figure 11 ◆ Examples of fittings made using triangulation.

7.1.0 Cutting With Hand Snips

You will use hand snips to make straight and curved cuts in sheet metal made from mild steel or nonferrous metals (see *Figure 12*). Never use hand snips to cut wire, bolts, nails, hardened steel, or double thicknesses of metal. In this module, the steps for making straight and curved cuts are written for both right- and left-handed workers. Cut with the hand you normally use for writing and hold the metal with your other hand.

DID YOU KNOW?
Sheet Metal and Flight

Until Orville Wright's famous flight on December 17, 1903, in Kitty Hawk, North Carolina, controlled flying seemed just a dream. But before Orville flew into history, he and his brother Wilbur spent hours in their shop testing and perfecting their glider.

The brothers had to understand the effect of airflow on their glider's wings. Even though other scientists around the world were also working on flying experiments, little or no reliable information on airflow and wind effects existed.

To better understand the effect of airflow, the brothers built a wind tunnel. The tunnel consisted of a wooden chase or duct attached to a sheet metal fitting. One end of the fitting tapered to fit inside one end of the wooden chase. The other end of the fitting widened out to house a blower fan. Inside the chase, the brothers hung model wings, also made of sheet metal, to test wind resistance and airflow.

The fan, driven by an overhead belt, could reproduce air speeds between 25 and 35 miles per hour, enabling the Wright brothers to measure the amount of lift they could expect to get from different wing designs.

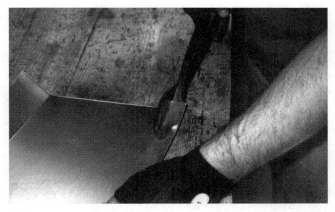
106F12.EPS

Figure 12 ◆ Making cuts with hand snips.

Riveting Ideas

Optical Illusion

When you look at the plan view in *Figure 10*, it will sometimes appear as though you are looking down into a box instead of at the top of the fitting. This is an *optical illusion* caused by the perspective of the lines DG, FC, EB, and AJ. Focus on the lines GFEJ. After a second or two, you will see them as the top of the fitting.

You must follow these guidelines when using snips:

- For straight cuts in 24-gauge or lighter mild steel, use straight-blade snips or combination snips.
- For straight cuts in 22- to 16-gauge mild steel, use bulldog snips, which are designed for notching or trimming extra-heavy stock.
- For cutting circles and curves, use right-hand or left-hand aviation snips.
- Keep narrower pieces above the lower blade of the snips.
- Check the snips for proper blade fit.
- Rest both the snips and the sheet metal on the workbench.
- Hold the blades of the snips at right angles to the cut.
- Trim off surplus metal before making the final cut.
- Avoid jagged cut edges by never closing the blades completely, except for notching.

7.1.1 Straight Cuts

To make straight cuts, follow these steps:

Step 1 Grasp the snips in one hand and hold the narrowest part of the sheet metal in the other hand.

Step 2 Rest both the snips and the sheet metal pattern on the workbench (see *Figure 13*).

106F13.EPS

Figure 13 ◆ Resting the snips and metal on the bench ensures accurate cutting.

 WARNING!
Always wear gloves when using snips. Remove all jewelry (rings, watches, bracelets) and tie back long hair.

Step 3 Open the blades as wide as possible and start the cut at the edge of the sheet.

Step 4 Close the blades just short of the full length to prevent jagged edges. The length of each cut is determined by the thickness of the metal. A good rule of thumb to follow is the heavier the metal, the shorter the cut.

Step 5 Start the next cut at the extreme end of the preceding cut. Finish the cut, keeping the snips on the cutting line.

7.1.2 Outside Curved Cuts

To make outside curved cuts, follow these steps:

Step 1 Cut off the corners of the pattern.

Step 2 Holding the metal in one hand and the snips in your other hand, rest the snips and metal on the workbench.

Step 3 Make a continuous cut, turning the metal as the cut progresses and removing waste metal in one piece.

Step 4 Trim away all burrs, jagged edges, and fishhooks (hook-shaped slivers of metal left on the edges of cut metal).

7.1.3 Inside Curved Cuts

You must start an inside curved cut away from the edges of the metal. Therefore, before you can make an inside curved cut, you must make a slit or starter hole in which to insert the snips. You can do this with a chisel or with a hollow punch.

To make an inside curved cut, follow these steps:

Step 1 Use a chisel to cut two slits in the center of the sheet metal, or make a starter hole with a hollow punch or drill.

Step 2 Insert the blades into the slit or starter hole.

 **Riveting Ideas** *Smooth Cutting*

For smooth cuts, turn the metal into the snips. Don't force the snips around the metal.

Step 3 Gradually increase the cut at the slit or starter hole until you can easily fit the snips in to begin cutting.

Step 4 Make a continuous cut, turning the metal as the cut progresses and removing waste metal in one piece.

Step 5 Trim away all burrs, jagged edges, and fishhooks.

7.1.4 Notching

A notch is a piece of metal cut out of the workpiece before it is formed or fitted. You will make a notch to eliminate an overlap or bulge at an edge or seam. There are several types of notches:

- The *square notch* can be either square or rectangular and is used to make boxes and pans or to make fittings that have boxlike shapes. It is used in fittings where seams and edges are required.
- The *straight notch* is a straight cut or slice in the metal. The straight notch is used in making fittings that require an outside edge or flange with a closed corner.
- The *slant notch* is a 45-degree angle cut from the corner of the pattern. This notch prevents single or double hems or edges from overlapping at the corners. It is also used for fittings that require a single hem around a flat surface.
- A *V-notch* is a 45-degree angle cut made on two sides to form a 90-degree angle or V shape. It is used in making a fitting with a 90-degree bend and an inside edge or flange.

To use snips to notch metal, follow these steps:

Step 1 Select either combination blade or straight blade snips.

Step 2 Rest the snips and workpiece on the workbench.

Step 3 Open the blades so that they do not extend beyond the end of the line to be notched.

Step 4 Hold the blades of the snips completely vertical to the plane of the cut and make the cut by closing the blades completely.

Step 5 Repeat these steps to cut the opposite side of each notch on the pattern.

You may also use notchers for specific notching jobs. The hand notcher is a lightweight hand tool designed for fast, accurate work (see *Figure 14*). The jaw design permits notching to the exact depth without slippage. The notch configuration is in the shape of a V.

The dovetail notcher is used on the ends of pipes, collars, and Y-branches. It has the advantage of allowing you to cut the notch and fold down the tab in one motion (see *Figure 15*).

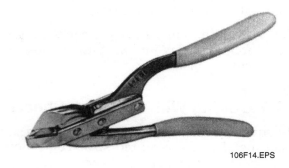

106F14.EPS

Figure 14 ◆ A hand notcher.

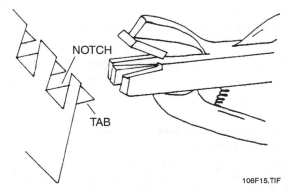

106F15.TIF

Figure 15 ◆ A dovetail notcher.

7.1.5 Double Cutting

To cut light-gauge pipe, you will use double-cutting snips. This tool has a center cutting blade that will not leave burrs. It is designed so that neither side of the metal has to slide over the bottom blade.

To double-cut pipe, follow these steps (see *Figure 16*):

106F16.EPS

Figure 16 ◆ Cutting pipe with double-cutting snips.

Step 1 Make a starter hole along the layout line with a chisel or a punch.

Step 2 Cut with one hand while turning the pipe with the other hand so that the cut is always on the top surface.

Step 3 Keep the snips at an angle to the pipe and follow the layout line with the nose of the cutting blade.

7.2.0 Cutting With Squaring Shears

The squaring shear is used to cut, trim, and square sheet metal to the required size. The following rules apply to the squaring shear:

- You must use it only for straight cutting.
- You must cut only one sheet of metal at a time.
- You must never use it to cut wires, rods, seams, or double edges.

The shear is equipped with one of two types of hold-down devices. The first type is set by hand before cutting. The other type is controlled with a foot treadle while the cutting takes place.

 WARNING!

The squaring shear can slice through your fingers as easily as it slices through metal. Avoid putting your fingers anywhere near the blade or the hold-down bar.

Never cut metal that is too small to fit under the hold-down bar.

Always keep foreign objects off the work surface.

Operate the foot treadle with only one foot. Keep your other foot clear of the treadle to avoid pinching or crushing your toes. Never jump on the foot treadle.

As a general rule, only one person at a time should operate a squaring shear. However, if you work with an assistant, make sure that your assistant's hands and feet are clear of the hold-down bar, the blade, and the foot treadle.

The squaring shear, like many large shop machines, comes equipped with safety guards and controls. Never turn off or disable any safety guards or controls.

The shear also contains front, back, and bevel gauges that you can use to cut many pieces of the same size. Setting these gauges requires set-up time, so consider the number of pieces to be cut before you use them.

7.2.1 Side Gauge Cutting

When using the side gauge on the squaring shear, follow these steps:

Step 1 Insert the metal from the front of the machine.

Step 2 Place the edge to be cut about ¼ inch past the bottom blade.

Step 3 Use both hands to hold the left-hand edge of the sheet firmly against the left-hand side gauge.

Step 4 If your shear has a hand-operated hold-down bar, place it in the holding position. If your shear is foot operated, depress the treadle with your right foot to set the hold-down bar.

Step 5 Make the cut with a steady downward motion. Release the hold-down bar gradually until it returns to the original position. When using a hand-operated hold-down bar, don't allow the handle to fly out of your hands. When using a foot-operated hold-down bar, don't allow the treadle to spring back. Work with a steady, even pressure.

Step 6 Place the cut edge against the side gauge and repeat the holding and cutting operations when squaring a corner.

7.2.2 Marked Sheet Cutting

Usually you will not use the gauges on the squaring shear when you cut sheet metal to a scribed line. Instead, you will use your line of sight to set the cut lines in position. To cut sheet metal to a scribed line, follow these steps:

Step 1 Insert the metal from the front of the machine while you look down between the hold-down bar and the upper cutting blade.

 **Riveting Ideas**   *Coper*

Many sheet metal shops use a machine called a coper to notch sheet metal patterns. The machine is a combination notcher and shear and can do many of the operations done with hand snips, only much faster.

Special Cutting

In the sheet metal trade, many additional types of snips and cutting equipment are used for special cutting operations. When large arcs or circles are to be cut, a power-operated ring-and-circle shear or an electric hand-operated shear may be used.

 CAUTION

Never cut sheet metal that is too short for the hold-down devices (called dogs) to hold down.

Step 2 Position the cut line to align the mark with the lower cutting blade edge.

Step 3 Hold the metal in place until the hold-down bar engages.

Step 4 Depress the treadle and complete the cut.

You can also make notches and partial angle cuts on the squaring shear, but it is sometimes difficult to control the cut distance.

8.0.0 ◆ PUNCHING HOLES

You can punch holes in sheet metal with solid or hollow punches. It is better to use a punch than a drill on light-gauge sheet metal (24 gauge or thinner) because a drill is apt to leave burrs at the edge of the hole. Punching is also faster than drilling. Note that the use of hollow punches is no longer common in the sheet metal industry. This tool has largely been replaced by lever punches and hydraulic multiple-task machine punches like the Ironworker (see *Figure 17*).

You must use a drill when cutting holes in heavy-gauge metal. The speed of the drill makes it more accurate on heavy metal and causes less distortion than a punch would.

106F17.EPS

Figure 17 ◆ Ironworker.

8.1.0 Using a Lever Punch

A lever punch consists of a die and a punch, which are moved by levers. The punch forces the metal through the die, cutting out a blank of metal (see *Figure 18*). This blank is known as a **slug**. The die acts as backing for the edge of the metal that is not cut out.

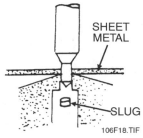

106F18.TIF

Figure 18 ◆ The lever punch cuts out a blank of metal, or slug.

To punch holes with a hand lever, follow these steps:

Step 1 Lay out and prick-punch all of the holes.

Step 2 Install a lever punch and die that are the correct size for the task.

Step 3 Place the sheet metal on the workbench with the area to be punched extending 1 to 2 inches beyond the edge of the workbench.

Step 4 Place the centering point of the lever punch on the prick-punch mark.

Step 5 Squeeze the handles of the lever punch to punch the hole (see *Figure 19*).

106F19.EPS

Figure 19 ◆ Using the hand lever punch.

Other types of lever punches are available:

- The *bottom punch* is used to indent several thicknesses of metal together to provide a secure fastening method that can be used instead of rivets.
- The *clip punch* is used to join ductwork seams together. It turns down an ear that is later hemmed tight with a hammer.
- *Floor and bench lever punches* are used on heavier gauges of sheet metal and to make large holes.
- The *snap lock punch* (see *Figure 20*) forms ears that lock firmly on the seamed edge of a joining piece.

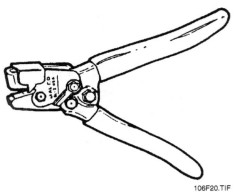

106F20.TIF

Figure 20 ◆ A snap lock punch.

9.0.0 ◆ FORMING

To make a fitting, you must form the sheet metal into square, rectangular, round, oblong, conical, or other geometric shapes. You may complete this forming process by using hand tools such as stakes and mallets or by using machines specially designed for this purpose.

9.1.0 Stakes

As you learned in the Sheet Metal Level One Module, *Tools of the Trade,* you can form sheet metal by working on it with a mallet over a stake made of hardened steel. You will use stakes when a suitable machine is not available or adaptable for the work. Stakes vary in shape and size, and you can form square, round, or conical workpieces on them. You can also set and finish edges and seams on stakes.

If you have ever seen a blacksmith forming metal over an anvil, you have a good idea of how a sheet metal mechanic works a piece of metal over a stake.

9.2.0 Forming Machines

In the shop, you will use forming machines to form pipes and other cylindrical objects. The most commonly used machines include the slip-roll forming machine, the easy edger, and the crimping and beading machine.

9.2.1 Slip-Roll Forming Machine

The slip-roll forming machine forms metal into curves or cylinders (see *Figure 21*). It consists of a housing; a base; upper, lower, and rear rolls; an upper roll release; lower and rear roll adjusting screws; and an operating handle. The lower roll has grooves in it used for forming parts with wired edges and to form wire.

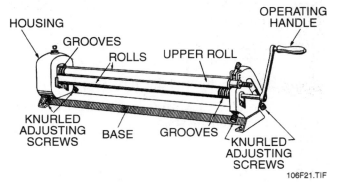

106F21.TIF

Figure 21 ◆ A slip-roll forming machine.

To use a slip-roll forming machine, follow these steps:

Step 1 Insert the metal between the two front rolls (see *Figure 22*).

Step 2 Adjust the front rolls by turning the front screws.

Step 3 Raise the rear roll for a small radius or lower it for a large radius.

Step 4 Turn the operating handle to pull the metal through the rolls.

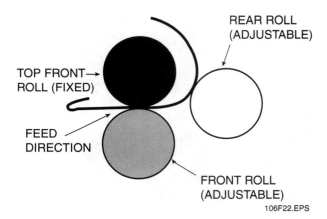

106F22.EPS

Figure 22 ◆ Roll configuration for the slip-roll forming machine.

9.2.2 Easy Edger

The easy edger is a bench-type machine used for making a 90-degree bend on flat, curved parts (see *Figure 23*). It is also used to turn a flange (measuring ³⁄₁₆ of an inch) on cheeks of elbows and offsets for insertion into a Pittsburgh lock.

106F23.EPS

Figure 23 ◆ An easy edger.

10.0.0 ◆ EDGES

Every time you make a sheet metal fitting, you must finish it with some type of edge. An edge provides a finished look and additional strength, and it eliminates the ragged metal that can cause cuts. Some edges provide only a small amount of strength, while others give maximum rigidity. The commonly formed sheet metal edges are the single hem, the double hem, and the wired edge (see *Figure 24*).

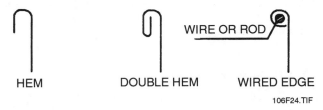

106F24.TIF

Figure 24 ◆ Examples of sheet metal edges.

The single hem is a folded edge on the metal made to increase strength and to provide a smoothly finished edge. The allowance for a single hem is generally ½ inch.

The double hem is simply a single hem done twice. It is an easy edge to make and provides more strength than the single hem. The allowance for the double hem is twice the hem size less ¹⁄₁₆ of an inch. The inside allowance made to the hem size is usually ⁵⁄₁₆ of an inch or ⅜ of an inch. The outside allowance is ¹⁄₁₆ of an inch less than the hem size because the outside line is formed first and must be short so that it does not cover the second bend line (see *Figure 25*).

Wired edges are stronger than the double hem. You make a wired edge by wrapping the sheet metal around a piece of wire. The wired edge is not used as often as it once was because it takes longer to produce.

The allowance added to the pattern for a wired edge depends on the diameter of the wire. For 26-gauge and lighter sheet metal, 2½ times the diameter of the wire is added to the pattern. For 24-gauge and heavier sheet metal, allowances must be made for the thickness of the metal and the diameter of the wire, which vary from 2 to 2½ times the thickness of the metal.

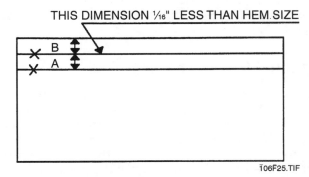

THIS DIMENSION ¹⁄₁₆" LESS THAN HEM SIZE

106F25.TIF

Figure 25 ◆ Hem allowance.

11.0.0 ◆ SEAMS (LOCKS)

Seams (or locks) are used to join the edges of the metal. They may be made by mechanical methods or by welding. You can choose the best method for joining the seams based on the thickness of the metal, the kind of metal, the cost of fabrication, and the equipment available. Common seams include the grooved lock seam, snap lock seam, and the Pittsburgh lock.

11.1.0 Grooved Lock Seam

The grooved lock seam is also sometimes called the acme, or pipe lock (see *Figure 26*). The seam consists of two folded edges that are hooked together and locked with a grooving machine or hand groover.

106F26.TIF

Figure 26 ◆ Cross section of a grooved lock seam.

The hand groover is a hardened steel tool with one end recessed to offset the grooved lock. It has a range of grooves ranging from ³⁄₃₂ to ¹⁹⁄₃₂ of an inch wide. You should select a groover with a groove that is approximately ¹⁄₁₆ of an inch wider than the width of the seam. Grooved seams are rarely used in metals heavier than 20 gauge.

The formula for finding the amount of material needed for a grooved seam is as follows:

24 gauge or heavier =
(3 × lock width) + (5 × metal thickness)

11.2.0 Snap Lock Seam

The snap lock seam consists of a pocket lock and another edge that is inserted into the pocket. This edge is formed using a snap lock punch to raise buttons or bumps that produce a tighter fit inside the pocket.

11.3.0 Pittsburgh Lock

The Pittsburgh lock is the most commonly used seam in the sheet metal shop. This seam consists of one edge formed into a pocket and a second edge that is bent and inserted into the pocket. The important feature of this seam is that after the bent edge is inserted into the pocket, the pocket edge is folded over to permanently lock the seam shut (see *Figure 27*).

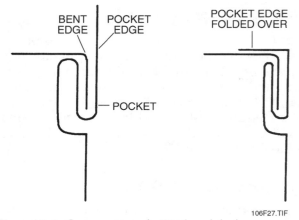

Figure 27 ◆ Cross section of a Pittsburgh lock.

This seam is used so often that a roll-forming machine called the Pittsburgh lock machine has been developed. The metal is inserted in one end of the machine, runs through a series of rolls, and comes out at the other end with the pocket lock completely formed. If no roll-forming machine is available, you must form the Pittsburgh lock on a brake. The allowance for the Pittsburgh lock formed on a brake is 1¼ inches.

12.0.0 ◆ CONNECTORS

Connectors are used to join individual pieces of duct. Connectors include the drive connector, S-slip, standing seam, standing S, standing drive slip, and Ductmate®.

12.1.0 Drive Connector

The drive connector is made in a two-step process. First, the edges of two pieces of metal to be joined are turned to form two pockets, each about a ½ inch wide. The drive is formed from a separate piece of metal, the edges of which are also turned, forming a sleeve. You will pull this sleeve over the folded edges of the pieces to be connected and drive it on with a hammer (see *Figure 28*). Drives are used to connect the sides of ductwork.

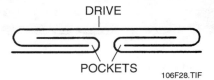

Figure 28 ◆ Cross section of a drive connector.

12.2.0 S-Slip

The S-slip is an S-shaped connector that forms two pocket locks for metal edges to slip into (see *Figure 29*). S-slips are used to connect the top and bottom edges of ductwork. The S-slip is sometimes also called a flat slip.

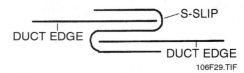

Figure 29 ◆ Cross section of an S-slip connector.

12.3.0 Standing Seam

The standing seam eliminates the need for additionally reinforcing a run of duct because this type of connector supplies its own reinforcement. This lock is easily made and is also used as a cross-seam on larger ducts (see *Figure 30*).

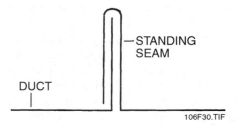

Figure 30 ◆ Cross section of a standing seam.

12.4.0 Transverse Duct Connector

The transverse duct connector is used to connect two sections of duct. Sometimes called a pocket lock, it is used in the same way as the S-slips and drive slips. The difference is that the finished transverse duct connector is not flush with the duct.

12.5.0 Other Connectors

Three other commonly used duct connectors include the standing S, standing drive slip, and Ductmate®. The standing S is an S-shaped connector with an additional hem reinforcement (see *Figure 31*). The standing drive slip is a drive connector with this same type of additional reinforcement (see *Figure 32*). Ductmate® is a patented duct connection system for sealing connecting duct sections. This system is used primarily to prevent air leaks in medium-pressure air systems. It also gives further reinforcement to larger ducts.

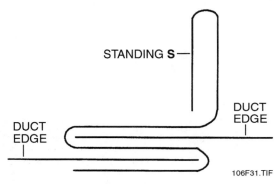

Figure 31 ◆ Cross section of a standing S connector.

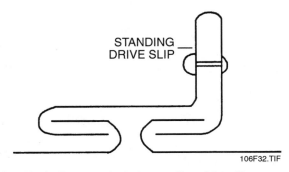

Figure 32 ◆ Cross section of a standing drive slip.

Review Questions

Sections 6.0.0–12.0.0

1. To lay out rectangular and round duct, elbows, tees, roof gutters, cornices, or offsets, you would use _____.
   a. radial line development
   b. parallel line development
   c. triangulation
   d. offset triangle development

2. To develop fittings in which all sides meet at an apex, you must use _____.
   a. parallel line development
   b. triangulation
   c. radial line development
   d. true lengths

3. Before you can make an inside curved cut, you must first _____.
   a. square up the edges of the metal sheet
   b. cut away the outside corners of the metal sheet
   c. make a starter hole with the blades of the snips
   d. make a starter hole with a chisel or a punch

4. To raise buttons or bumps to form a tight seam inside a pocket, you will use a _____.
   a. hollow punch
   b. snap lock punch
   c. hand groover
   d. Pittsburgh lock machine

5. Three formed sheet metal edges are the _____.
   a. curved edge, the double-curved edge, and the mitered edge
   b. grooved edge, the snap lock edge, and the pocket lock edge
   c. single hem, the double hem, and the wired edge
   d. grooved hem, the double-lock hem, and the mitered edge

Summary

All layout work is done by one of three methods: parallel line development, radial line development, and triangulation. As an apprentice, you will use parallel line development most often. This module covered the basics of parallel line and radial line development. It also introduced you to some basic concepts in triangulation, a layout method that you will learn more about later in your training. You also learned how to properly select and use layout tools. You will find that a good background in math and geometry will help you to master layout techniques. Equally important is your ability to visualize what your finished fitting will look like. Seeing the fitting in your head will help you to properly lay it out.

Once you are ready to lay out a fitting, you will follow these basic steps: laying out the pattern, cutting out the pattern, forming the metal into fittings, putting edges on the fittings, and joining the fittings. Taking the time now to practice these steps and perfect your skills will enable you to quickly produce high-quality fittings that are ready for installation.

Maynard Kettner

Retired Manager
Hewitt Heating and Air, Shiocton, Wisconsin

Maynard was born and raised on a farm in Wisconsin, where he did everything from milking cows to plowing the earth. After completing a tour in the Army in 1961, he worked in a woodworking factory but soon switched to the field of heating and air conditioning. Maynard completed a five-year apprenticeship with a local contractor, where he learned all the basics—layout, fabrication, forming, welding, and soldering. After work, he took additional classes and seminars to improve his skills and rise within the profession. He became a shop foreman within 10 years. In March 2001, Maynard retired as manager of a heating and air conditioning company after nearly 40 years in the industry and 15 years as a college instructor. The Associated Builders and Contractors, Inc. (ABC), honored Maynard by naming him Instructor of the Year.

How did you become interested in the construction industry?

When I came home from the Army, I worked for a while in a woodworking shop. But there was no advancement, so I left pretty quickly. Sheet metal looked to me like it had a lot of interesting challenges. I liked the idea that I could make anything out of metal. A person can learn how to take control of metal, instead of letting it control them. I used to build tin men and tin women in class. I enjoyed that, and I learned a lot at the same time.

How did you decide to become a manager?

I felt that it was time for me to try running my own business. I came in right off the street to take over a business that was failing. In six years, the company went from 6 to 24 employees. When I left, we were generating $2 million a year in business. It was stressful, but I enjoyed going in to work most of the time. It was that way with all my jobs. Sometimes, companies don't know how to treat people. When that used to happen to me, I would never stay there for long. I believe it's important to make sure your people and your customers are happy.

What do you think it takes to be a success in your trade?

Above all, it takes honesty. That means being honest with your people, with your customers, and with the world. From the time I started as an apprentice, my goal was not just to move up the ladder, but to do it honestly. I believe that's what got me here today.

It's also important to work hard. I've seen some young people brought up to expect that things will be given to them. They usually end up learning that they can't get along like that for very long in this business. I always told my people that if they're not working hard, they're basically just stealing hours. And stealing hours is no different from stealing off the grocery shelf.

I think that trainees need more instruction in basic psychology—how to work with people and handle situations that come up on a daily basis. To succeed on the job, people need to be able to pull together and work together. Not everybody knows how to do that.

(continued)

What are some things you did in your jobs as manager and instructor?

You name it, I did it! At the time I retired as manager of Hewitt Heating and Air, I supervised 24 employees. It was very important to me to make sure that everybody was happy there. It was my responsibility to find new work for them, and that took a lot of time and effort. We earned a lot of our new business through word-of-mouth. That's where honesty and hard work always pay off. I also managed the company's finances, and hired and fired people. I usually worked 50-hour weeks to get everything done. Every day on the job I tried to set a good example.

Until I retired, I taught two nights a week for 15 years at a local technical college. I mentioned before that when I was starting out as an apprentice, I loved the idea of being able to control metal; I tried to instill that same interest in my students. I made them design and fit their own tin men and women, just like I used to do when I was a student. They had to use all the proper tools and codes, so it was a real challenge for them. It was also a way for them to demonstrate to themselves what they had learned.

What did you like most about being a manager?

What I liked the most was meeting new people and facing new challenges every day. I never got tired of that. I've done everything from setting units using helicopters to working on coal elevators on Christmas Eve, because that was the only time the mill shut down. My formal training lasted five years, but the learning did not end there.

What would you say to someone entering the trade today?

Be aggressive in pursuing your education. I've always told my workers and students: "If you're waiting for something to turn up, start with your shirt sleeves." Don't be afraid of work. Enjoy your work, and have fun doing it. The way to make it fun is to be educated; that way, you can understand your work. You control your destiny in the profession, but success is not about downgrading somebody to get higher yourself. Everyone can climb the ladder together.

Trade Terms Introduced in This Module

Many of the terms in this glossary also appear in the section of this module titled *Layout Terminology*. Shorter forms of these definitions have been included in this glossary for your convenience.

Angle: In layout, angular fittings, branches, or sections of round or rectangular duct.

Apex: A narrow or pointed end at the uppermost part of an object. The peak of a pointed object.

Axis: An imaginary line around which an object rotates.

Centerlines: Lines used to show the centers, or axes, of parts or circles shown on a layout.

Cheek: The flat side of any rectangular curved elbow or fitting, as opposed to the curved sides.

Constructions: Two-dimensional representations or drawings of three-dimensional objects.

Curved lines: Lines with a constantly changing direction.

Development: The act of creating a sheet metal pattern.

Dimension lines: Lines on plans or patterns that indicate size (width and height).

Elevation: A drawing of any object as if it were being viewed face-on.

Extension lines: Lines that extend from a plan or pattern to the dimension lines.

Fitting: Any irregularly shaped sheet metal object for which a pattern must be developed.

Gore: A section of a round sheet metal elbow cut at an angle at one or both ends.

Heel: The long side or longest curved surface on any rectangular curved elbow or fitting.

Horizontal lines: Straight lines that are parallel to the horizon.

Miter line: The line of intersection for two pipes or other fittings joined together at any angle.

Oblique lines: Lines drawn at any angle between vertical and horizontal.

Offset: An angled fitting, such as a duct, that shifts direction to move around an obstruction.

Parallel lines: In layout, straight lines equally spaced apart that never meet or intersect and are finite (come to an end).

Pattern: The flat outline of a fitting or object to be fabricated.

Perpendicular line: A line that is at a right angle to another line or a plane.

Plane: A surface having two dimensions (length and width) that may be horizontal, vertical, or oblique (at an angle).

Plan view: A drawing of an object or room as it would appear if you could see it from directly overhead.

Profile: In curved pipe layout, the shape of half of a fitting at any given point, shown as a plan view.

Radius: In layout, the distance from a center position to the *throat* or *heel* of any curved fitting.

Scribing: The act of drawing lines on metal or wood using a pointed instrument such as a scratch awl.

Slug: The blank of metal ejected when a lever punch forces the metal through a die.

Stock: The supply of sheet metal in a shop; an individual piece of sheet metal.

Stretchout: The pattern for a three-dimensional object stretched out flat. The measurement around or across the flattened object.

Tee: A configuration consisting of two intersecting pipes that form a T shape.

Template: A master pattern used to trace the shape of a given fitting or object onto sheets of metal.

Throat: The short side or the shortest curved surface on any rectangular curved elbow or fitting.

True length: In a layout, a line whose true length is not distorted by perspective.

Vertical lines: Straight lines that are perpendicular (at right angles) to the horizon.

Additional Resources

This module is intended to present thorough resources for task training. The following reference works are suggested for further study. These are optional materials for continued education rather than for task training.

Basic Mathematical Skill with Geometry, 1997. James Streeter, Donald Hutchison, and Louis F. Hoelzle. New York, NY: McGraw-Hill.

Bob Miller's Geometry for the Clueless, 2000. Robert Miller. New York, NY: McGraw-Hill.

Cliff's Quick Review Geometry, 1998. Edward Kohn. Lincoln, NE: Cliff's Notes Publishing Company.

Figure Credits

Edwards Manufacturing Company, Inc.	106F17
New York State Education Department	106F21
Glenn Schwenneker of MSI Encompass	106F12, 106F13, 106F16, 106F19
Malco Products, Inc.	106F03, 106F20
Parrott Mechanical, Inc.	106F23
Roper Whitney of Rockford, Illinois	106F04, 106F14

NCCER CRAFT TRAINING USER UPDATES

The NCCER makes every effort to keep these textbooks up-to-date and free of technical errors. We appreciate your help in this process. If you have an idea for improving this textbook, or if you find an error, a typographical mistake, or an inaccuracy in the NCCER's Craft Training textbooks, please write us, using this form or a photocopy. Be sure to include the exact module number, page number, a detailed description, and the correction, if applicable. Your input will be brought to the attention of the Technical Review Committee. Thank you for your assistance.

Instructors – If you found that additional materials were necessary in order to teach this module effectively, please let us know so that we may include them in the Equipment and Materials list in the Instructor's Guide.

Write: Curriculum Revision and Development Department
National Center for Construction Education and Research
P.O. Box 141104, Gainesville, FL 32614-1104

Fax: 352-334-0932

E-mail: curriculum@nccer.org

Craft _____   Module Name _____

Copyright Date _____   Module Number _____   Page Number(s) _____

Description _____

_____

_____

_____

(Optional) Correction _____

_____

_____

(Optional) Your Name and Address _____

_____

_____

Trade Math One

COURSE MAP

This course map shows all of the modules in the first level of the Sheet Metal curriculum. The suggested training order begins at the bottom and proceeds up. Skill levels increase as you advance on the course map. The local Training Program Sponsor may adjust the training order.

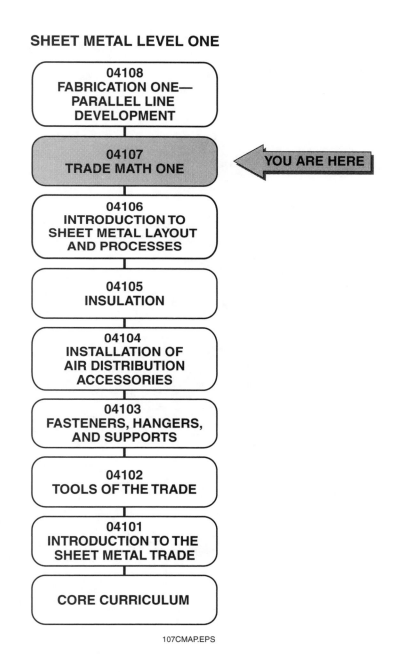

SHEET METAL LEVEL ONE

04108
FABRICATION ONE—
PARALLEL LINE
DEVELOPMENT

04107
TRADE MATH ONE ◀ YOU ARE HERE

04106
INTRODUCTION TO
SHEET METAL LAYOUT
AND PROCESSES

04105
INSULATION

04104
INSTALLATION OF
AIR DISTRIBUTION
ACCESSORIES

04103
FASTENERS, HANGERS,
AND SUPPORTS

04102
TOOLS OF THE TRADE

04101
INTRODUCTION TO THE
SHEET METAL TRADE

CORE CURRICULUM

107CMAP.EPS

Copyright © 2001 National Center for Construction Education and Research, Gainesville, FL 32614-1104. All rights reserved. No part of this work may be reproduced in any form or by any means, including photocopying, without written permission of the publisher.

Figures

Tables

Trade Math One

Objectives

When you finish this module, you will be able to do the following:

1. Convert denominate numbers and solve problems using them.
2. Calculate using rules.
3. Calculate using metric, linear, square, volume, and weight measurements.
4. Calculate the stretchouts for selected fittings.
5. Construct simple geometric figures.

Prerequisites

Before you begin this module, it is recommended that you successfully complete the following modules: Core Curriculum; Sheet Metal Level One, Modules 04101 through 04106.

Required Trainee Materials

1. Pencil and paper
2. Appropriate personal protective equipment

1.0.0 ◆ INTRODUCTION

In the sheet metal trade, you will work with measurements and calculations every day to make fittings, to create patterns, and to solve problems as they come up on the job. In this module, you will build on your basic math skills to learn how to do calculations with **denominate numbers**, how to use rules to do simple calculations, and how to convert measurements in both the American and metric systems. You will also learn how to calculate stretchouts for selected fittings, and you will be introduced to some basic geometry.

2.0.0 ◆ DENOMINATE NUMBERS

Numbers that have units of measure associated with them are called denominate numbers. Examples of such measures are feet and inches, feet and yards, pounds and ounces, square feet and square inches, cubic feet and cubic inches, and so forth.

When you do calculations with denominate numbers, you work on math problems that you can apply to real-world situations instead of to abstract theories. You will probably agree that mathematics makes the most sense when you use it to solve problems that involve real things that you can see, cut, bend, or fabricate.

It's important to remember that you are working with units of measurement and not simply numbers. You have probably heard the expression, "you cannot add apples and oranges." Let's see if that is true. Say that you are asked to add 10 apples and 6 oranges. How would you state your answer? You can't just say the answer is 16. To state the answer properly, you must find a common term that applies to both apples and oranges. You could say, "I have 16 pieces of *fruit*." But, as you can see, the word *fruit* cannot describe *exactly* what kinds of fruit you have.

When you work with units of measurement, however, you can convert different units into a common unit so that you can state your answer in exact terms. You know, for example, that 12 inches = 1 foot, 3 feet = 1 yard, and 16 ounces = 1 pound. If you are asked to add 12 inches and 3 feet, you can convert 12 inches to 1 foot and state your answer as 4 feet.

When you work with denominate numbers you must always remember what system you are in. When you work with feet and inches, you are in the 12-piece system. When you work with feet and yards, you are in the 3-piece system. When you work with ounces and pounds, you are in the 16-piece system. How do you apply this knowledge? If you are working in the 12-piece system, you know that 12 inches equal 1 foot. When you divide 1 foot into equal parts, each fractional part is $\frac{1}{12}$ of a foot. If you are working in the 3-piece system, you know that 3 feet equal 1 yard. When you divide 1 yard into equal parts, each fractional part is $\frac{1}{3}$ of a yard. If you are working in the 16-piece system, you know that 16 ounces equal 1 pound. When you divide 1 pound into equal parts, each fractional part is $\frac{1}{16}$ of a pound.

2.1.0 Adding Denominate Numbers

You add denominate numbers in the same way that you add whole numbers. But you must always remember to include the units of measurement. Look at the following example:

```
    6 feet   6 inches
+   9 feet   7 inches
   15 feet  13 inches
```

You can also state this answer as $15\frac{13}{12}$ or as $\frac{193}{12}$. You know that fractions must always be reduced to their lowest form. If you reduce both fractions to their lowest form, you will get the same answer both times.

To reduce $15\frac{13}{12}$ to its lowest form, you first divide 13 by 12, and then add the result to the whole number:

$$\frac{13}{12} = 1\frac{1}{12}$$

$$1\frac{1}{12} + 15 = 16\frac{1}{12}$$

To reduce $\frac{193}{12}$ to its lowest form, divide 193 by 12 as follows:

$$\frac{193}{12} = 16 \text{ } remainder \text{ } 1$$

The remainder is expressed as a fraction, $\frac{1}{12}$. So your answer in both cases is $16\frac{1}{12}$. But $16\frac{1}{12}$ what? Look back at the beginning of the problem. You started out with feet and inches, so you must state your answer in those units. In this case, you would state your answer as 16 feet, 1 inch ($\frac{1}{12}$ of 1 foot is 1 inch).

You must always state the answer to problems involving denominate numbers in the units with which you start. This means that if you work on a problem involving feet and inches, you must state your answer in feet and inches (even if you later convert to yards or meters). This is very important to remember. You may find it easy to add $\frac{1}{2}$ and $\frac{3}{4}$, but you must also remember to keep the units straight in your mind when you are adding $\frac{1}{2}$ of a *foot* to $\frac{3}{4}$ of an *inch*.

2.2.0 Subtracting Denominate Numbers

Keeping the units straight in your mind is especially important when you subtract denominate numbers. Study the following example:

```
    7 feet   4 inches
-   5 feet   6 inches
```

You can see that you cannot subtract 6 inches from 4 inches, so you must borrow from the whole number that appears to the left of the 4. Here is where you must be careful and remember to keep the units in mind. You are not just borrowing 1 from 7 and adding it to 4. You are borrowing 1 *foot* from 7 *feet* and adding it to 4 *inches*. You must convert the 1 foot into inches before you can add it to the 4 inches as follows:

12 inches + 4 inches = 16 inches

Now that you have borrowed correctly, you can subtract.

```
    6 feet  16 inches
-   5 feet   6 inches
    1 feet  10 inches
```

2.3.0 Multiplying Denominate Numbers

When you multiply feet and inches for an **area**, you must state your answer in square units. A square unit of measurement is one in which the measurements are the same along all sides—provided that the corners are perpendicular (all corners are at 90 degrees to one another).

Thus, a square is a geometric figure with four equal sides and four equal angles. A square foot is a geometric figure in which each side measures exactly 1 foot. A square inch is a geometric figure in which each side measures exactly 1 inch.

When you calculate the area of a geometric figure, you must first determine if all the measurements are stated in a common unit. If they are, you can simply multiply the measurements. If they are not, you must convert the measurements to a common unit. In either case, you must state your answer in square units.

For example, let's say that you must calculate the area of a sheet of metal measuring 9 feet along one side and 6 feet along the other side (see *Figure 1*). Because the measurement along each side is stated in a common unit (feet), you simply multiply the two measurements and state your answer in the proper unit: 54 square feet.

You can prove this calculation is accurate by constructing a proof (an illustration that proves that the calculation is true). To construct a proof, follow these steps (you will need a piece of paper, a pencil, and a straightedge):

Step 1 Draw a rectangle that is 6 inches on the short side and 9 inches on the long side (each inch represents 1 foot in *Figure 1*).

Step 2 Measure and make a mark at 1-inch intervals on the 6-inch side. Repeat this process for the 9-inch side.

Step 3 Use a straightedge and draw horizontal lines connecting all the marks along the sides. Then draw vertical lines to connect all the marks at the top and bottom of the rectangle.

When you are done, you will have 54 little squares inside your big rectangle. And that's exactly what is meant by multiplying side measurements to get the square measure of a given area.

Now let's find the area of a rectangle when the sides are stated in different units of measure. In the following example, the long side of the rectangle is 9 *yards* and the short side is 6 *feet*. You are multiplying two different things—yards and feet. How can you properly state your answer? You must convert to a common unit of measure that applies equally to both sides. You can convert either yards to feet or feet to yards. To convert 9 yards to feet, *multiply* by 3 (there are 3 feet in 1 yard) for a total of 27 feet. Now your calculation is 27 feet × 6 feet. To convert 6 feet to yards, *divide* by 3 for a total of 2 yards. Now your calculation is 9 yards × 2 yards. Will both calculations result in the same answer?

27 feet × 6 feet = 162 square feet

9 yards × 2 yards = 18 square yards

These answers certainly don't look the same, but they are. That is because the answers are expressed in square units. If you count all the little squares in *Figure 2*, you will find 162 of them. If you count all the large squares in *Figure 3*, you will see that there are 18. In each case, you have exactly the same *total area*, even though each rectangle is measured in different units. Therefore, you can say that 162 square feet is the *equivalent* of 18 square yards.

Of course, you won't have time to draw proof boxes while you're on the job. You did this exercise to help you see how seemingly different numbers can express the same overall measurement. At work, you will rely on math as well as conversion charts that help you quickly convert units of measure (see *Table 1*).

DID YOU KNOW?

Geometry

Geometry might sound like a difficult subject, but it basically involves working with familiar shapes such as squares, rectangles, circles, and triangles. Each shape has its own set of rules that describes how the shape is constructed and what measurements apply to it. For example, a square has four equal sides with four 90-degree angles. A triangle, on the other hand, has three sides and three angles. Although the angles in a triangle can vary, the sum of the three angles is always 180 degrees. As you progress in your apprenticeship, you will learn more about geometry and how it helps you do your job.

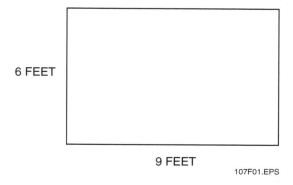

6 FEET

9 FEET

107F01.EPS

Figure 1 ◆ Calculating area.

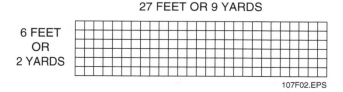

27 FEET OR 9 YARDS

6 FEET OR 2 YARDS

107F02.EPS

Figure 2 ◆ Area of 162 square feet.

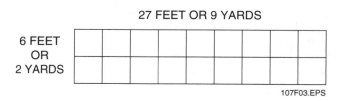

27 FEET OR 9 YARDS

6 FEET OR 2 YARDS

107F03.EPS

Figure 3 ◆ Area of 18 square yards.

2.3.1 Multiplication Exercises

When you multiply feet by inches you can express your answer in either feet or inches. However, on the job site, it is best to use the larger unit of measurement. For example, say you are asked to multiply the following:

8 feet × 24 inches

You can state the answer correctly as 2,304 inches, but it is more practical to state the answer as 16 feet. Multiply the following:

1. 4 feet × 15 feet = _____

2. 6 feet × 1½ feet = _____

3. 9 feet × 18 inches = _____

4. 2 yards 2 feet × 5 yards 1 foot = _____

5. 10 feet 4 inches × 6 feet 2 inches = _____

2.4.0 Dividing Denominate Numbers

To divide two units of different denominations, you must first convert the units to the smaller denomination. Look at the following problem:

6 feet 6 inches ÷ 2

To solve this problem, convert 6 feet to inches and then add the 6 inches to your total:

$6 \times 12 = 72$

$72 + 6 = 78$

Now you can divide by 2:

$$\begin{array}{r} 39 \text{ inches} \\ 2\overline{)78} \\ -6 \\ \hline 18 \\ -18 \\ \hline 0 \end{array}$$

Whenever you get an answer that is 12 or more inches, you should convert the answer to feet and inches. To do this, divide the answer by 12 (the number of inches in 1 foot). You would then state the remainder, if any, as inches. In this example, you would convert 39 inches to 3 feet 3 inches as follows:

$$\begin{array}{r} 3 \text{ feet 3 inches} \\ 12\overline{)39} \\ -36 \\ \hline 3 \end{array}$$ (*remainder* ³/₁₂ of a foot or 3 inches)

Table 1 Examples of Weights and Measures

Linear Measure		Liquid Measure	
foot	= 12 inches; 0.333 yard	pint	= 4 gills
yard	= 3 feet; 36 inches	quart	= 2 pints
rod	= 5-1/2 yards; 16-1/2 feet	gallon	= 4 quarts; 8 pints
furlong	= 40 rods; 220 yards; 660 feet	**Fluid Measure**	
statute mile	= 8 furlongs; 1,760 yards; 5,280 feet	fluid dram	= 60 minims
Area Measure		fluid ounce	= 8 fluid drams
square foot	= 144 square inches	pint	= 16 fluid ounces
square yard	= 9 square feet; 1,296 square inches	quart	= 2 pints
square rod	= 30-1/4 square yards; 272-1/4 square feet	gallon	= 4 quarts; 8 pints
acre	= 160 square rods; 4,840 square yards; 43,560 square feet	**Troy Weight**	
		pennyweight	= 24 grains
square mile	= 640 acres	troy ounce	= 20 pennyweight
Cubic Measure		troy pound	= 240 pennyweight; 12 troy ounces
cubic foot	= 1,728 cubic inches	**Avoirdupois Weight**	
cubic yard	= 27 cubic feet	dram	= 27 11/32 grains
Circular/Angle Measure		ounce	= 16 drams; 437-1/2 grains
second	= 1/60 minute	pound	= 16 ounces; 256 drams; 7,000 grains
minute	= 60 seconds	hundredweight (short or net)	= 100 pounds
degree	= 60 minutes; 1/360 circle	ton (short or net)	= 20 hundredweight; 2,000 pounds
right angle	= 90 degrees	long hundredweight (gross)	= 112 pounds
straight angle	= 180 degrees	long ton (gross)	= 20 gross hundredweight; 20 long hundredweight; 2,240 pounds
circle	= 360 degrees		
Dry Measure			
quart	= 2 pints		
peck	= 8 quarts		
bushel	= 4 pecks		

2.4.1 Division Exercises

In the following exercise, express your answer in feet and inches:

1. 4 feet 3 inches ÷ 2 = _____

2. 7 feet 7 inches ÷ 4 = _____

3. 3 feet 6 inches ÷ 5 = _____

4. 8 feet 4 inches ÷ 3 = _____

5. 3 feet 2 inches ÷ 2 = _____

3.0.0 ◆ RULES

One of the most frequently used tools of the sheet metal trade is the standard rule. Rules come in a variety of sizes and shapes, but the common feature of all standard rules is that they measure lengths. Some rules may include both the American and the metric scale, or they may contain only one scale specific to the measurement task.

The flexible steel rule, also called a machinist's rule, is one of the simplest and most useful measuring tools. Because it is used to measure close dimensions in layout and development, you must handle it carefully to keep the edges from becoming nicked or worn. The edges of the steel rule are marked by fine lines that show different parts of an inch, such as fourths, eighths, sixteenths, and sometimes thirty-seconds. Some rules are divided into tenths and hundredths of an inch. Some rules have American measures on one side and metric measures on the other (see *Figure 4*).

The four-foot bench rule, is 48 inches long. The markings on this tempered steel rule are etched in a permanent black ink for ease in reading the markings. This rule also has circumference markings on it and may have formulas for calculating such measurements as circumference diameter and area on the reverse side (see *Figure 5*).

The tape rule is handy for taking measurements almost anywhere and is especially useful on the job site. It comes in different lengths, widths, and degrees of stiffness. It may have a locking switch to hold the tape in place, and a rewind feature (either manual or automatic) to wind the tape back into the case for storage (see *Figure 6*).

3.1.0 Reading Rules and Making Calculations

When you look at a standard rule, you will notice that every inch is divided into parts that are marked off by lines of different lengths. The longest line between any two numbered inches divides the inch into halves. The next longest line divides the half-inch in half. This process is repeated down to the smallest unit your rule measures. The halves are divided into quarters, the quarters are divided into eighths, and the eighths are divided into sixteenths. Some rules may show the sixteenths divided into thirty-seconds and the thirty-seconds divided into sixty-fourths of an inch.

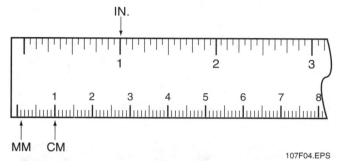

Figure 4 ◆ American and metric rules.

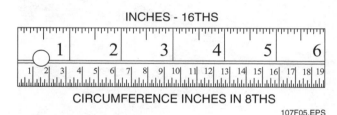

Figure 5 ◆ Four-foot bench rule.

Figure 6 ◆ Tape rules.

The whole numbers on rules are found at each inch mark. The lines between the inch marks are fractions. You can use rules to quickly and easily calculate fractional measures.

Use the following steps to solve this problem (you will need two rules):

1¾ inches + 7½ inches

Step 1 Place one rule on the table so that the measurements read upside down. Position a second rule below it with the measurements reading right side up.

Step 2 Slide the 1¾-inch mark of the lower rule against the 7½-inch mark of the upper rule. Note that since the upper rule is upside down, you will read 7½ inches to the *left* of the 7-inch mark (see *Figure 7*).

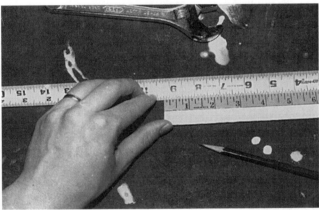

107F07.EPS

Figure 7 ◆ Adding with the two-rules method.

Step 3 Look at the point on the upper rule where the lower rule begins (at the zero mark). It will be lined up with the 9¼-inch mark. So your answer is 9¼ inches. Remember to read 9¼ inches to the *left* of the 9-inch mark on the upper rule.

Using this method is the same as drawing a line measuring 7½ inches and then adding on a line that measures 1¾ inches. When you measure the total line, you will have a line that is 9¼ inches long.

You can use this same method to subtract fractional measures. To subtract, you will line up the rules so that the numbers on both rules read right side up. Use the following steps to solve this problem:

9¼ inches − 1¾ inches

Step 1 Place one rule on the table so that the measurement numbers read right side up. Position a second rule below it so that the measurement numbers also read right side up.

Step 2 Slide the lower rule until the 1¾-inch mark lines up with the 9¼-inch mark of the upper rule (see *Figure 8*). In this case, you will read both measurements to the *right*, as usual.

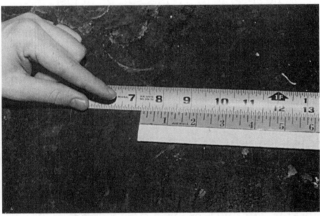

107F08.EPS

Figure 8 ◆ Subtracting with the two-rules method.

Step 3 Look at where the lower rule begins (at the zero mark). It should line up with the 7½-inch mark of the upper rule.

Helpful Measuring Features

Some measuring tapes used in the trade include helpful features that make doing the job easier. You'll notice that the numbers 16, 32, 48, and so on are highlighted in red. These measurements are all 16 inches apart. They are highlighted to mark the distance from the center of one wall stud to the center of the next, as wall studs are generally 16 inches on center.

You will also notice small black diamonds every 19.2 inches. These indicate the spacing for engineered lumber joists and studs. Several wood product manufacturers offer engineered lumber as a substitute for conventional lumber. Tables for engineered lumber provide ratings for spacing of 12 inches, 16 inches, 19³⁄₁₆ inches, and 24 inches. Engineered lumber is used where codes allow because its greater strength enables the use of fewer joists and studs.

DID YOU KNOW?

Measurement Standards

Suppose there were no tape measures. You and two friends want to cut a salami into three parts. How would you measure each part to ensure that each of you gets an equal share? You might decide to use the length of one person's hand as a measuring stick. This is how people in ancient times measured. In fact, the inch was originally based on the width of a man's thumb. Buildings and horses were described as being so many hands high. But this system became complicated because the lengths and widths of people's hands and thumbs aren't always the same, and this system is not very useful for large measurements. If you had to rely on the length of another person's hand for measurements, you would probably try to find a better way. Chances are you and your friends would decide to use a long stick, marked off into segments that all of you could agree on. And that's exactly how people first solved the problem of establishing a fixed set of measurements. Of course, total agreement was not always possible. Measurement standards have varied from village to village and from country to country throughout history.

Today there are two widely accepted standards: the American measure and the metric system. Efforts to adopt the metric system in America date back to the time of Thomas Jefferson, who lobbied Congress unsuccessfully for this change.

Using this method is the same as drawing a line measuring 9¼ inches, then measuring 1¾ inches along that line and erasing only that part. You will be left with a line that measures 7½ inches.

Of course, you can work out both of these problems using math, but once you have practiced it, the two-rules method is a lot faster.

The two-rules method demonstrates the wisdom of the KISS Principle: Keep It Simple and Short. The expert sheet metal mechanic is always alert to ways that the job can be done more quickly but still effectively by using the simple tools at hand. Practice the two-rules method until you too can easily and quickly arrive at the correct answer. And always be alert to ways in which you can do your job more effectively.

4.0.0 ◆ THE METRIC SYSTEM

Why should you learn the metric system if you live in the United States? Many countries around the world use the metric system as their standard. The company you work for may have customers in foreign markets, or you might work in the foreign office of an American company. So you must learn the metric system in case the projects you work on require metric system measurements. You are already using the metric system for many everyday things. For example, you have probably purchased a 2-liter bottle of soda and you may have run in a 10K (kilometer) race.

The metric system is a very easy measuring system to learn and use. The basic unit of length is a meter. Anything longer than 1 meter is a multiple of the meter. For example, *kilo-* is a prefix meaning thousand. So a kilometer is 1,000 meters. Anything shorter than a meter is a part of a meter and can be calculated using division. The most common small units of a meter are the centimeter and the millimeter. The prefix *centi-* means one hundredth (¹⁄₁₀₀). The prefix *milli-* means one thousandth (¹⁄₁₀₀₀). So a centimeter is one hundredth of a meter and a millimeter is one thousandth of a meter.

All the units of measure in the metric system are based on the number 10. This makes it easy to convert units within the system:

- Centimeter = 1×0.01
- Millimeter = 1×0.001
- Meter = 1
- Kilometer = $1 \times 1,000$

To convert 1 kilometer to meters, you multiply by 1,000. Thus, 1 kilometer equals 1,000 meters ($1 \times 1,000$). To convert 1 meter to centimeters, you divide by .01. Thus, 1 meter equals 100 centimeters ($1 \div 0.01 = 100$).

4.1.0 Converting From the Metric System to the American System

Converting dimensions from one system to another must be done very carefully. You can use charts such as the one shown in *Table 2*, which will help you convert a measurement in one system to its counterpart measure in the other system.

One meter is equal to 39.37 inches. To find what 1 centimeter equals, you can look at the conversion chart. But you can also divide by 100 to get 0.3937 of an inch. To find what 1 millimeter equals, divide by 1,000 to get 0.03937 of an inch.

Table 2 Conversion Chart:
American–Metric Equivalent Measurements

LINEAR MEASURE

inch	=	25.4 millimeters
inch	=	2.54 centimeters
foot	=	0.3048 meter
yard	=	0.9144 meter
mile	=	1.609 kilometers
millimeter	=	0.03937 inch
centimeter	=	0.3937 inch
meter	=	39.37 inches
meter	=	3.28084 feet
meter	=	1.09361 yards
kilometer	=	0.62137 mile

AREA MEASURE

square inch	=	645.16 square millimeters
square inch	=	6.4516 square centimeters
square foot	=	0.092903 square meter
square yard	=	0.836127 square meter
square millimeter	=	0.001550 square inch
square centimeter	=	0.155 square inch
square meter	=	10.763910 square feet
square meter	=	1.19599 square yards

VOLUME MEASURE for Solids

cubic inch	=	16.387064 cubic centimeters
cubic foot	=	0.028317 cubic meters
cubic yard	=	0.764555 cubic meters
cubic centimeter	=	0.061024 cubic inch
cubic meter	=	35.314667 cubic feet
cubic meter	=	1.307951 cubic yards

VOLUME MEASURE for Fluids

gallon	=	3785.411 cubic centimeters
gallon	=	3.785411 liters
quart	=	0.946353 liter
ounce	=	29.573530 cubic centimeters
cubic centimeter	=	0.00264 gallon
liter	=	0.264172 gallon
liter	=	1.056688 quarts
cubic centimeter	=	0.033814 ounce

WEIGHT MEASURE

metric ton	=	1,000 kilograms
kilogram	=	1,000 grams
gram	=	1,000 milligrams
pound	=	0.453592 kilogram
pound	=	453.59237 grams
ounce	=	28.349523 grams
ounce	=	0.028350 kilogram
kilogram	=	2.204623 pounds
gram	=	0.002205 pound
kilogram	=	35.273962 ounces
gram	=	0.035274 ounce

Once you know that 1 centimeter equals 0.3937 of an inch, you can get the value of 1 inch in terms of centimeters by dividing 1 centimeter by 0.3937.

Thus, 1 inch is 2.54 centimeters, or 25.4 millimeters. To convert inches into centimeters you multiply by the conversion factor 2.54. To convert inches into millimeters you multiply by the conversion factor 25.4. Look at the following examples:

To convert 5 inches into centimeters:

5 inches × 2.54 centimeters = 12.7 centimeters

To convert 5 inches into millimeters:

5 inches × 25.4 millimeters = 127 millimeters

What about fractions? You must first convert the fraction to its decimal equivalent, and then multiply by the conversion factor. To convert ¾ of an inch into centimeters, do the following:

¾ inch = 0.75 inch

.75 inch × 2.54 centimeters = 1.905 centimeters

To convert ¾ of an inch into millimeters, do the following:

¾ inch = 0.75 inch

.75 inches × 25.4 millimeters = 19.05 millimeters

 **Project Calculators**

It's good to learn how to use conversion charts to convert measurements and how to calculate using denominate numbers. On the job, however, it's also important to be quick and accurate. Special calculators can help you do this.

One, called ProjectCalc®, looks and works like a standard calculator. However, it has additional keys that allow you to make calculations in yards, feet, inches, and fractions. You can use it for American and metric measurements. You can also use it to calculate square and cubic measurements.

4.1.1 Conversion Exercises

Convert the following to centimeters:

1. 1⅝ inches = _____

2. 30 inches = _____

3. 12 inches = _____

4. 6¾ inches = _____

5. 2 feet 6 inches = _____

Convert the following to millimeters:

6. .25 inch = _____

7. ⅝ inch = _____

8. 25⁄32 inch = _____

9. 7.375 inch = _____

10. 3¾ inches = _____

Convert the following to meters:

11. 2.5 feet = _____

12. 100 yards = _____

13. 16½ feet = _____

14. 660 feet = _____

15. 5,280 feet = _____

Review Questions

Sections 2.0.0–4.0.0

1. Numbers that have units of measure associated with them are called _____.
   a. whole numbers
   b. mixed numbers
   c. denominate numbers
   d. conversion numbers

2. When you multiply feet and inches for an area, you must express your answer in _____.
   a. square feet
   b. its lowest form
   c. its metric equivalent
   d. common units

3. To divide two units of different denominations, you must first _____.
   a. convert the units to fractions
   b. convert the units to decimals
   c. convert the units to the larger denomination
   d. convert the units to the smaller denomination

4. One inch is the equivalent of _____ centimeters.
   a. 0.254
   b. 2.54
   c. 25.4
   d. 254

5. To convert 1 kilometer to meters, you multiply by _____.
   a. 0.01
   b. 0.001
   c. 100
   d. 1,000

5.0.0 ◆ LINEAR MEASURE

A line is the basic single dimension. It is defined as the distance between two points in space. In the sheet metal shop, a line connects two points on a flat surface. This measure of a line is called **linear measure**. You can work out conversions for linear measures using math, but it is much easier to use a conversion chart.

You can express the linear measure for one length in a number of ways. For example,

    12 inches = 1 foot

    1 foot = 0.3048 meter

Do these equal signs mean that the left side of the equation is *identical* to the right side of the equation? At first, it seems that the answer must be yes. But in actuality, the left and right sides of the equation are not identical. To express that they are equal but not identical, you can say that the left side is *equivalent* to the right side. Although they may look different, they each measure the same length.

6.0.0 ◆ SQUARE MEASURE

A two-dimensional object has height and width. You must have these two dimensions to define a surface or area. The area of a geometric shape (A) is equal to its length (L) times its width (W).

    A = L × W

Whatever area you calculate, you must state the answer in the proper units. Thus you must express areas measured in feet as square feet, areas measured in yards as square yards, areas measured in centimeters as square centimeters, and so on.

6.1.0 Square Measure Example

This example shows how to calculate an area measured in centimeters and then how to convert that answer to square inches.

To find the area in square inches of a rectangle measuring 30 centimeters wide and 40 centimeters long, first find the area:

A = L × W
A = 40 centimeters × 30 centimeters
A = 1,200 square centimeters

To convert this number to square inches, refer back to the conversion chart in *Table 2* and then multiply 1,200 by the number of square inches per square centimeter.

1,200 × 0.155 = 186 square inches

There is another way to solve this problem. You could first convert length and width from centimeters to inches and then multiply the new numbers. To do the conversion you would multiply each measurement by the conversion factor (0.3937) from the conversion chart and then multiply the answers:

30 centimeters × .0.3937 = 11.81 inches
40 centimeters × 0.3937 = 15.75 inches
11.81 inches × 15.75 inches = 186 square inches

When you multiply each measurement by the conversion factor, you should round your answers to the nearest hundred. So 11.811 becomes 11.81 and 15.748 becomes 15.75. When the number in the thousandths place is 4 or lower, the number in the hundredths place remains the same. When the number in the thousandths place is 5 or higher, round the number in the hundredths place up one.

6.1.1 Square Measure Exercises

Note: Refer to *Table 2* to solve the first problem.

1. How many square inches are in a galvanized sheet 150 millimeters wide and 250 millimeters long? _____

2. What is the area of a piece of sheet of metal 3½ feet by 12¼ feet? _____

3. You are in a classroom that measures 10 feet by 12 feet. What is the area of your classroom? _____

4. What is the area of a roof to be covered if one side measures 37 feet and the other measures 13 feet 9 inches? _____

7.0.0 ◆ VOLUME MEASURE

A solid object has three dimensions: height, width, and depth. The inside, or **volume**, measurement of a three-dimensional object results in a **cubic measure**. When you multiply these three dimensions together, you must state your answer in the proper units—for example, cubic inches, cubic feet, or cubic yards.

The volume (V) of a geometric shape is equal to its length (L) times its width (W) times its height (H). You may use this basic formula to calculate the volume of a stack of sheet metal, for example, or the volume of air inside a duct.

V = L × W × H

Objects such as cones, cylinders, pyramids, and other specially shaped fittings you will fabricate all have special formulas for calculating their volumes. However, these require more complicated computations than are necessary for you to learn as a first-year sheet metal apprentice.

7.1.0 Volume Measure Example

A box is 1 yard long, 23 inches wide, and 18 inches high. How many cubic inches are in its volume?

V = L × W × H
V = 1 yard × 23 inches × 18 inches

You can see that before going any further, you must first convert to a common unit of measure. You know that 1 yard is equal to 3 feet, which, in turn, is equal to 36 inches.

V = 36 inches × 23 inches × 18 inches
V = 14,904 cubic inches

7.1.1 Volume Measure Exercises

1. A stack of metal is 12 feet long, 6 feet wide, and 3 feet high. What is its volume? _____

2. How much air is contained in a duct 15 feet by 4 feet by 2½ feet? _____

3. What is the volume of an air conditioning plenum measuring 35 inches by 20½ inches by 12¾ inches? _____

4. A rectangle is 5 feet high, 6 feet thick, and 13 feet long. What is the volume? _____

5. What is the volume of a 3½-foot cube? _____

8.0.0 ◆ WEIGHT MEASURE

The most common weight measurement in the American system is **avoirdupois** (pronounced *ah-ver-de-poise*), which uses ounces, pounds, and tons as units of measure. The common weight measurement in the metric system is the gram.

8.1.0 Weight Measure Examples

The following example shows how to convert pounds to grams:

1 pound = 453.59237 grams
(or 453.6 grams rounded off)

Therefore:

5 pounds = 5 pounds × 453.6 grams = 2,268 grams

The following example shows how to convert pounds to kilograms:

1 pound = 453.59237 grams
(or 453.6 grams rounded off)

1 gram = 0.001 kilogram

Therefore:

5 pounds = 5 pounds × 453.6 grams × 0.001 kilogram

5 pounds = 2,268 grams × 0.001 kilogram

5 pounds = 2.268 kilograms

Therefore:

100 pounds = 100 pounds × 453.6 grams × 0.001 kilogram

100 pounds = 45,360 grams × 0.001 kilogram

100 pounds = 45.36 kilograms

8.1.1 Weight Measure Exercises

Refer to *Table 2* and convert the following to grams. Round up your answers.

1. 8 ounces   = _____
2. 16 ounces   = _____
3. 32 ounces   = _____
4. 8 pounds   = _____
5. 20 pounds   = _____

Refer to *Table 2* and convert the following to kilograms. Round up your answers.

6. 200 pounds   = _____
7. 2,500 pounds = _____
8. 1,500 pounds = _____
9. 400 pounds   = _____
10. 5,000 pounds = _____

Refer to *Table 1* and convert the following to American tons:

11. 3,800 pounds = _____
12. 4,600 pounds = _____
13. 1,500 pounds = _____
14. 8,500 pounds = _____
15. 12,800 pounds = _____

9.0.0 ◆ WORKING WITH FORMULAS

You will solve many construction problems by using formulas. These formulas, which you can find in reference manuals, are used to calculate volumes, strength of materials, and other technical data. The letters and symbols used in formulas have definite values that you can use to solve a particular problem. For example, the formula for calculating the area of a circle is as follows:

Area = pi × r²

The symbol for **pi** is π. Whether you use π or the word *pi*, it always stands for the same number:

$^{22}\!/_7$ or $3\frac{1}{7}$ or approximately 3.14

The figure 3.14 is the rounded-off decimal equivalent of $^{22}\!/_7$.

In the formula above, the lowercase letter *r* stands for the radius of the circle. The radius equals half of the **diameter**. So, if you know the radius of any circle, you can compute its area in square units of measure. Study the following example, which shows how to calculate the area of a circle with a 4-inch radius:

Area = pi × r²
Area = 3.14 × 4²
Area = 3.14 × 16
Area = 50.24 square inches

Recall that the square of any number equals the product of that number times itself. So 4^2 is 4×4, or 16.

10.0.0 ◆ CALCULATING STRETCHOUTS

When layout work is done directly on the metal, you must calculate the size of the stretchout to avoid wasting material. You must also add allowances for edges, seams, or notches that will be included on the finished pattern. The stretchout is also called the **blank size** because this is the amount of metal needed to make the fitting.

10.1.0 Rectangular Fittings

For rectangular duct, the length of the stretchout (SO) is equal to the sum of all four sides or twice the height (H) of the fitting plus twice the width (W) of the fitting. The formula is as follows:

SO = (2H) + (2W)

To calculate the stretchout for a rectangular duct with a Pittsburgh seam, you use the same formula, but you must add three times the seam allowance (SA) (see *Figure 9*):

SO = (2H) + (2W) + (3SA)

10.1.1 Rectangular Fitting Exercise

For the following problem, calculate stretchout for a rectangular duct with a Pittsburgh seam:

H =   5 inches
W =   20 inches
SA = 1¼ inches
SO = _____

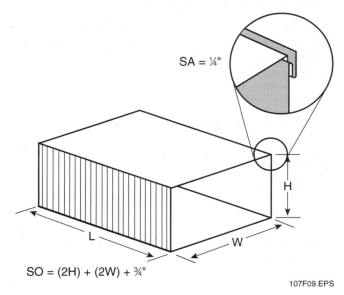

SA = ¼"

SO = (2H) + (2W) + ¾"

107F09.EPS

Figure 9 ◆ Rectangular duct with a Pittsburgh seam.

Working With Formulas

Formulas often contain numbers that must be added, subtracted, multiplied, or divided. It's important to perform the calculations in the right order. When you work with denominate numbers, you must also make sure that the proper unit of measure stays with its arithmetic number while you do the calculation.

To help you remember the correct order for performing math calculations in formulas, memorize this phrase: *My Dear Aunt Sally*. The first letter in each word stands for the correct order: *M* ultiply
     D ivide
     A dd
     S ubtract

You will find this simple phrase to be a great help when you work on a formula, especially one that is long and complex. Study the following example:

$3 + 3 \times 2 - 6 \div 3 + 6 =$

You could arrive at several different answers, depending on the order in which you do the math functions. But only one way will give you the correct answer.

M (Multiply)
$3 + (3 \times 2) - 6 \div 3 + 6$
gives you $3 + 6 - 6 \div 3 + 6$
D (Divide)
$3 + 6 - (6 \div 3) + 6$
gives you $3 + 6 - 2 + 6$
A (Add)
$(3 + 6 + 6) - 2$
S (Subtract)
$15 - 2 = 13$

10.2.0 Box Fittings

For box fittings you must make allowance for the tabs. The formula for calculating the stretchout of boxes (length and width) without edges or hems is as follows:

Stretchout length = (L + 2H)
Stretchout width = (W + 2H)

10.2.1 Box Fitting Exercise

To calculate the length and width of the stretchout for a fitting with a hem allowance (HA), you would use the same formula but add two times the hem allowance to the width. In this exercise you will calculate the stretchout (length and width) for a box fitting with a single hem edge (see *Figure 10*). The formula is as follows:

Stretchout length = (L + 2H)
Stretchout width = (W + 2H) + (2HA)
L = 12 inches
W = 9¾ inches
H = 2 inches
HA = ½ inch

Stretchout length _____
Stretchout width _____

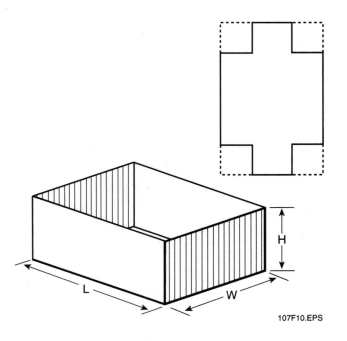

Figure 10 ◆ Box with a single hem edge.

10.3.0 Circular Fittings

One dimension of the stretchout for a circular or cylindrical fitting is the circumference, and the other dimension is the length. When measurements are stated for a circular fitting, the diameter (D), not the circumference, is usually stated. To calculate the stretchout for a circular fitting, you must find the circumference and add the seam allowance. The formula for calculating the stretchout for a circular fitting follows (see *Figure 11*).

Stretchout circumference = 3.14 × D
Stretchout length = L

To calculate the stretchout circumference for a circular fitting with a lap seam, you would use the same formula and add the seam allowance to the circumference as follows:

Stretchout circumference = 3.14 × D + SA

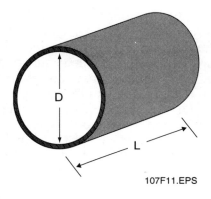

107F11.EPS

Figure 11 ◆ Circular or cylindrical fitting.

10.3.1 Circular Fitting Exercise

For the following problem, calculate the stretchout (circumference and length) for a cylinder with a lap seam:

D = 10½ inches
L = 12 inches
SA = ½ inch
Stretchout circumference = _____
Stretchout length = _____

11.0.0 ◆ GEOMETRY

Three-dimensional objects are called geometric solids. In the sheet metal trade, you will work with three-dimensional objects. However, to make the patterns for these objects, you will draw two-dimensional representations, or constructions. To make these constructions, you will use geometry.

In the following section you will learn the proper names and definitions for lines, shapes, and angles. Then you will practice some simple geometry exercises.

11.1.0 The Point

A point indicates a position only. Because it has no length, width, or thickness, it has no dimension. A point is an origin or beginning. For example, the starting place for a circle is a point. Two points are necessary to define a line, and three points may define a flat surface, or plane. Lines and planes may have many other points as well.

11.2.0 The Line

A line has only one dimension—length. A straight line is defined as the shortest distance between two points. If a line merely passes through one or two points, its length may be undetermined, or *infinite* (see *Figure 12*). If a line begins at one point and ends at another, it has a *finite* length (see *Figure 13*).

A *straight line* is an unbroken line that travels in the same direction throughout its length. A *broken line* is a series of connected straight lines that travel in different directions (see *Figure 14*). A *curved line* is a line that continuously changes direction (see *Figure 15*).

A *horizontal line* is a straight line that is level with the horizon. A *vertical line* is a straight line that extends up from the horizon. When you work on two-dimensional constructions, a horizontal line runs from left to right on your paper or metal and a vertical line runs from bottom to top.

Parallel lines are two or more straight lines that are the same distance apart from each other (see *Figure 16*). Parallel lines never intersect (cross) or touch each other.

A *perpendicular line* is a line that forms a right angle (90 degrees) with one or more other lines (see *Figure 17*). Lines that are perpendicular to horizontal lines are vertical lines.

11.3.0 The Circle

The circle is a finite curved line that connects with itself and has the following properties (see *Figure 18*):

Figure 12 ◆ Infinite straight line.

Figure 13 ◆ Finite straight line.

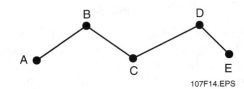

Figure 14 ◆ Broken line.

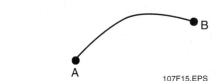

Figure 15 ◆ Curved line.

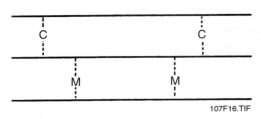

Figure 16 ◆ Parallel lines.

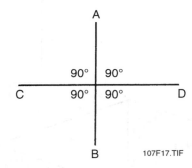

Figure 17 ◆ Perpendicular lines.

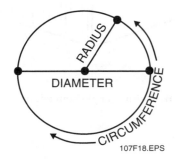

Figure 18 ◆ Circle.

DID YOU KNOW?

Why Study Geometry?

The word *geometry* comes from two Greek words meaning *earth* and *to measure*. From the earliest times, people have used geometry as a way to measure the things around them: the sizes of their fields, the dimensions of their buildings, and the distances between places.

Geometry is a very useful tool in the construction industry. Say that you must use a crane to lift a large piece of steel framing onto the eighth floor of a 12-story building that is next door to an 18-story building. You have only so much room to work with between the buildings, and you know that the framing will swing as it is lifted. What must you do to make sure that you can safely lift the framing into place without damaging either building or the piece of framing?

Say that you must install a large fan and access panel in a section of ductwork. You have the dimensions of the ductwork and the fan, and you know that you must allow for the mounting brackets that will hold the fan in place. You also want to make sure that the access panel is wide enough to allow for easy installation and future service.

To solve these and many other construction problems, you will use mathematics and geometry. You may not think that doing geometric exercises now will ever have a practical application. However, as you advance in your apprenticeship, you will see firsthand how useful geometry can be.

The radius from the center to any point on the curved line is always the same.

The total measure of all angles formed by all consecutive *radii* (more than one radius) equals 360 degrees.

The diameter passes through the center and is equal to twice the distance of the radius. The diameter is also the longest possible straight line that can be constructed within a circle.

11.4.0 Angles

Two straight lines that meet at a point, called the **vertex**, form an angle (see *Figure 19*). These two lines form the sides of the angle. These lines are also called the **rays** of the angle.

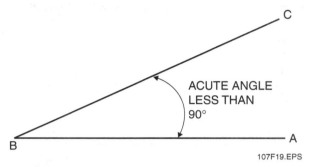

Figure 19 ◆ Angle.

There are two ways to identify angles. One way is to assign a letter to the vertex. In the figure the vertex angle is B, which is written <B. You read this aloud as *angle B*. The other way is to name the two end points of the rays and put the vertex angle letter between them, like this: <ABC.

To indicate the degree of the angle, write that number inside the angle (if possible). If the angle is too small for you to write the measurement in, you may write it outside the angle and draw an arrow to the inside to show that the measurement applies to that angle. You can indicate degrees in one of two ways: with the word (47 degrees) or with the symbol (47°).

You will use a protractor to measure angles on a plane (see *Figure 20*). Place your protractor so that the angle vertex lines up with the center point and one ray lines up with the bottom edge of the protractor. The other ray will point to a number on the protractor's scale. That number is the measure of the angle.

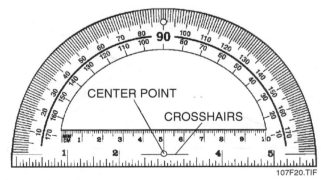

Figure 20 ◆ Protractor.

Following are the most common types of angles:

The *right angle* has rays that are perpendicular to each other (see *Figure 21*). A right angle always measures 90 degrees. *Note:* A circle measures 360 degrees, so a right angle represents one-fourth of a complete circle (360 degrees ÷ 4 = 90 degrees).

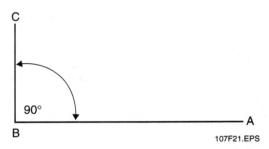

Figure 21 ◆ Right angle.

The *straight angle* does not look like an angle at all. But note that it has a vertex indicated by the letter B (see *Figure 22*). The rays of the straight angle lie in a straight line, and their angle measures 180 degrees, or one-half of a complete circle (360 degrees ÷ 2 = 180 degrees). If the rays were the same length, you could think of this construction as the diameter of a circle.

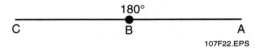

Figure 22 ◆ Straight angle.

The *acute angle* measures between 0 and 90 degrees (see *Figure 23*). The most common acute angles are 30, 45, and 60 degrees. As you can see in the figure, the angle is measured between the rays indicated by the letters A and C.

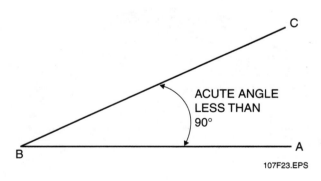

Figure 23 ◆ Acute angle.

The *obtuse angle* is greater than 90 degrees but less than 180 degrees (see *Figure 24*). As you can see in the figure, the angle is measured between the rays indicated by the letters A and C.

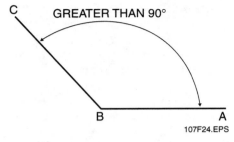

Figure 24 ◆ Obtuse angle.

Adjacent angles occur when three or more rays meet at the same vertex. In *Figure 25*, <ABC and <CBD are adjacent angles. The ray BC is common to both angles.

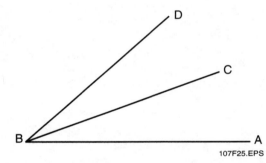

Figure 25 ◆ Adjacent angles.

Complementary angles are two angles that have a combined total measure of 90 degrees. In *Figure 26*, <ABC is complementary to <CBD.

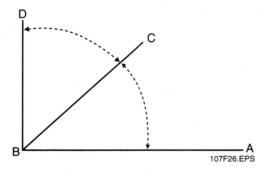

Figure 26 ◆ Complementary angles.

Supplementary angles are two angles that have a combined total measure of 180 degrees. In *Figure 27*, <ABC is supplementary to <CBD.

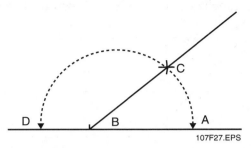

Figure 27 ◆ Supplementary angles.

11.5.0 Polygons

A closed-plane figure bounded by three or more line segments is a **polygon**. When all sides are of equal length and all internal angles are equal, the figure is called a regular polygon. You are already familiar with several polygons, such as the triangle, the square, and the rectangle. These and other polygons are described in the following section.

11.5.1 Three-Sided Polygons

A polygon with three sides is called a triangle (see *Figure 28*). The *equilateral triangle* is a regular polygon with three equal sides. The *isosceles triangle* is an irregular polygon with only two equal sides. The *scalene triangle* is also an irregular polygon. None of its sides are equal in length.

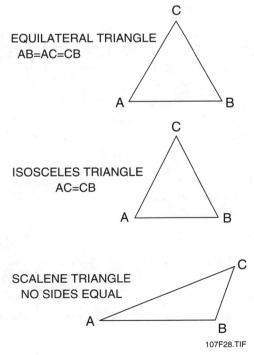

Figure 28 ◆ Types of triangles.

Triangles are also classified by the degree of their angles. If one of the three internal angles is 90 degrees, the figure is called a right triangle (see *Figure 29*). If one of the three internal angles is greater than 90 degrees, the figure is called an obtuse triangle (see *Figure 30*). If each of the interior angles is less than 90 degrees, the figure is called an acute triangle (see *Figure 31*). Both acute and obtuse triangles are also called *oblique triangles*.

You should note that when you add up all the interior angles of any triangle, the sum is always 180 degrees. This is helpful to remember when you know two angles of a triangle and must calculate the third angle.

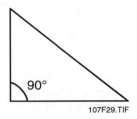

Figure 29 ◆ Right triangle.

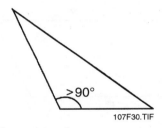

Figure 30 ◆ Obtuse triangle.

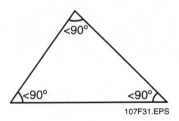

Figure 31 ◆ Acute triangle.

11.5.2 Four-Sided Polygons

A four-sided polygon is called a **quadrilateral**. When all four sides and all interior angles are equal, the figure is called a *square* (see *Figure 32*). In a square, each interior angle must equal 90 degrees.

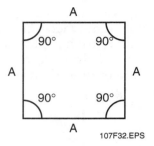

Figure 32 ◆ Square.

In the *parallelogram* (see *Figure 33*) each side is equal to the side opposite and each angle is equal to the angle opposite. Note that unlike the square, the four sides of a parallelogram are not equal.

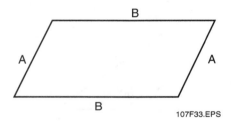

Figure 33 ◆ Parallelogram.

When all the interior angles are equal (90 degrees each) and only the opposite sides are equal, the figure is called a *rectangle* (see *Figure 34*). Note that the rectangle is similar to the square.

Figure 34 ◆ Rectangle.

A *trapezoid* is a quadrilateral with two parallel sides (called bases) that are not equal in length (see *Figure 35*). The perpendicular distance between the bases is called the altitude. The non-parallel sides are called legs. When the legs of a trapezoid are of equal length, the figure is called an *isosceles trapezoid*.

Figure 35 ◆ Trapezoid.

A regular *pentagon* has five equal sides (see *Figure 36*). All of its internal angles are also equal. An irregular pentagon has five unequal sides.

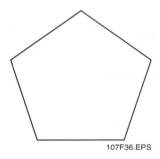

Figure 36 ◆ Pentagon.

 DID YOU KNOW?

The Pentagon

One of the most famous buildings in the world is named for its shape. The Pentagon, a five-sided building located in Arlington, Virginia, is the headquarters of the United States Department of Defense. The Pentagon is one of the world's largest office buildings. It is twice the size of the Merchandise Mart in Chicago, and has three times the floor space of the Empire State Building in New York. The area of the heating and refrigeration plant alone is 1 acre. But in spite of its 17.5 miles of hallways, it takes only 7 minutes to walk between any two points in the building.

A regular *hexagon* has six equal sides, and all of its internal angles are equal (see *Figure 37*). You probably recognize this figure as a honeycomb shape.

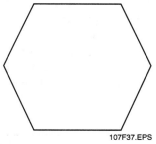

107F37.EPS

Figure 37 ◆ Hexagon.

A regular *octagon* has eight sides (see *Figure 38*). All eight sides and internal angles are equal. You probably recognize this figure as the familiar shape of the stop sign.

107F38.EPS

Figure 38 ◆ Octagon.

The ellipse (see *Figure 39*) is of special interest to sheet metal mechanics. This is a figure bounded by a curved line. The sum of the distances from each of two fixed points to any point on the perimeter is a **constant** (it is always the same). In the figure, the two fixed points (which are called *foci*) are labeled F1 and F2. The points on the perimeter are labeled P1 and P2.

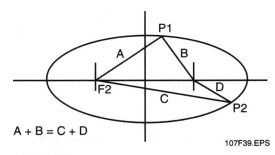

A + B = C + D

107F39.EPS

Figure 39 ◆ Ellipse.

What is of most interest to sheet metal mechanics is that the shape of a mitered pipe section is an ellipse. Only cuts made perpendicular to the pipe length will produce a perfect circle. Any angular cut will produce an ellipse.

11.6.0 Geometry Exercises

In the following exercises, you will use a compass or a divider, which you learned about in the Sheet Metal Level One Module, *Tools of the Trade*, to construct geometric figures. When you work on paper, you will use a compass. When you work on metal, you will use a divider. As you do the following exercises, complete each step in the process before proceeding to the next. Your instructor will decide how many of these exercises you will do.

11.6.1 Exercise One: Erecting a Perpendicular Bisector Line

To erect a perpendicular bisector line from a straight line, follow these steps:

Step 1 Place the point of your compass or divider on point A and extend the free leg to a length longer than the distance from A to B. Then swing the leg and draw an arc both above and below the line (see *Figure 40*).

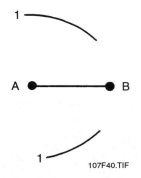

107F40.TIF

Figure 40 ◆ Erecting a perpendicular from a straight line: Step 1.

Step 2 Move the point of the compass or divider to point B, making sure you do not change the compass setting. Then draw another arc both above and below the line (see *Figure 41*).

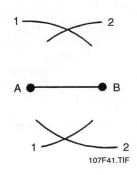

107F41.TIF

Figure 41 ◆ Erecting a perpendicular from a straight line: Step 2.

Step 3 Draw a line connecting each point, above and below, where the arcs intersect (see *Figure 42*). That line CD is perpendicular to line AB. It also passes through line AB at point E.

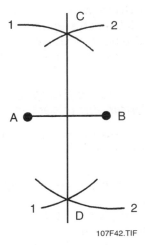

107F42.TIF

Figure 42 ◆ Erecting a perpendicular from a straight line: Step 3.

DID YOU KNOW?

Pythagoras Makes a Deal

Students in ancient times were as reluctant to study geometry as are students of today. Many did not see any practical use in the subject. Pythagoras (who developed the **Pythagorean theorem**) wanted to make sure that his work in geometry would not die with him. He offered to pay an intelligent young man a small sum of money for every arithmetic and geometry principle that he could master. Pythagoras hoped that the young man would enjoy the lessons so much that he would keep studying without being paid. This arrangement worked very well. One day Pythagoras mentioned that he would have to spend more time earning a living instead of teaching mathematics and geometry. By this time, the young man had become so interested that he offered to pay Pythagoras to teach him more.

11.6.2 Exercise Two: Erecting a Perpendicular Line Near the End of a Given Line

To erect a perpendicular line *near* the end of a given line, follow these steps.

Step 1 Near the end of given line AB, locate a point C about ½ inch from B. You will erect the perpendicular line from point C (see *Figure 43*).

107F43.TIF

Figure 43 ◆ Erecting a perpendicular line near the end of a given line: Step 1.

Step 2 With C as your center and using any convenient radius, draw the arc from point 1 to point 2 (see *Figure 44*).

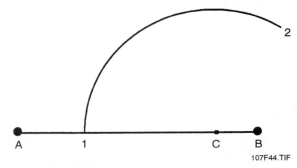

107F44.TIF

Figure 44 ◆ Erecting a perpendicular line near the end of a given line: Step 2.

Step 3 Using the same radius, mark off that distance from point 1 to 3 and from point 3 to 4 (see *Figure 45*).

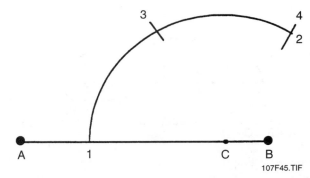

107F45.TIF

Figure 45 ◆ Erecting a perpendicular line near the end of a given line: Step 3.

Step 4 Using any radius with points 3 and 4 as centers, draw arcs 5 and 6 intersecting each other at point 7 (see *Figure 46*).

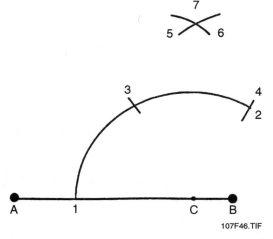

Figure 46 ◆ Erecting a perpendicular line near the end of a given line: Step 4.

Step 5 Draw a line from C through point 7. This line produces the required perpendicular line at given point C (see *Figure 47*).

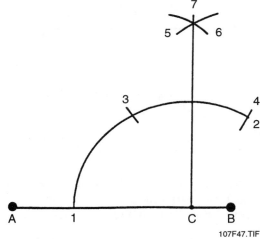

Figure 47 ◆ Erecting a perpendicular line near the end of a given line: Step 5.

11.6.3 Exercise Three: Erecting a Perpendicular Line at the End of a Given Line

To erect a perpendicular line *at* the end of a given line, follow these steps:

Step 1 Set the compass or divider point on A at the given line AC (see *Figure 48*).

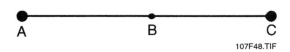

Figure 48 ◆ Erecting a perpendicular line at the end of a given line: Step 1.

Step 2 Using any radius, draw arc 2 coming up from the line at point B (see *Figure 49*).

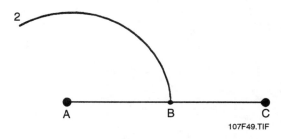

Figure 49 ◆ Erecting a perpendicular line at the end of a given line: Step 2.

Step 3 Using the radius AB, draw arc 3 intersecting arc 2B at point D (see *Figure 50*).

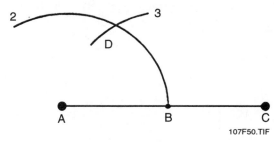

Figure 50 ◆ Erecting a perpendicular line at the end of a given line: Step 3.

Step 4 Connect D and B with a straight line that extends infinitely (see *Figure 51*). Note that an infinite line has no end point.

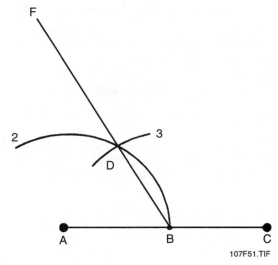

Figure 51 ◆ Erecting a perpendicular line at the end of a given line: Step 4.

Step 5 Using the radius AB, draw arc 4 from point D to intersect the straight line at point E. Note that radius AB = BD = DE (see *Figure 52*).

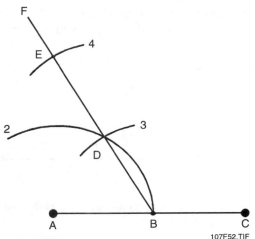

Figure 52 ◆ Erecting a perpendicular line at the end of a given line: Step 5.

Step 6 Connect E to end point A, which will give you the perpendicular line required (see *Figure 53*).

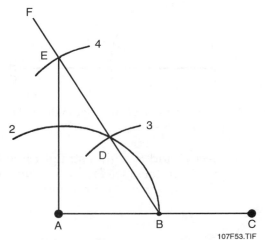

Figure 53 ◆ Erecting a perpendicular line at the end of a given line: Step 6.

11.6.4 Exercise Four: Bisecting Lines

To bisect lines, follow these steps:

Step 1 To bisect straight line AB, or the arc AB, make A and B the center points for your compass or divider (see *Figure 54*).

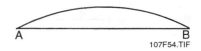

Figure 54 ◆ Bisecting lines: Step 1.

Step 2 Using any radius greater than one-half of the line or arc, place the compass or divider point at A and draw arc 1 (see *Figure 55*).

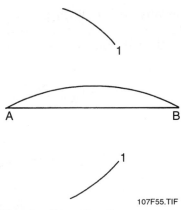

Figure 55 ◆ Bisecting lines: Step 2.

Step 3 Place the point at B and draw arc 2 (see *Figure 56*). Make sure that you do not change the setting on the compass or divider.

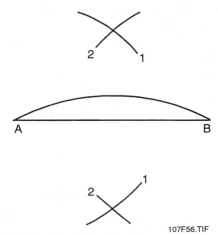

Figure 56 ◆ Bisecting lines: Step 3.

Step 4 Draw a straight line through both intersecting points of arcs 1 and 2, and through line AB and arc AB (see *Figure 57*).

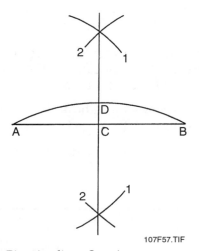

Figure 57 ◆ Bisecting lines: Step 4.

This line now evenly bisects both the line and the arc. This means that line AC equals line CB and arc AD equals arc DB.

11.6.5 Exercise Five: Bisecting Angles With Equal Rays

To bisect a 90-degree or 45-degree angle or any angle with rays of equal length, use given points C and B as the center points for your compass or divider (see *Figure 58*) and follow these steps:

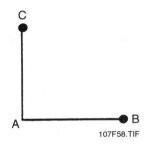

Figure 58 ◆ Right angle.

Step 1 Place the point of your compass or divider on point B and draw arc 1B. Then without changing the setting, place the point on point C and draw arc 1C (see *Figure 59*).

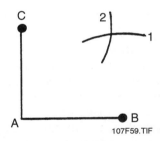

Figure 59 ◆ Bisecting angles with equal rays: Step 1.

Step 2 Draw a straight line from the intersection of arcs 1 and 2 to point A. The angle is now divided in half (see *Figure 60*). Since the original angle CAB is 90 degrees, each of these new angles is 45 degrees.

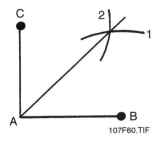

Figure 60 ◆ Bisecting angles with equal rays: Step 2.

Step 3 You may now continue to bisect each of these new angles into 22½-degree angles by following steps one and two. To do this, you must place your compass or divider at points C and D and then at points D and B. But you must first find point D. To find point D, set your compass or divider at point A and use radius AC or AB (they are the same) to draw the arc that connects C and B. The spot at which that arc intersects the first bisecting line is the location for point D (see *Figure 61*).

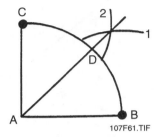

Figure 61 ◆ Bisecting angles with equal rays: Step 3.

Step 4 You can now continue to bisect each of these new angles to produce additional angles (see *Figure 62*).

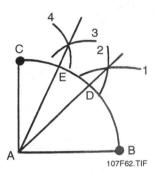

Figure 62 ◆ Bisecting angles with equal rays: Step 4.

11.6.6 Exercise Six: Bisecting Angles With Unequal Rays

The steps for bisecting an angle with unequal rays are similar to the steps for bisecting an angle with equal rays. However, because the rays are of unequal length, you cannot use the end points A or C as a starting place (see *Figure 63*). Instead, you must put your compass or divider at point B and, using any convenient radius, draw arcs 1 and 2 (see *Figure 64*). To continue, follow these steps:

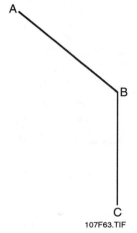

Figure 63 ◆ Angle with rays of unequal length.

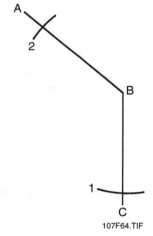

Figure 64 ◆ Drawing arcs 1 and 2.

Step 1 Place your compass or divider at the point where arc 1 intersects ray CB and draw arc 3. Repeat this procedure by placing your compass or divider at the point where arc 2 intersects ray AB and draw arc 4. (see *Figure 65*).

Step 2 At the point where arcs 3 and 4 intersect, draw a straight line to point B. This divides angle ABC into two equal parts (see *Figure 66*).

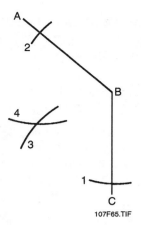

Figure 65 ◆ Bisecting angles with unequal rays: Step 1.

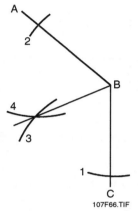

Figure 66 ◆ Bisecting angles with unequal rays: Step 2.

The steps in this exercise are used often in the sheet metal trade. You can use these steps to find the miter line to divide a sheet metal angle. The dashed lines in *Figure 67* show this process. You simply extend the bisecting line through point B to the end point of the metal angle. You can use this line to cut the metal sheet in half.

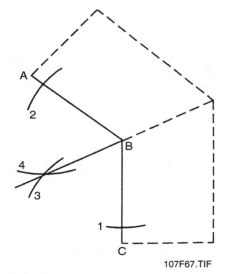

Figure 67 ◆ Finding a miter line.

11.6.7 Exercise Seven: Copying Angles

In this exercise, you will use geometry to make an exact copy of a given angle.

Step 1 Use angle CAB as the given angle (see *Figure 68*).

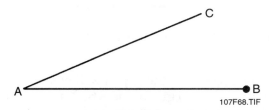

Figure 68 ◆ Constructing angles: Step 1.

Step 2 With point A as the center and using any convenient radius less than either ray, draw arc 1–2 (see *Figure 69*). Arc 1–2 identifies the curved line between points 1 and 2.

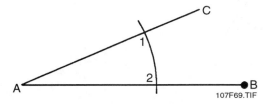

Figure 69 ◆ Constructing angles: Step 2.

Step 3 Move to another spot on your paper below the angle you just drew. Draw a line DE to equal line AB (see *Figure 70*).

Figure 70 ◆ Constructing angles: Step 3.

Step 4 Using D as the center, set your compass or divider to the same radius you used to produce arc 1–2 and draw arc 3–4 (see *Figure 71*). Now place your compass or divider at point 2 of the given angle ABC and adjust the radius to the exact distance from point 2 to point 1.

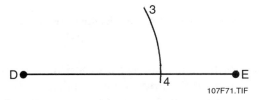

Figure 71 ◆ Constructing angles: Step 4.

Step 5 Set your compass or divider at point 4 on line DE and draw arc 5 (see *Figure 72*). This is point F.

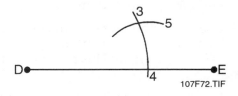

Figure 72 ◆ Constructing angles: Step 5.

Step 6 Draw a line from point D through point F. You have made an exact copy of the given angle ABC (see *Figure 73*). (Note that you can also measure ray AC from the original angle and then make this new ray equal to it.)

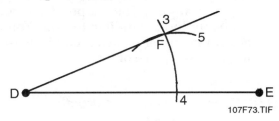

Figure 73 ◆ Constructing angles: Step 6.

11.6.8 Exercise Eight: Constructing the Parts of a Circle

This exercise will familiarize you with the various parts of a circle (see *Figure 74*). To construct these parts, follow these steps:

Step 1 Draw the diameter line AB 3¾ inches long.

Step 2 Bisect line AB to locate point C. This point is the center of the circle.

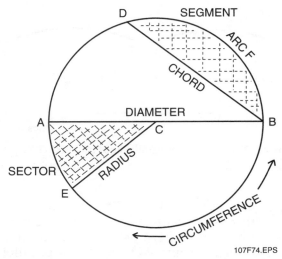

Figure 74 ◆ Constructing the parts of a circle.

Step 3 Set your compass or divider at point C, measure radius CA, and draw the entire circle. Note that your circumference line will pass through point B.

Step 4 Use the method for copying an angle (refer back to exercise seven) to reproduce angle DBA in the circle. This procedure also produces arc F.

Step 5 Draw a straight line to connect the end points of the arc to create a **chord**. The area between the chord and the arc is called a segment. When you reproduced angle DBA, you actually copied arc DB and chord DB.

Step 6 By drawing any two radii, you describe an area within a circle known as a sector. You can copy sector ACE using the method for copying angles. The shape of the sector probably looks familiar to you. You can easily remember what a sector is by thinking of it as a piece of pie.

11.6.9 Exercise Nine: Constructing Parallel Lines

To draw a line parallel to a given line, you have to locate only two points on the new line, both of which are the same distance from the given line. This exercise includes two methods.

The first method is quick, but not as precise as the second method. For the first method, follow these steps:

Step 1 Place your compass or divider at point A and draw arc 1. Then, keeping the same setting, place the compass or divider at point B and draw arc 2 (see *Figure 75*).

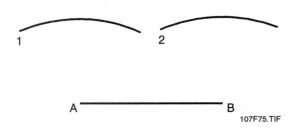

Figure 75 ◆ Constructing parallel lines (method 1): Step 1.

Step 2 Connect arcs 1 and 2 with a straight line that is **tangent** to both. (The line should touch the outermost points of each arc.) Your new line CD should be parallel to line AB (see *Figure 76*).

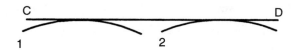

Figure 76 ◆ Constructing parallel lines (method 1): Step 2.

In the second method, you will erect two equal perpendiculars to given line AB. Refer back to the steps and figures shown in exercise three for erecting a perpendicular at the end of given line.

Step 1 Note that the first figure in this exercise is similar to the last figure in exercise three. Draw radius AC (see *Figure 77*).

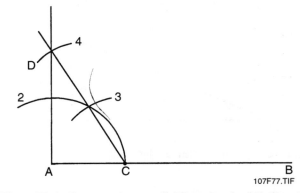

Figure 77 ◆ Constructing parallel lines (method 2): Step 1.

Step 2 Draw radius BE. Make sure that it is equal to radius AC (see *Figure 78*).

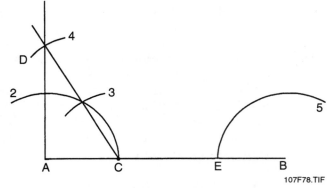

Figure 78 ◆ Constructing parallel lines (method 2): Step 2.

Step 3 Follow the steps for erecting a perpendicular at the end of a given line to draw arcs 6 and 7 and to construct line EF (see *Figure 79*).

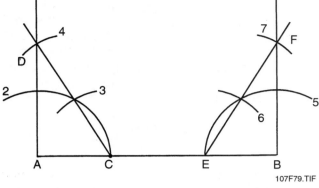

Figure 79 ◆ Constructing parallel lines (method 2): Step 3.

Step 4 Connect arc 4 to arc 7 with line DF, which is exactly parallel to the original given line AB (see *Figure 80*).

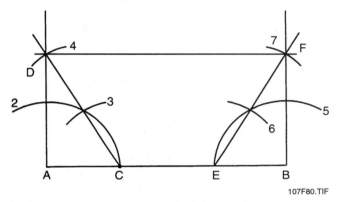

Figure 80 ◆ Constructing parallel lines (method 2): Step 4.

11.6.10 Exercise Ten: Locating the Center of a Circle

To find the center of any circle, you simply bisect two arcs. This exercise includes two methods.

For the first method, follow these steps:

Step 1 Note that the perpendicular bisector of any chord of a circle will establish the diameter of the circle (see *Figure 81*). Place your compass or divider at a point along the side of the circumference of the circle and draw arc 1. Move the compass or divider to a point on the opposite side of the circle and draw arc 2. Draw a vertical line to cross where the arcs intersect to establish the diameter of the circle.

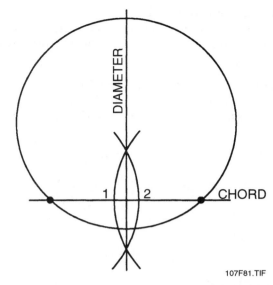

Figure 81 ◆ Locating the center of a circle (method 1): Step 1.

Step 2 Note that the perpendicular bisectors of any two chords of a circle will cross at the center of the circle (see *Figure 82*). Set your compass or divider at a different point along the side of the circumference of the circle and draw arc 3. Move the compass or divider to a point on the opposite side of the circle and draw arc 4. Draw a vertical line to cross where the arcs intersect, extending this second line to intersect with the first line you established in step 1. This intersection is the center of the circle.

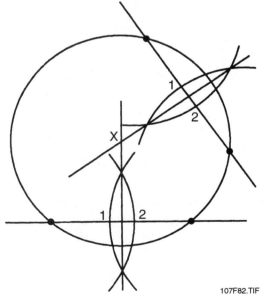

Figure 82 ◆ Locating the center of a circle (method 1): Step 2.

The second method of locating the center of a circle is convenient because the same distance is used for all steps. For the second method, follow these steps:

Step 1 From any point on the circle (A) and with any convenient radius, draw arc 1 to establish points B and C (see *Figure 83*).

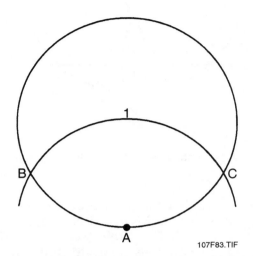

Figure 83 ◆ Locating the center of a circle (method 2): Step 1.

Step 2 With the same radius, establish point D from B and establish point E from C (see *Figure 84*).

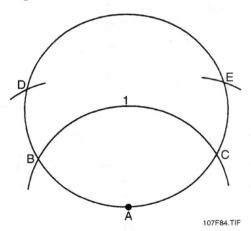

Figure 84 ◆ Locating the center of a circle (method 2): Step 2.

Step 3 Keeping the same radius, use point D to draw arc 2. Where arc 2 intersects arc 1, establish point F. Keeping the same radius, use point E to draw arc 3. Where arc 3 intersects arc 1, establish point G. *Note:* Arcs 2 and 3 intersect at points B and C (see *Figure 85*).

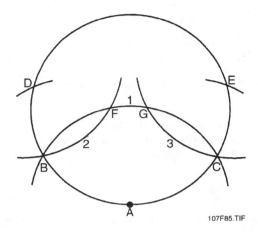

Figure 85 ◆ Locating the center of a circle (method 2): Step 3.

Step 4 Draw a straight line, extending through the circle circumference, that joins points B and F, and an additional line that joins points C and G (see *Figure 86*). These lines intersect at the center of the circle (point X).

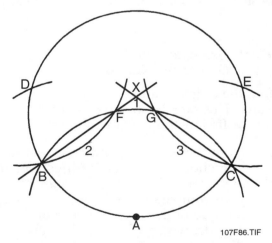

Figure 86 ◆ Locating the center of a circle (method 2): Step 4.

1. To find the area of a rectangle, you would use the formula _____.
   a. $A = L \times W$
   b. $A = D \times W$
   c. $A = L^2 \times W$
   d. $A = D^2 \times W$

2. The inside measurement of a three-dimensional object is called a _____.
   a. square measure
   b. cubic measure
   c. linear measure
   d. box measure

3. The most common weight measurement in the American system is _____
   a. troy weight
   b. apothecaries weight
   c. avoirdupois weight
   d. pennyweight

4. To help you remember the proper order for performing calculations in formulas, think of this phrase: _____.
   a. My Dear Aunt Sally
   b. My Aunt Drives Slow
   c. Aunt Sally Makes Doughnuts
   d. Sally's Aunt Makes Doughnuts

5. A line that begins at one point and ends at another is _____.
   a. infinite
   b. horizontal
   c. curved
   d. finite

6. Two straight lines that form an angle meet at a point; that point is called the _____
   a. focus
   b. radial
   c. vertex
   d. apex

7. To measure angles on a plane, you must use a _____.
   a. protractor
   b. divider
   c. machinist's rule
   d. compass

8. A triangle with three unequal sides is called a(n) _____.
   a. equilateral triangle
   b. isosceles triangle
   c. scalene triangle
   d. 90-degree triangle

9. The shape of a mitered pipe section is a(n) _____.
   a. triangle
   b. square
   c. arc
   d. ellipse

10. When layout work is done directly on metal, you must calculate the _____ to avoid wasting material.
    a. size of the seams
    b. length of the fitting
    c. size of the stretchout
    d. height of the fitting

Summary

You will use mathematics every day in your job in the sheet metal trade. You will work most often with denominate numbers—numbers that are associated with units of measurement. You must be able to convert these units within the American system so that you can perform mathematical functions such as addition, subtraction, multiplication, and division. Depending on where you work, you may also need to learn how to convert American measurements into metric measurements and vice versa.

When you make sheet metal fittings, you will begin with a blank of sheet metal. Your goal is to cut out a pattern to form the fitting. You want to do this in the most efficient way possible to avoid wasting material. You also want to ensure that when you fold the metal and form the edges that the finished piece will be of the correct dimensions. In this module, you learned some of the formulas that will help you calculate how much metal you will need for the finished fitting.

Finally, a good understanding of geometry will be very helpful to you in your career. In this module, you learned the terminology and some basic geometric concepts, which will serve as a good basis for your future studies in this subject.

Curtis McMullen

Sheet Metal Shop Foreman and Director of Craft Training
Interstate Mechanical Corp., Phoenix, Arizona

Curtis was born and raised in Des Moines, Iowa. After graduating from high school, he worked for a short time as a laborer, but soon decided to follow his father and older brother into the sheet metal trade. In 1972, Curtis entered a four-year apprenticeship training program, where he learned how to fabricate and install HVAC duct and to install copper roofing and other architectural items. In his next job, he welded nuclear powerhouses for one of the country's largest nuclear plant contractors. In 1987, he joined Interstate Mechanical as a fabricator and welder. As a result of his lifelong dedication to learning new skills and gaining experience, Curtis is now a shop foreman and administrator of an accredited craft training program.

How did you become interested in the construction industry?
My father and my older brother were sheet metal workers, and almost everybody in my family is in construction. My father was a very good craftsman— he made a lot of useful things for around the house. I thought it would be nice to become that skillful myself. I didn't work very long as a laborer— I wanted to learn how to work smarter, not harder! The craftsmanship aspect of sheet metal work really appealed to me.

How did you decide to become a foreman?
I have been a skilled fabricator and a skilled welder throughout my career. When I came to work at Interstate Mechanical, I did a lot of specialty work. The company offered me the foreman position more than once. About four years ago a foreman left, and I finally decided it was time to advance both my position and my wages. About a year later, I also became director of craft training.

What do you think it takes to be a success in your trade?
Sign your work with excellence every day. You have to want to produce a quality product, and you need to have a real desire for craftsmanship. Try to do everything you can when you are in training—take every opportunity to learn something new.

It's important for people to understand not only the details, but also how those details fit into the big picture. When I started as an apprentice, I thought the work was just about making and putting in duct. But I learned very quickly that there is a lot more to the craft. I learned layout, fabrication, mechanical drawing, and basic mathematics, as well as trigonometry and geometry. The courses provided me with a good overall view of complete systems, duct designs, air quality, and things like that.

There's a true story I like to tell that shows trainees they can go anywhere in this profession if they just work for it. About 14 years ago, a helper named Mark Moore started out in the shop measuring metal for cutting. He didn't have a tape measure, so he had to borrow one. He cut the tape measure on the shears. He ended up cutting three tape measures on his first day! Well, about a year ago, Mark became president of the company, but we still won't lend him a tape measure! That's a true story, and a classic example of how a person can become anything they want to become.

What are some things you do on the job?

As a foreman, I supervise about 20 people on the shop floor. I oversee all sheet metal fabrication and production for the company, and purchase all the necessary materials to maintain our inventories and job requirements. We receive orders from job site foremen for fittings and duct, and our job is to meet their time frames and their deadlines. We process 50,000 pounds of metal a week here, so there's a lot to keep track of.

As director of craft training, I manage the company's in-house apprenticeship program—a state-approved four-year training program, accredited by NCCER and the state of Arizona. I actively recruit trainees from our employee base, and also make sure we have enough instructors to staff the program. I oversee all the administrative work, including grades, attendance, and report cards, and make sure we keep up our accreditation. I try to get trainees to think about the training as the starting point for their education and their careers. The amount of material they have to learn can be intimidating, so we break things down into basic building blocks. We make sure they learn one thing at a time so that they get a good grasp of the whole by the time they finish the program.

What do you like most about your job?

I've worked as a fabricator and a welder for many years. I always enjoy working, and I take pride in my work. I am very fortunate to work for a company that is full of hard-working, smart people.

What would you say to someone entering the trade today?

In our apprenticeship classes, I tell trainees up front how to succeed, and I try to be very honest and straightforward. I tell them it is very easy to be successful—you have to show up every day, and you have to put out a good effort every day. That's it. We give good opportunities to people; all they have to do is take them and they will succeed.

Success is about what you do with your abilities. The apprenticeship program is only the beginning. In this field, you can be anything you want—a foreman, an estimator, a contractor, a business owner. I tell trainees that the apprenticeship is the foundation. It determines your view of the job and your perspective on your life.

Trade Terms Introduced in This Module

Area: The surface or amount of space occupied by a two-dimensional object, such as a rectangle, circle, or square.

Avoirdupois: A weight system based on a pound of 16 ounces and an ounce of 16 drams.

Blank size: The amount of sheet metal needed to produce a fitting.

Chord: A straight line that joins two points on a curve.

Constant: A fixed quantity whose value does not change in relation to any variable.

Cubic measure: A measurement found by multiplying a number against itself three times. It describes volume.

Denominate numbers: Numbers that have units of measure associated with them.

Diameter: The length of a straight line that crosses from one side of the circle through the center point to a point on the opposite side. It is the longest straight line you can draw inside a circle.

Linear measure: A measure of length or a system of measures of length.

Pi: A mathematical constant value of approximately 3.14 (or $^{22}/_{7}$) used to determine the area and circumference of circles. It is sometimes expressed as the symbol π.

Polygon: A closed plane figure bounded by straight lines.

Pythagorean theorem: A theorem in geometry that states the square of the length of the hypotenuse of a right triangle equals the sum of the squares of the lengths of the other two sides.

Quadrilateral: A polygon with four sides.

Ray: Any one of a group of lines that extend or move out in different directions from a common center.

Tangent: The point where a straight line meets or touches a curve without intersecting it.

Vertex: A point at which two or more lines or curves come together.

Volume: The amount of space occupied in three dimensions (length, width, and height).

Answers to Exercises

Section 2.3.1 Multiplication Exercises
1. 60 square feet
2. 9 square feet
3. 13½ square feet
4. 14.2 square yards
5. 63.72 square feet

Section 2.4.1 Division Exercises
1. 2 feet 1½ inches
2. 1 foot 10¾ inches
3. ⅔ of a foot
4. 33⅓ inches
5. 19 inches

Section 4.1.1 Conversion Exercises
1. 4.1275 centimeters
2. 76.2 centimeters
3. 30.48 centimeters
4. 17.145 centimeters
5. 76.2 centimeters
6. 6.35 millimeters
7. 15.875 millimeters
8. 19.84375 millimeters
9. 187.325 millimeters
10. 95.25 millimeters
11. 0.762 meter
12. 91.44 meters
13. 5.0292 meters
14. 201.168 meters
15. 1,609.344 meters

Section 6.1.1 Square Measure Exercises
1. 58.125 square inches
2. 42.875 square feet
3. 120 square feet
4. 508.75 square feet

Section 7.1.1 Volume Measure Exercises
1. 216 cubic feet
2. 150 cubic feet
3. 9,148⅛ cubic inches
4. 390 cubic feet
5. 42.875 cubic feet

Section 8.1.1 Weight Measure Exercises
1. 226.8 grams
2. 453.6 grams
3. 907.20 grams
4. 3,628.8 grams
5. 9,702 grams
6. 90.8 grams
7. 1,135 kilograms
8. 681 kilograms
9. 181.6 kilograms
10. 2,270 kilograms
11. 1.9 tons
12. 2.3 tons
13. .75 tons
14. 4.25 tons
15. 6.4 tons

Section 10.1.1 Rectangular Fitting Exercise
SO = 51¼ inches

Section 10.2.1 Box Fitting Exercise
Strechout length: 16 inches
Stretchout width: 14¾ inches

Section 10.3.1 Circular Fitting Exercise
SO (circumference) = 33⁷⁄₁₆ inches
SO (length) = 12½ inches

Additional Resources

This module is intended to present thorough resources for task training. The following reference works are suggested for further study. These are optional materials for continued education rather than for task training.

Geometry Plane and Practical, 1991. Bruce Stephan. New York, NY: Harcourt Brace Jovanovich.

Geometry the Easy Way, 1991. Lawrence Leff. Hauppauge, NY: Barrons Educational Series.

Mastering Math for the Building Trades, 2000. James Gerhart. New York, NY: McGraw-Hill.

Workshop Math, 1989. Robert Scharff. New York, NY: Sterling Publications.

Figure Credits

Stanley Tools   107F06

NCCER CRAFT TRAINING USER UPDATES

The NCCER makes every effort to keep these textbooks up-to-date and free of technical errors. We appreciate your help in this process. If you have an idea for improving this textbook, or if you find an error, a typographical mistake, or an inaccuracy in the NCCER's Craft Training textbooks, please write us, using this form or a photocopy. Be sure to include the exact module number, page number, a detailed description, and the correction, if applicable. Your input will be brought to the attention of the Technical Review Committee. Thank you for your assistance.

Instructors – If you found that additional materials were necessary in order to teach this module effectively, please let us know so that we may include them in the Equipment and Materials list in the Instructor's Guide.

Write: Curriculum Revision and Development Department
National Center for Construction Education and Research
P.O. Box 141104, Gainesville, FL 32614-1104

Fax: 352-334-0932

E-mail: curriculum@nccer.org

Craft _____ Module Name _____

Copyright Date _____ Module Number _____ Page Number(s) _____

Description _____

_____

_____

_____

(Optional) Correction _____

_____

_____

(Optional) Your Name and Address _____

_____

_____

_____

Module 04108-01

Fabrication One— Parallel Line Development

COURSE MAP

This course map shows all of the modules in the first level of the Sheet Metal curriculum. The suggested training order begins at the bottom and proceeds up. Skill levels increase as you advance on the course map. The local Training Program Sponsor may adjust the training order.

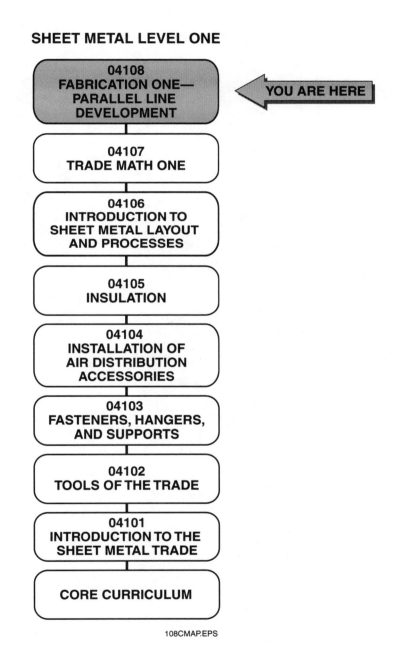

SHEET METAL LEVEL ONE

04108
FABRICATION ONE—
PARALLEL LINE
DEVELOPMENT

YOU ARE HERE

04107
TRADE MATH ONE

04106
INTRODUCTION TO
SHEET METAL LAYOUT
AND PROCESSES

04105
INSULATION

04104
INSTALLATION OF
AIR DISTRIBUTION
ACCESSORIES

04103
FASTENERS, HANGERS,
AND SUPPORTS

04102
TOOLS OF THE TRADE

04101
INTRODUCTION TO THE
SHEET METAL TRADE

CORE CURRICULUM

108CMAP.EPS

Copyright © 2001 National Center for Construction Education and Research, Gainesville, FL 32614-1104. All rights reserved. No part of this work may be reproduced in any form or by any means, including photocopying, without written permission of the publisher.

Figures

Fabrication One— Parallel Line Development

Objectives

When you finish this module, you will be able to do the following:

1. Explain procedures for parallel line development.
2. Lay out and fabricate selected ductrun fittings.

Prerequisites

Before you begin this module, it is recommended that you successfully complete the following modules: Core Curriculum; Sheet Metal Level One, Modules 04101 through 04107.

Required Trainee Materials

1. Pencil and paper
2. Appropriate personal protective equipment

1.0.0 ◆ INTRODUCTION

As you learned in the Sheet Metal Level One Module, *Introduction to Sheet Metal Layout and Processes*, sheet metal layout work is done by one of three methods. The most basic method is parallel line development. It is the method you are most likely to use as a first-year sheet metal apprentice and is the method you will use in this module. Most of the work done by sheet metal workers consists of laying out, fabricating, and installing duct fittings. These fittings are joined to form an air distribution or heating, ventilating, and air conditioning (HVAC) system.

The main components in the HVAC system are as follows:

- *Duct:* The square, rectangular, or round fabrication that carries air from a heating, ventilating, or cooling source to an outlet. Round ducts are usually called *pipes*.
- *Fitting:* A fabricated metal part that changes the direction of the airflow, that has ends of different size or shape, or that has both of these features.
- *Ductrun:* The complete assembly of ducts and fittings.

In *Introduction to Sheet Metal Layout and Processes*, you learned how to visualize a layout—how to see it in your head before beginning to do the actual layout. You also were introduced to parallel line development. Following is a brief review of the steps involved in this process:

Step 1 Draw the plan and elevation views.

Step 2 Locate the measuring lines on the elevation.

Step 3 Draw the stretchout of the pattern.

Step 4 Locate the measuring lines from the elevation onto the pattern.

Step 5 Transfer the lengths of the measuring lines from the elevation to their proper locations on the pattern.

Step 6 Connect the points located on the measuring lines.

Step 7 Make allowances for connections.

Visualizing Layouts

Visualizing a layout in your head is a very important skill to develop. Practice visualizing the pattern for a simple object, such as a box. With a little effort you will be able to see all of the folds, tabs, and edges that make up the box. The more clearly you can visualize a fitting in your head, the easier it will be for you to do the layout.

1.1.0 About the Tasks in This Module

In this module you will get hands-on practice in layout and fabrication. Each task includes a tools and materials list and step-by-step procedures. Your instructor will determine the number of tasks that you will complete and the order in which you will complete them.

As you make the fittings described in this module, you may discover that each fitting is easier to make than you might think. Take some time to study the drawings for each task. (Note that the figures are not drawn to scale.) On some tasks, you may need to look at two drawings for one step. You will probably recognize many of the steps you learned in the geometry exercises in the Sheet Metal Level One Module, *Trade Math One*. If you can't fully understand something, ask your instructor for help. Once you master the fundamentals, you will be able to make much more complex fittings.

Some of the tasks in this module include an isometric drawing to help you visualize the fitting. Some also include a plan view or working drawing. The plan view is the one you will most often receive when fittings are sent from the field to the shop for fabrication.

The tasks assume a small Pittsburgh seam (1 inch and ¼ inch) and a ½-inch notch for standard S and drive-end connectors. You may have to adjust your allowances to meet local requirements.

Some of the tasks include steps to fabricate the fittings; in some tasks, your instructor will provide the fabrication steps.

2.0.0 ◆ PATTERN DEVELOPMENT

For many of the tasks in this module, you will first develop a pattern. In the sheet metal shop, you will lay out patterns directly on the metal. For practice purposes, you may find it helpful to first lay out the patterns on paper using drafting tools. Patterns may vary to some degree, but the layout steps are always the same.

You must follow these steps in order to avoid error and waste:

Step 1 Square up the edges.

Step 2 Always start your layout in the lower left-hand corner of the sheet.

Step 3 Take all of your measurements from the squared bottom edge or a line you have drawn to square up the left-hand edge. Never measure from the right-hand side of the metal toward the left, or from the top toward the bottom.

Step 4 Always measure two points for each line and connect the points for a straight line.

Step 5 Draw all lines in one direction first. Do not keep turning your straightedge from horizontal to vertical or vice versa.

Step 6 Prick-punch all bend lines. Do this at each end of the line at which the bend is to be made.

Step 7 Study the basic shape of the patterns to help you visualize the finished job from the flat pattern.

Step 8 Check your overall dimensions for accuracy when you have completed the layout.

CAUTION

Before doing any of the tasks in this module, you must have and wear the appropriate personal protective equipment—eye and ear protection, gloves, leather boots—whatever is appropriate for the task at hand. Dress properly. Do not wear loose-fitting clothing, ties, or scarves that could get caught in machinery. Do not wear any jewelry. Securely tie long hair back away from your face. If you are taking medication that could make you drowsy, you must tell your instructor. Think of safety first and always.

3.0.0 ◆ TASK 1: GROOVED LOCK SEAM

In this task you will measure and lay out metal to fabricate a grooved lock seam, form the metal edges of the seam, and, using a hand groover, correctly lock the grooved lock seam. The grooved lock seam, also called a pipe lock seam, consists of two folded edges called locks. This seam is used to join two metal edges. It is used most often to form round or rectangular duct using 20-gauge or lighter sheet metal.

When constructing grooved lock seams, you must make allowances for the extra bends at each edge. These allowances depend on the width of the lock and the thickness of the metal.

3.1.0 Tools and Materials

1. Appropriate personal protective equipment
2. Two pieces of precut 26- or 28-gauge galvanized sheet metal, measured as indicated in the figures or according to your instructor's specifications
3. Hand groover
4. Mallet
5. Riveting hammer
6. Scriber
7. Combination square
8. Bar folder or brake

3.2.0 Procedure

Step 1 Lay out the metal and mark the edges to be seamed with a scriber. Allow an extra one and a half times the width of the seam on each seam edge (see *Figure 1*).

Step 2 Form one seam edge up to about 90 degrees at ⅜ of an inch from the edge.

Step 3 Make another 90-degree bend at ³⁄₁₆ of an inch from the first bend.

Step 4 Turn the piece over and repeat steps 2 and 3 to form the other seam edge. You should have a pocket on each piece—one facing up and one facing down.

Step 5 Fit one formed edge pocket inside the other edge pocket to make one workpiece.

Step 6 Use your hand groover and riveting hammer to form and flatten the lock. This will form the top piece into a locking pocket (see *Figure 2*).

Step 7 Check the overall measurements of the workpiece (see *Figure 3*) and the measurement of the lock seam (see *Figure 4*) and present the workpiece to your instructor.

Step 8 Clean up your work area.

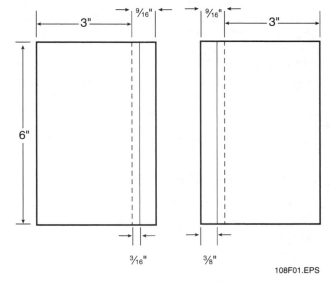

Figure 1 ◆ Scribed edges for a grooved lock seam.

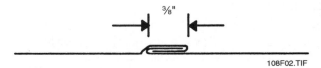

Figure 2 ◆ Formed grooved lock seam.

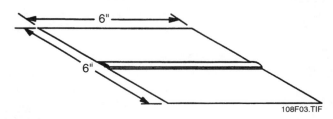

Figure 3 ◆ Overall measurements.

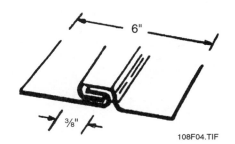

Figure 4 ◆ Lock seam measurements.

4.0.0 ◆ TASK 2: FLEXIBLE CONNECTION

In this task you will form and assemble a typical flexible connection. Vibration noise from a fan or blower can be carried through the ductwork into a building's occupied spaces. Flexible connections isolate the noise at the source to solve this problem. These connections are made of a special fabric that is attached to the sheet metal on both sides and is then inserted between the fan or blower and the ductwork. The fabric may be made from a variety of materials to suit the application, but it must conform to the National Fire Protection Association (NFPA) **Standard 90A**. In addition, the fabric must be sealed with a sealant that also conforms to this standard.

4.1.0 Tools and Materials

1. Appropriate personal protective equipment
2. One piece of 26-gauge galvanized sheet metal, measured as indicated in the figures or according to your instructor's specifications
3. Snips
4. Hand notcher
5. Hand groover
6. Mallet
7. Riveting hammer
8. Prefabricated flexible connection material that conforms to NFPA Standard 90A
9. NFPA-approved sealant (for the fabric-to-fabric connection)
10. Heavy-duty staple gun and staples

CAUTION

When bending a flexible connection, be careful to avoid damaging the fabric.

4.2.0 Procedure

Step 1 Study the **oblique drawings** and **detail drawings** for the dimensions of the fabricated fitting (see *Figure 5*).

Step 2 Select the sheet metal and the fabric needed for the connection.

Step 3 Notch the metal at the bend lines where the locks and hems intersect.

Step 4 Form the hems and fabric locks.

Step 5 Set the fabric in place.

Step 6 Fold the edge of the fabric to be stapled.

Step 7 Bend the flexible connection fitting to complete the rectangular shape.

Step 8 Apply the sealant on the fabric ends, stretch and fold into position, and staple the fabric on 1-inch centers.

Step 9 Present the finished fitting to your instructor.

Step 10 Clean up your work area.

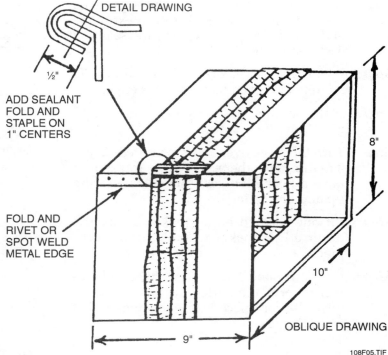

Figure 5 ◆ Flexible connection.

5.0.0 ◆ TASK 3: RECTANGULAR PITTSBURGH LOCK DUCT

In this task you will lay out, form, and assemble a rectangular duct seamed with a Pittsburgh lock. As you will recall, the Pittsburgh lock is a seam made up of a flanged end that fits into a pocket.

5.1.0 Tools and Materials

1. Appropriate personal protective equipment
2. One piece of 26-gauge galvanized sheet metal, measured as indicated in the figures or according to your instructor's specifications
3. Scratch awl
4. Straightedge
5. Wing dividers
6. Scriber
7. Felt-tipped marker
8. Framing square
9. Combination square
10. Prick punch
11. Mallet
12. Riveting hammer
13. Snips
14. Hand seamer
15. Hand notcher
16. Brake
17. Squaring shear

5.2.0 Procedure

Step 1 Study the shape of the finished workpiece (see *Figure 6*). Compare it to the pattern (see *Figure 7*). You will refer to the pattern for every step in this task. Can you visualize how the pattern will be formed into the workpiece?

Step 2 Lay out the pattern on the metal, allowing the correct dimensions for a Pittsburgh pocket lock and a single lock. Note that the letter *D* denotes a drive edge, which you will turn to receive a drive connector. The letter *S* denotes a slip edge, which will receive a slip connector. You can mark these letters on the ductwork with a felt-tipped marker.

Step 3 Prick-punch *both ends* of each bend line. Use a felt-tipped marker to write "up 90 degrees" on the duct faces that are to be bent upward 90 degrees.

Step 4 Use the combination square to lay out accurate angles at the notch positions.

Step 5 Cut out and notch the pattern.

Step 6 Form the Pittsburgh pocket lock.

Step 7 Form up the pattern with the brake.

Step 8 Assemble the duct and lock the seam. Use the mallet to hammer the pocket lock flange over the ¼-inch single lock inserted into the Pittsburgh pocket.

Step 9 Turn the drive edges, using the hand seamer.

Step 10 Present the finished workpiece to your instructor.

Step 11 Clean up your work area.

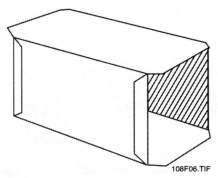

Figure 6 ◆ Rectangular Pittsburgh lock duct.

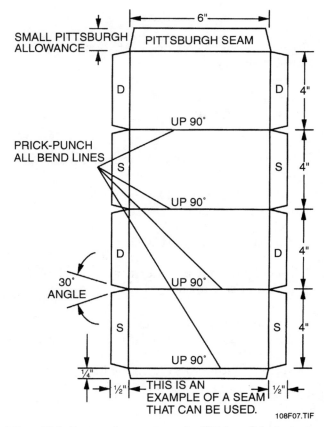

Figure 7 ◆ Pattern for a rectangular Pittsburgh lock duct.

Duct Measurement

When making duct measurements, you must be consistent. Some shops may measure from finished edge to finished edge, from drive to drive, or from connector to connector. Some shops will add the seam allowance to measurements, while others let the computer add in the allowance. Become familiar with how duct is measured in your shop so that callouts on your patterns will be consistent and so that you will always measure duct accurately. When in doubt, ask.

Review Questions

Sections 1.0.0–5.0.0

1. The complete assembly of ducts and fittings is called a _____.
   a. ventilation system
   b. heating and cooling system
   c. ductrun
   d. chase

2. The *final* step at the end of your work period is to _____.
   a. verify that all your fittings are the right measurements
   b. reset all the shop machines to their original settings
   c. prepare a stack of sheet metal for the next day's work
   d. clean up your work area

3. To isolate vibration noise at its source, you must make and install a _____.
   a. grooved lock seam
   b. flexible connection
   c. Pittsburgh seam
   d. neoprene ring

4. The fabric for a flexible connection must conform to _____.
   a. NFPA Standard 80D
   b. SMACNA Standard 29-2
   c. NFPA Standard 90A
   d. SMACNA Standard 30-3

5. When laying out a pattern, you must prick-punch all bend lines _____.
   a. at both ends
   b. in the center of the lines
   c. 1½ inches from the right-hand side on the line to be bent
   d. at 2-inch intervals along the line

6.0.0 ◆ TASK 4: MITERED FITTING

In this task you will learn how to lay out, fabricate, and assemble a mitered duct fitting. The procedure is the same whether you are working with round duct (pipes) or square duct.

It is fairly easy to develop a pattern for a square duct. The length of the edges and the distances between the edges are the same on the finished workpiece as they are on the stretchout of the pattern (see *Figure 8*). In the pattern for a round duct, the length of the stretchout of the edges is equal to the circumference of the finished job. To calculate the circumference, you multiply the diameter by 3.14 (pi).

For a mitered duct piece, you must project the height of the elements on the cut surface from the elevation view to the stretchout of the pattern. You then connect those measuring lines with a curved line. The projection from the elevation view must always be at right angles to the elements of the stretchout of the pattern.

6.1.0 Tools and Materials

1. Appropriate personal protective equipment
2. A piece of 26-gauge sheet metal, measured as indicated in the figures or according to your instructor's specifications
3. Mallet
4. Riveting hammer
5. Scriber
6. Combination square
7. Bar folder or brake

6.2.0 Procedure

Step 1 Draw the plan and elevation views of the mitered duct (see *Figure 9*). These views show the component in a right-view position, in which the parallel lines of the solid are shown in their true length.

Step 2 Draw the pattern from a right view of the object in which the miter line (or line of intersection) is shown.

Pattern Notes

It is best to write pattern notes or instructions on the side of the metal that will be inside the duct once it is fabricated, leaving the outside clean and neat.

Step 3 Draw a stretchout line at right angles to the parallel measuring lines of the object. Draw each space in the plan view on the stretchout.

Step 4 Draw the measuring lines at right angles to the stretchout line on the pattern. Note that the lines drawn from the points of intersection on the miter line in the right view intersect similarly numbered measuring lines drawn from the stretchout.

Step 5 Connect the intersection points to show the outline of the pattern. Note that allowances must be made for seams and joint connections.

Step 6 Assemble the mitered duct piece following your instructor's directions.

Step 7 Present the finished fitting to your instructor.

Step 8 Clean up your work area.

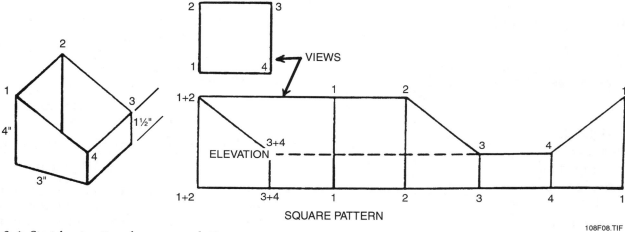

Figure 8 ◆ Stretchout pattern for a square duct.

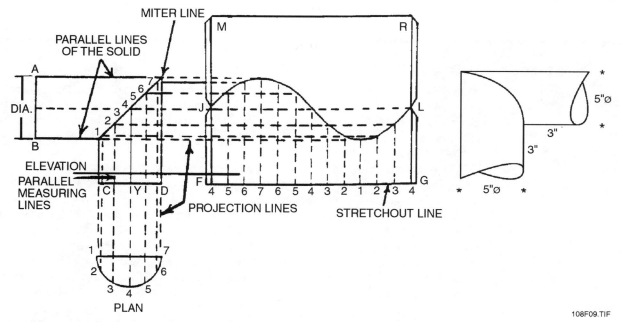

Figure 9 ◆ Elevation, plan view, and stretchout for a mitered fitting.

FABRICATION ONE—PARALLEL LINE DEVELOPMENT — TRAINEE MODULE 04108 **8.7**

Cleaning Up is Part of the Job

You show pride of craftsmanship each time you fabricate a fitting well. But you also show pride of craftsmanship by taking care of your tools and your work area. In every task in this module, the last step is to clean up your work area. Do not skip this step. It is important not only in apprentice training, but also on the job. At the end of your work period, you must sweep up and properly dispose of any bits of metal that could injure you or a co-worker, or that could fall into and damage shop machines. You must also clean your tools and store them carefully so that they will be ready to use when you report for work the next day.

7.0.0 ◆ TASK 5: SQUARE ELBOW

In this task you will learn how to lay out and fabricate a square elbow with a square throat and heel. The square elbow is a fitting that connects two ducts at a right angle.

7.1.0 Tools and Materials

1. Appropriate personal protective equipment
2. Sheets of 26-gauge galvanized sheet metal, measured as indicated in the figures or according to your instructor's specifications
3. Scratch awl
4. Straightedge
5. Scriber
6. Felt-tipped marker
7. Framing square
8. Combination square
9. Prick punch
10. Mallet
11. Riveting hammer
12. Hand seamer
13. Snips
14. Hand notcher
15. Hand brake
16. Squaring shear
17. Bar folder or brake
18. Slip-roll machine
19. Pittsburgh roll-forming machine

7.2.0 Procedure

Step 1 Study the isometric drawing and the plan view (see *Figure 10*).

Step 2 Lay out the pattern on the metal (*Figure 11*).

Step 3 Cut and notch the metal pattern.

Step 4 Fabricate the Pittsburgh locks on the hand brake or run the metal through the Pittsburgh roll-forming machine to form the locks.

Airflow, Elbows, and Pressure Drop

You've heard the expression *lighter than air.* Well, air does have weight, and it is inert (does not move) until it is set into motion. Once air starts moving, it moves in a straight line and in a single direction. It takes energy to make air change direction. When air moving in a ductrun enters an elbow, it does not easily make the turn; instead, it tends to compress against the turn of the elbow.

As the air compresses, it can create turbulence (irregular air waves). Turbulence can cause a drop in pressure at the elbow. **Pressure drop** at an elbow may be 10 times greater than that in an equal length of straight duct.

Various elbow designs can reduce elbow pressure drop. The most efficient design is the round elbow. It offers the least resistance to airflow. A rectangular elbow with a curved throat and heel, though not as efficient as a round elbow, also offers little airflow resistance. The elbow designs with the most resistance to airflow are the rectangular elbow with a square throat and heel, and the square elbow with a square throat and heel. These elbow designs have the greatest amount of pressure drop. Installing vanes in these elbows helps lessen the problem.

Riveting Ideas

True Lengths

Any lines that are *perpendicular to your line of vision* are true lengths. Any lines that are *at an angle to your line of vision* are not true lengths.

Step 5 Form the metal pieces using the bar folder, hand brake, and hand-forming tools.

Step 6 Assemble one cheek.

Step 7 Assemble the throat (see *Figure 12*) and the heel (see *Figure 13*).

Step 8 Assemble the remaining cheek.

Step 9 Set the lock seams.

Step 10 Turn the drive edges.

Step 11 Present the fitting to your instructor.

Step 12 Clean up your work area.

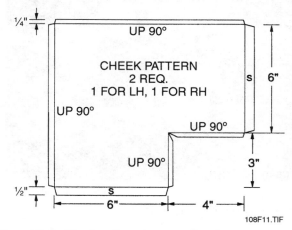

Figure 11 ◆ Cheek pattern (square elbow).

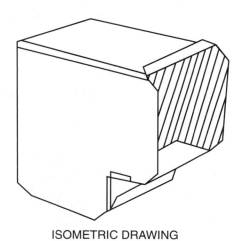

ISOMETRIC DRAWING

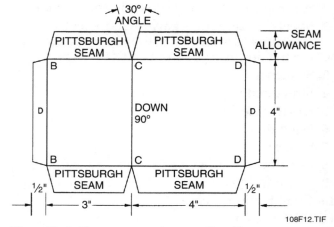

Figure 12 ◆ Throat pattern (square elbow).

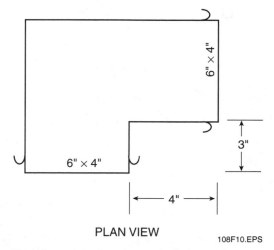

PLAN VIEW

108F10.EPS

Figure 10 ◆ Isometric drawing and plan view (square elbow).

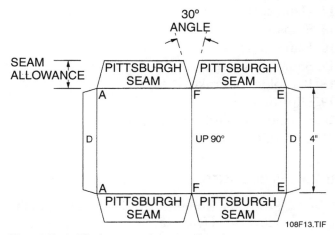

Figure 13 ◆ Heel pattern (square elbow).

8.0.0 ◆ TASK 6: 90-DEGREE ELBOW

In this task, you will learn how to lay out and fabricate a 90-degree elbow with a radius throat and heel. A very large example of this fitting is shown in *Figure 14*.

108F14.EPS

Figure 14 ◆ A large 90-degree elbow.

8.1.0 Tools and Materials

1. Appropriate personal protective equipment
2. Sheets of 26-gauge galvanized sheet metal, measured as indicated in the figures or according to your instructor's specifications
3. Scratch awl
4. Straightedge
5. Flexible steel rule
6. Wing dividers
7. Scriber
8. Felt-tipped marker
9. Framing square
10. Combination square
11. Prick punch
12. Mallet
13. Riveting hammer
14. Hand seamer
15. Snips
16. Hand notcher
17. Squaring shear
18. Bar folder or brake
19. Slip-roll machine
20. Pittsburgh roll-forming machine
21. Easy edger

8.2.0 Procedure

Step 1 Study the isometric drawing and the plan view (see *Figure 15*).

Step 2 Lay out the cheek pattern (see *Figure 16*). Leave an allowance for the ¼-inch male flange. This flange mates with the Pittsburgh pocket lock on the throat and heel.

Step 3 Establish points A, B, and C (prick-punch point A). Using AB as the radius and A as the center, scribe the curved throat BB. Using AC as the radius and A as the center, scribe the curved heel CC.

Step 4 Lay out the heel and throat patterns (see *Figure 17*). Establish the length BB for the throat pattern. Measure this length with a flexible steel rule or step it off with dividers. Then lay out the heel pattern in the same manner. Leave allowances for the locks and S and D edges.

Step 5 Cut and notch the pieces.

Step 6 Form the pocket locks on the Pittsburgh roll-forming machine.

Step 7 Form the pieces using the slip-roll machine, the hand seamer, and the easy edger.

Step 8 Assemble the parts and set the Pittsburgh lock seams to complete the fitting.

Step 9 Present the fitting to your instructor.

Step 10 Clean up your work area.

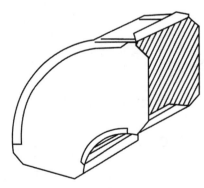

ISOMETRIC DRAWING

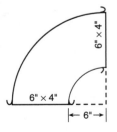

6" × 4"

6" × 4"

6"

PLAN VIEW

108F15.EPS

Figure 15 ◆ Isometric drawing and plan view (90-degree elbow).

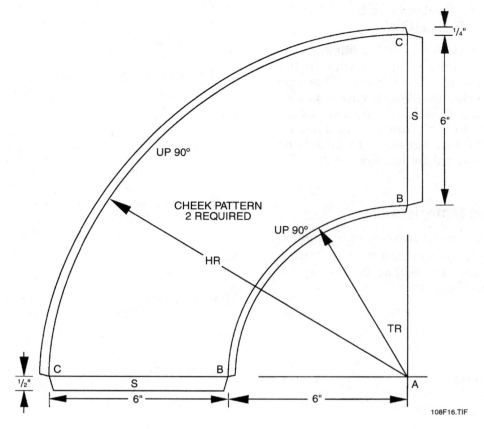

Figure 16 ◆ Cheek pattern (90-degree elbow).

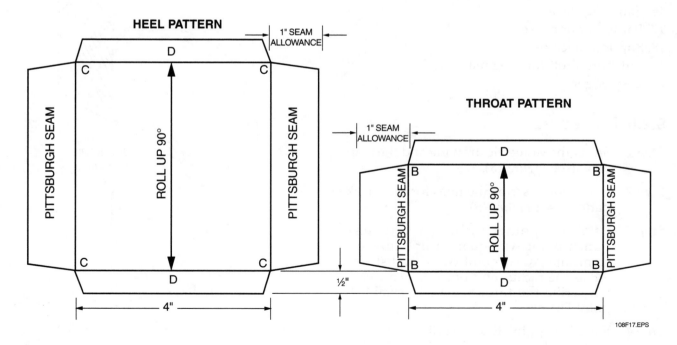

Figure 17 ◆ Heel and throat patterns (90-degree elbow).

9.0.0 ◆ TASK 7: 90-DEGREE CHANGE ELBOW

In this task you will learn how to lay out and fabricate a 90-degree elbow with a change in the cheek and with a radius throat and heel. This type of elbow is called a change elbow because the size on the cheek changes. This change in size allows a section of duct to branch off from a main ductrun. Branching off may be necessary to allow for reduced airflow required by locations served by this branch.

9.1.0 Tools and Materials

1. Appropriate personal protective equipment
2. Sheets of 26-gauge galvanized steel, measured as indicated in the figures or according to your instructor's specifications
3. Scratch awl
4. Straightedge
5. Wing dividers
6. Scriber
7. Felt-tipped marker
8. Framing square
9. Combination square
10. Prick punch
11. Mallet
12. Riveting hammer
13. Hand seamer
14. Snips
15. Hand notcher
16. Squaring shear
17. Bar folder or brake
18. Slip-roll machine
19. Pittsburgh roll-forming machine
20. Easy edger

9.2.0 Procedure

Step 1 Study the isometric drawing and the plan view (see *Figure 18*).

Step 2 Lay out and scribe the lines for the cheek pattern (see *Figure 19*).

Step 3 Establish points A, B, and C (prick-punch point A). Square a line upward from line AC at point A. With distance AB as the radius and point A as the center, scribe the throat curve to establish point D.

Step 4 Establish point E and scribe a straight horizontal line to the left of line ADE at point E.

Step 5 Set the dividers from point A to E. Prick-punch point C and, using point C as the center, scribe an arc across line ABC to establish point F.

Step 6 Scribe a line upward from point F on line ABFC and establish point G.

Step 7 Prick-punch point F. Using point F as the center and distance GF as the radius, scribe the heel curve line CG.

Step 8 Lay out the heel and throat patterns (see *Figure 20*). To determine the length of the heel, measure length CE on the cheek pattern. To determine the length of the throat, measure length BD on the cheek pattern.

Step 9 Make allowances for the Pittsburgh locks and the S and D edges.

Step 10 Using the squaring shear and proper hand tools, cut out and notch the patterns.

Step 11 Form the locks on the Pittsburgh roll-forming machine.

Step 12 Form the pieces by using the slip-roll machine, the brake, the easy edger, and the hand seamer.

Step 13 Assemble the pieces and set the Pittsburgh seams.

Step 14 Present the finished fitting to your instructor.

Step 15 Clean up your work area.

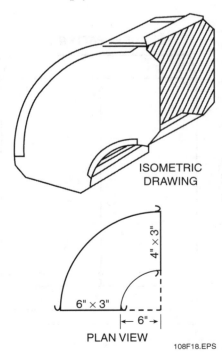

ISOMETRIC DRAWING

PLAN VIEW

4" × 3"

6" × 3"

6"

108F18.EPS

Figure 18 ◆ Isometric drawing and plan view (90-degree change elbow).

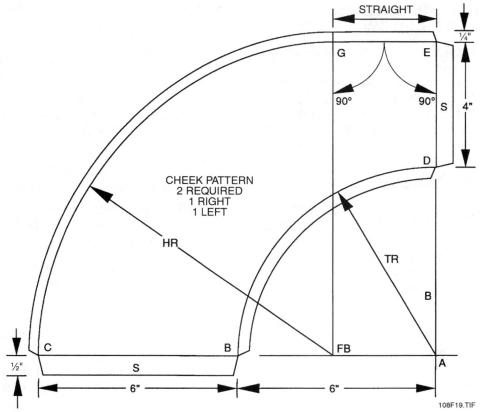

Figure 19 ◆ Cheek pattern (90-degree change elbow).

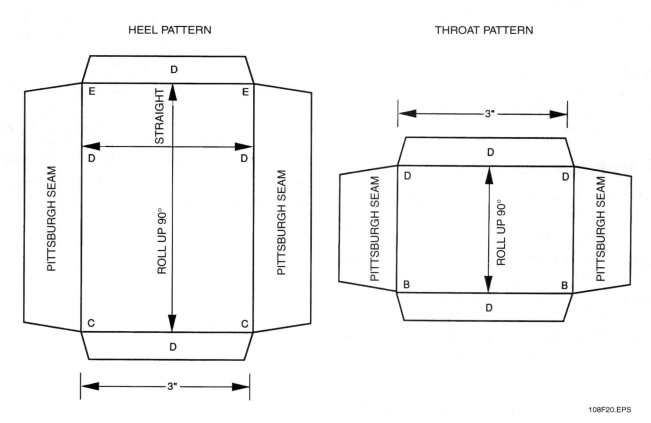

Figure 20 ◆ Heel and throat patterns (90-degree change elbow).

10.0.0 ◆ TASK 8: 45-DEGREE CHANGE ELBOW

In this task you will learn how to lay out and fabricate a 45-degree change elbow with a radius throat and heel. This elbow is called a change elbow because the dimensions change in the cheek pattern. This type of elbow is used to downsize a ductrun to create a change in air volume and direction.

10.1.0 Tools and Materials

1. Appropriate personal protective equipment
2. Sheets of 26-gauge galvanized sheet metal, measured as indicated in the figures or according to your instructor's specifications
3. Scratch awl
4. Straightedge
5. Wing dividers
6. Scriber
7. Felt-tipped marker
8. Framing square
9. Combination square
10. Prick punch
11. Mallet
12. Riveting hammer
13. Hand seamer
14. Snips
15. Hand notcher
16. Squaring shear
17. Bar folder or brake
18. Slip-roll machine
19. Pittsburgh roll-forming machine
20. Easy edger

10.2.0 Procedures

Step 1 Study the isometric drawing and plan view (see *Figure 21*).

Step 2 Lay out the cheek pattern (see *Figure 22*).

Step 3 Establish points A, B, and C (prick-punch point A).

Step 4 Scribe a horizontal line left from point A and a vertical line up from point A.

Step 5 Using point A as the center and point B as the radius, scribe the throat radius so that the arc crosses the vertical line at point F.

Step 6 Bisect the curve that was scribed between points B and F to establish line A to E.

Step 7 Measure the small cheek duct width from D to establish point E.

Step 8 Scribe a line perpendicular to line ADE at point E to make line EG, and extend it to the baseline ABC.

Step 9 Scribe a vertical line from point C on line ABC to intersect the perpendicular line from E and establish point I.

Step 10 Using point I as the center and distance IC as the radius, scribe an arc from point C to line EI to establish point G.

Step 11 Scribe a perpendicular line from line EG at point G and establish point H on the baseline ABC.

Step 12 Using point H as the center and distance GH as the radius, scribe the curve from C to G.

Step 13 Lay out the heel and throat patterns (see *Figure 23*). To determine the length of the heel pattern, measure from points C to E on the cheek pattern. To determine the length of the throat pattern, measure from points B to D on the cheek pattern.

Step 14 Make allowances for locks and edges, scribe the lines, and cut out and notch the patterns using the squaring shear and appropriate hand tools.

Step 15 Curve the throat and heel patterns on the slip-roll machine.

Step 16 Form the Pittsburgh pocket locks with the Pittsburgh roll-forming machine, and turn the single locks with the easy edger.

Step 17 Assemble the parts and lock the seams.

Step 18 Present the fabricated fitting to your instructor.

Step 19 Clean up your work area.

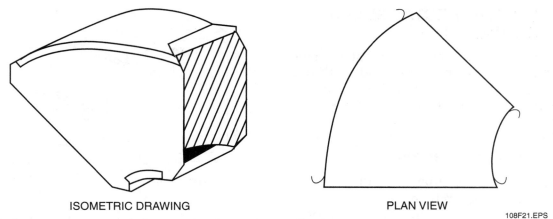

ISOMETRIC DRAWING

PLAN VIEW

108F21.EPS

Figure 21 ◆ Isometric drawing and plan view (45-degree change elbow).

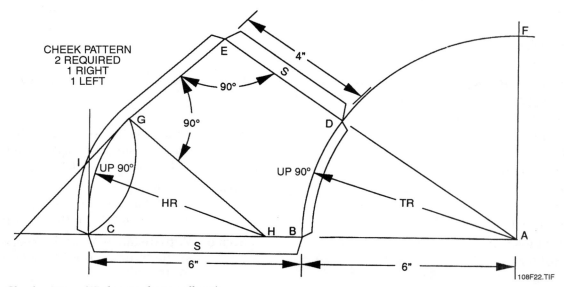

CHEEK PATTERN
2 REQUIRED
1 RIGHT
1 LEFT

108F22.TIF

Figure 22 ◆ Cheek pattern (45-degree change elbow).

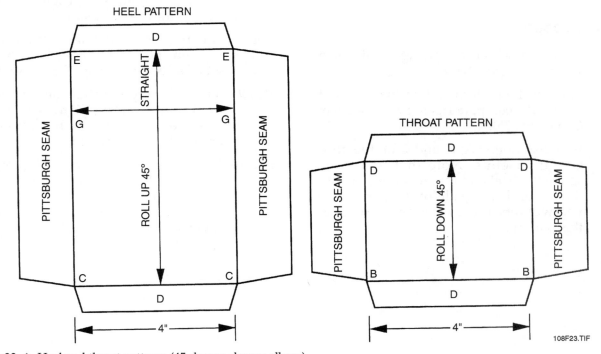

HEEL PATTERN

THROAT PATTERN

108F23.TIF

Figure 23 ◆ Heel and throat patterns (45-degree change elbow).

11.0.0 ◆ TASK 9: RECTANGULAR Y-BRANCH

In this task you will learn how to lay out and fabricate a one-way Y-branch with a radius throat and combination straight and radius heel. This **trunk line** branch fitting is designed to carry air to a branch ductrun.

11.1.0 Tools and Materials

1. Appropriate personal protective equipment
2. Sheets of 26-gauge galvanized sheet metal, measured as indicated in the figures or according to your instructor's specifications
3. Scratch awl
4. Straightedge
5. Wing dividers
6. Scriber
7. Felt-tipped marker
8. Framing square
9. Combination square
10. Prick punch
11. Mallet
12. Riveting hammer
13. Hand seamer
14. Snips
15. Hand notcher
16. Squaring shear
17. Bar folder or brake
18. Slip-roll machine
19. Pittsburgh roll-forming machine

11.2.0 Procedure

Step 1   Study the isometric drawing and the plan view (see *Figure 24*).

Step 2   Lay out the pattern so that the heel and the two cheek patterns are on one sheet (see *Figure 25*).

Step 3   Establish points A, B, and C on the horizontal baseline. Note that you must scribe the heel and throat curves on both the left and right side of the pattern, so you will repeat each step when scribing this pattern.

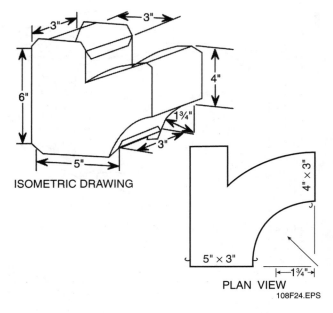

Figure 24 ◆ Isometric drawing and plan view (Y-branch).

Step 4   Scribe the throat curve with point A as the center. Using radius AB, establish point D (repeat for the other side).

Step 5   Square a perpendicular line upward from line AB at point A, through points D, and establish point E (repeat for the other side).

Step 6   With distance AE as the heel radius and A as the center, scribe the heel curve (repeat for the other side).

Step 7   Square perpendicular lines upward from line BC at point C to establish point F (repeat for the other side).

Step 8   Square a perpendicular line outward in one direction from line CF at point F to establish point G (repeat for the other side).

Step 9   Square a perpendicular line downward from point G on line GG to establish point H at the intersection with the heel curve (repeat for the other side).

Step 10 Lay out the heel pattern (see *Figure 26*). To determine the length of the heel pattern, measure the length of line HE and the length of line GH on the cheeks and back heel pattern.

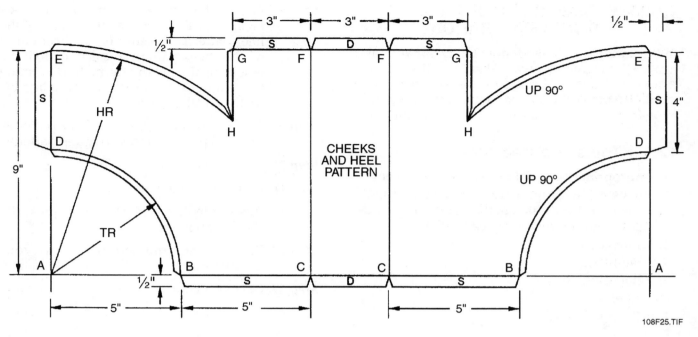

Figure 25 ◆ Cheeks and heel pattern (Y-branch).

Step 11 Lay out the throat pattern (see *Figure 27*). To determine the length of the throat pattern, measure the length of arc BD on the cheeks and back heel pattern.

Step 12 Complete the layout by adding the allowances for the Pittsburgh locks and the S and D edges and by double-checking the layout lines and dimensions.

Step 13 Cut out and notch the patterns, using the squaring shear and your hand tools.

Step 14 Form the Pittsburgh locks.

Step 15 Assemble the fitting and lock the seams.

Step 16 Present the finished fitting to your instructor.

Step 17 Clean up your work area.

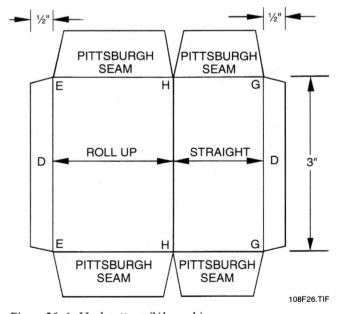

Figure 26 ◆ Heel pattern (Y-branch).

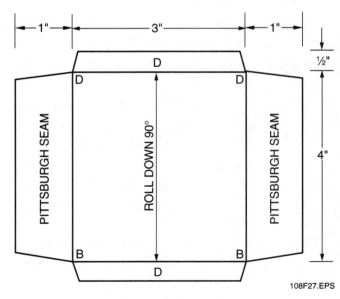

Figure 27 ◆ Throat pattern (Y-branch).

12.0.0 ◆ TASK 10: 90-DEGREE DOUBLE Y-BRANCH

In this task you will learn how to lay out and fabricate a 90-degree two-way Y-branch with a radius throat and heel. Y-branches are referred to as trunk line fittings. They are connected to the trunk takeoff and are used to carry air to the branches.

12.1.0 Tools and Materials

1. Appropriate personal protective equipment
2. Sheets of 26-gauge galvanized sheet metal, measured as indicated in the figures or according to your instructor's specifications
3. Scratch awl
4. Straightedge
5. Wing dividers
6. Scriber
7. Felt-tipped marker
8. Framing square
9. Combination square
10. Prick punch
11. Mallet
12. Riveting hammer
13. Hand seamer
14. Snips
15. Hand notcher
16. Squaring shear
17. Bar folder or brake
18. Slip-roll machine
19. Pittsburgh roll-forming machine

12.2.0 Procedure

Step 1 Study the isometric drawing and the plan view (see *Figure 28*).

Step 2 Lay out the pattern for the cheeks (see *Figure 29*).

Step 3 Establish a baseline between points A.

Step 4 Establish both points A so that distance AC is the throat radius. Scribe this radius.

Step 5 Square a perpendicular line upward from each point A and mark each point C.

Step 6 Extend both lines AC upward to establish both points D.

Step 7 With point A as the center and distance AD as the radius, scribe the heel curves.

Step 8 Lay out the heel and throat patterns (see *Figure 30*). To determine the length of the heel pattern, measure either heel curve on the cheek pattern to calculate half the length of the heel pattern. To determine the length of the throat, measure line BC on the cheek pattern.

Step 9 Cut out and notch the two cheek patterns, one heel pattern, and two throat patterns.

Step 10 Form the Pittsburgh locks.

Step 11 Form up all the patterns.

Step 12 Assemble the patterns and lock the Pittsburgh seams.

Step 13 Present the finished fitting to your instructor.

Step 14 Clean up your work area.

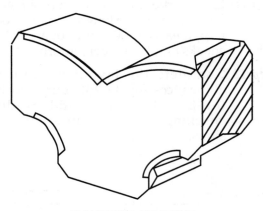

ISOMETRIC DRAWING

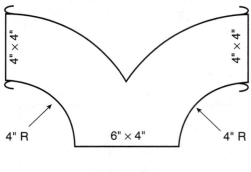

PLAN VIEW   108F28.EPS

Figure 28 ◆ Isometric drawing and plan view (double Y-branch).

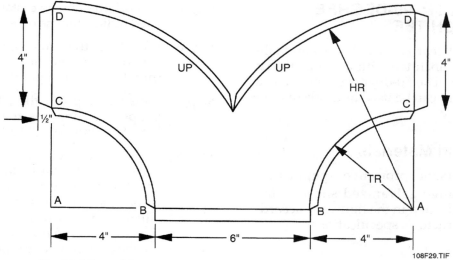

Figure 29 ◆ Cheek pattern (double Y-branch).

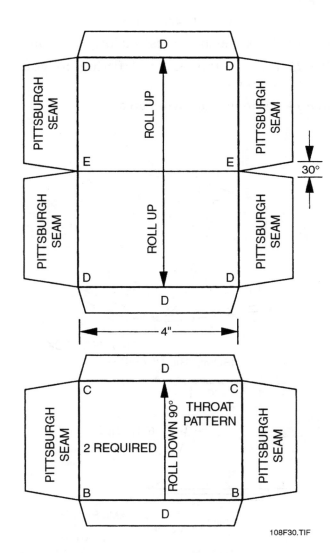

Figure 30 ◆ Heel and throat patterns (double Y-branch).

Review Questions

Sections 6.0.0–12.0.0

1. When moving air compresses, it can create a
   _____.
   a. pressure drop at an elbow
   b. noisy vibration that can transfer to occu-
      pied spaces
   c. vacuum
   d. reversal of airflow

2. The elbow design with the least resistance to
   airflow is _____.
   a. square
   b. round
   c. square with a square throat and heel
   d. rectangular with a curved throat and heel

3. A change elbow is used to _____ a ductrun.
   a. increase the size of
   b. close off a section of
   c. filter airflow to
   d. downsize

4. To calculate the circumference of a round duct,
   use the formula _____.
   a. diameter times pi
   b. diameter times pi^2
   c. diameter divided by pi
   d. diameter times radius

5. The _____ is a fitting that connects two ducts
   at a right angle.
   a. 45-degree change elbow
   b. square elbow
   c. flexible connection
   d. mitered connection

13.0.0 ◆ TASK 11: 90-DEGREE CLINCH TEE

In this task, you will learn how to lay out and fabricate a 90-degree clinch tee with a radius throat and a straight back. The 90-degree clinch tee is a trunk line fitting and can be used as a side takeoff for airflow efficiency.

13.1.0 Tools and Materials

1. Appropriate personal protective equipment
2. Sheets of 26-gauge galvanized sheet metal, measured as indicated in the figures or according to your instructor's specifications
3. Scratch awl
4. Straightedge
5. Wing dividers
6. Scriber
7. Felt-tipped marker
8. Framing square
9. Combination square
10. Prick punch
11. Mallet
12. Riveting hammer
13. Hand seamer
14. Snips
15. Hand notcher
16. Squaring shear
17. Bar folder or brake
18. Slip-roll machine
19. Pittsburgh roll-forming machine

13.2.0 Procedure

Step 1 Study the isometric drawing and the plan view (see *Figure 31*).

Step 2 Lay out the cheek pattern (see *Figure 32*).

Step 3 Establish points A, B, and C and scribe the lines through these points.

Step 4 To calculate dimension CD, add ⅛ inch for each inch of height to the height of the cheek line AB.

Step 5 Extend line BC the distance of this calculated radius dimension to establish point D.

Step 6 With D as the center and the calculated distance CD as the radius, scribe the throat curve from point C to point E.

Step 7 Finish laying out the pattern, allowing proper dimensions for the Pittsburgh locks and the S and D edges.

Step 8 Lay out the throat and heel patterns (see *Figure 33*). Measure length CE on the cheek pattern to find length BE on the throat pattern. Be sure to allow for the clinch and lock dimensions. Determine the length of the heel pattern by measuring length AB (with proper allowance) on the cheek pattern.

Step 9 Cut out and notch the patterns.

Step 10 Form the locks.

Step 11 Form the patterns.

Step 12 Assemble the pieces and lock the seams.

Step 13 Present the finished fitting to your instructor.

Step 14 Clean up your work area.

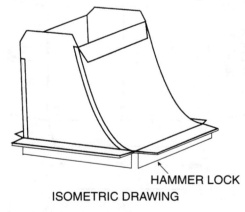

HAMMER LOCK
ISOMETRIC DRAWING

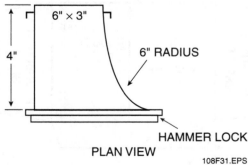

PLAN VIEW

108F31.EPS

Figure 31 ◆ Isometric drawing and plan view (clinch tee).

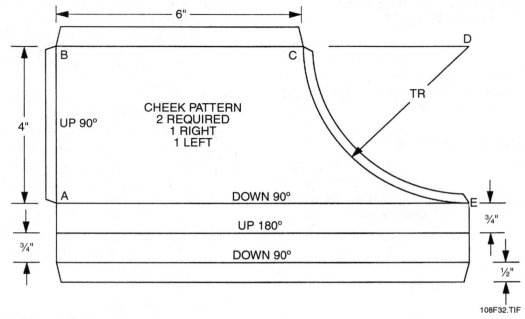

Figure 32 ◆ Cheek pattern (clinch tee).

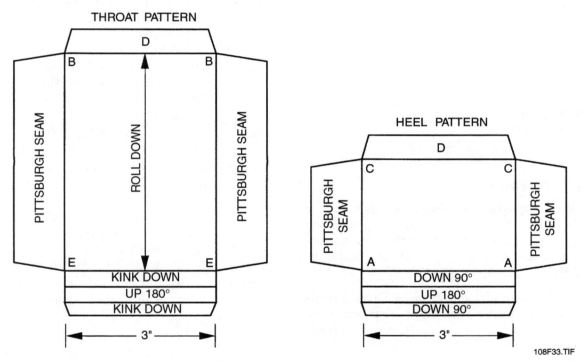

Figure 33 ◆ Throat and heel patterns (clinch tee).

14.0.0 ◆ TASK 12: THREE-PIECE ROUND OFFSET

In this task you will learn how to lay out and fabricate a three-piece round offset. This type of offset is required on installations where the amount and length of the offset make it difficult to use two angles and a short length of pipe.

14.1.0 Tools and Materials

1. Appropriate personal protective equipment
2. Two pieces of 26-gauge galvanized sheet metal, measured as indicated in the figures or according to your instructor's specifications
3. Scratch awl
4. Straightedge
5. Wing dividers
6. Scriber
7. Felt-tipped marker
8. Framing square
9. Combination square
10. Prick punch
11. Mallet
12. Riveting hammer
13. Hand seamer
14. Snips
15. Hand notcher
16. Squaring shear
17. Slip-roll machine
18. Soldering equipment (optional)

14.2.0 Procedure

For all of the working drawings for this task, see *Figure 34*. Study the isometric drawing and the drawing showing the assembled offset before beginning so that you can visualize this fitting in your head.

Step 1 Refer to the elevation view. Draw a horizontal baseline, mark the offset and pipe diameter on the baseline, and establish points A and B.

Step 2 Scribe a vertical line up from the offset dimension on the baseline and establish the height and diameter of the pipe on the top horizontal line.

Step 3 Draw the height of the throat by drawing line AC. Then establish point G from the top horizontal line using the same dimension as AC.

Step 4 To obtain the heights for the heel, use AB as the radius and points C and G as centers. Scribe an arc at the heel from the ver-

tical line to an undetermined length. Then, draw a straight line from point G, tangent to the arc, intersecting the vertical line at point D. Draw a straight line from point C, tangent to the arc, intersecting the vertical line at point H. These distances will be the height for the heel on both parts 1 and 3.

Step 5 Draw a half circle below the profile, and project lines to intersect the slant line CD.

Step 6 The distances C to E and G to F in the body, or part 2, are equal to the height A to C in part 1. Transfer the height AC from points C to E and G to F.

Step 7 The distances D to F and H to E in the body are equal to height B to D in part 1. Transfer the height BD from points D to F and H to E.

Step 8 Refer to the stretchout pattern. Lay out the stretchouts for the ends and the middle sections.

Step 9 Establish points A to B on the base horizontal line of the stretchout pattern equal to the circumference of A to B on the elevation view. Allow for seams.

Step 10 Divide line AB on the stretchout pattern into equal spaces (two times as many as the half circle). Number each point as indicated.

Step 11 Square a line upward from each point from line AB on the stretchout pattern.

Step 12 Set the dividers from point 5 on line AB on the elevation view to point 5 on the miter line CD. Transfer this distance to each point 5 on the end pattern to the squared lines on the stretchout pattern. Continue in the same manner for each numbered point.

Step 13 Draw a curved line to connect these points as indicated. Allow for the seam.

Step 14 Complete the middle and end patterns. Make proper seam allowances on the body pattern to allow for correct attachment of the end patterns (refer to the assembled offset).

Step 15 Transfer the pattern to the sheet metal and cut and form the patterns.

Step 16 Assemble the patterns and set and lock (or solder) the seams.

Step 17 Present the finished fitting to your instructor.

Step 18 Clean up your work area.

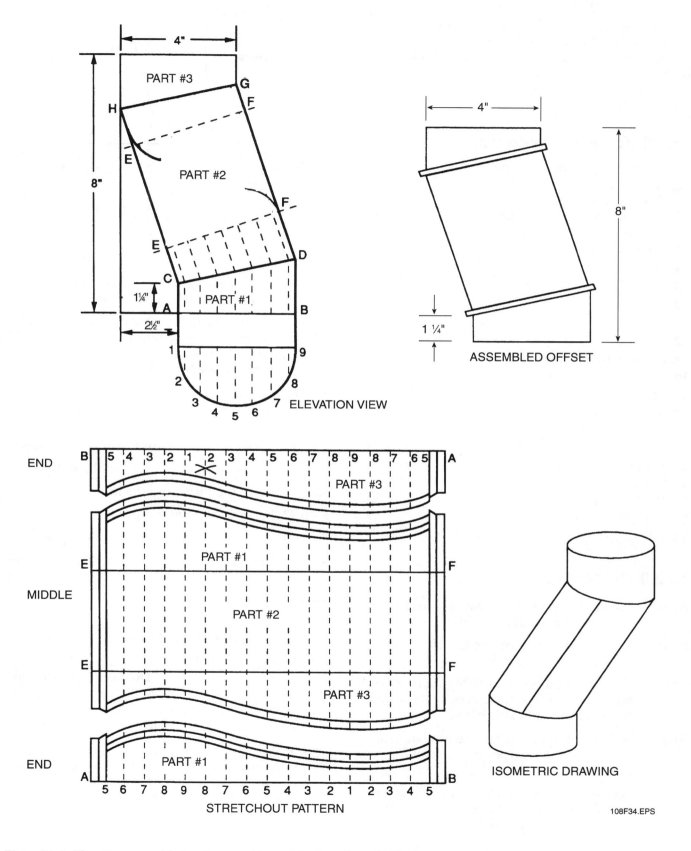

PART #3

G

H

F

E

PART #2

F

E

D

C

PART #1

A

1¼"

2½"

B

8"

4"

1

2

3

4

5

6

7

8

9

ELEVATION VIEW

4"

8"

1 ¼"

ASSEMBLED OFFSET

STRETCHOUT PATTERN

END

B 5 4 3 2 1 2 3 4 5 6 7 8 9 8 7 6 5 A

PART #3

E   PART #1   F

MIDDLE

E   PART #2   F

PART #3

END

A 5 6 7 8 9 8 7 6 5 4 3 2 1 2 3 4 5 B

PART #1

ISOMETRIC DRAWING

108F34.EPS

Figure 34 ◆ Elevation, assembled, pattern, and isometric views (round offset).

15.0.0 ◆ TASK 13: TRANSITION WITH THREE STRAIGHT SIDES

In this task you will learn how to lay out and fabricate a transition with three straight sides. This fitting is used to reduce the size of a trunk line for better air distribution. Note that any transition fitting is designed to change the ductrun from one volume size to another.

15.1.0 Tools and Materials

1. Appropriate personal protective equipment
2. One or two sheets of 26-gauge galvanized sheet metal, measured as indicated in the figures or according to your instructor's specifications
3. Scratch awl
4. Straightedge
5. Wing dividers
6. Scriber
7. Felt-tipped marker
8. Framing square
9. Combination square
10. Prick punch
11. Mallet
12. Riveting hammer
13. Hand seamer
14. Snips
15. Hand notcher
16. Squaring shear
17. Bar folder or brake
18. Slip-roll machine
19. Pittsburgh roll-forming machine

15.2.0 Procedure

Step 1 Study the isometric drawing and plan view (see *Figure 35*).

Step 2 Lay out the pattern for the cheeks and back heel (see *Figure 36*).

Step 3 Establish points A and B. Notice that you will establish these points on both the left side and the right side of the pattern.

Step 4 Square a perpendicular line upward from point B to establish point C (repeat for the other side).

Step 5 Scribe a horizontal line perpendicular to line BC at point C to establish point D (repeat for the other side).

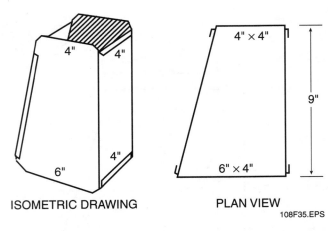

ISOMETRIC DRAWING   PLAN VIEW

108F35.EPS

Figure 35 ◆ Isometric drawing and plan view (transition with three straight sides).

Step 6 Scribe a straight line between point A and point D (repeat for the other side).

Step 7 Lay out the heel pattern (see *Figure 37*). To determine the length of the heel pattern line AD, measure the length of line AD in the cheeks and back heel pattern.

Step 8 Scribe the necessary lines on the heel pattern to establish the heel pattern dimensions.

Step 9 Make allowances for the locks and edges.

Step 10 Cut out and notch the metal patterns.

Step 11 Form the Pittsburgh locks.

Step 12 Form up the pattern pieces.

Step 13 Assemble the pieces and lock the seams.

Step 14 Present the finished fitting to your instructor.

Step 15 Clean up your work area.

15.2.1 Procedure for a One-Piece Pattern

If the fitting is small, this transition can be made from a one-piece pattern. The layout procedure for the one-piece pattern is the same as for the two-piece pattern, until you get to the heel pattern layout.

Step 1 Project lines outward from line AD at points A and D (both of these lines are perpendicular to line AD) to establish the second points A and D (see *Figure 38*).

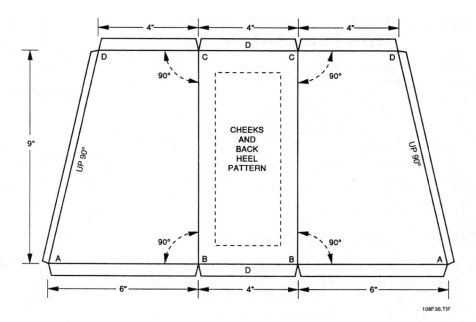

Figure 36 ◆ Cheeks and back heel pattern (transition with three straight sides).

Step 2 Measure line CC on the cheeks and back heel pattern to make sure that line DD on the one-piece pattern is the same.

Step 3 Scribe a straight line to connect the second points A and D.

Step 4 Then finish this fitting as usual: allow for the locks and edges, cut out and notch the metal patterns, form the Pittsburgh locks, form up the pattern pieces, assemble the pieces, and lock the seams.

Step 5 Present the finished fitting to your instructor.

Step 6 Clean up your work area.

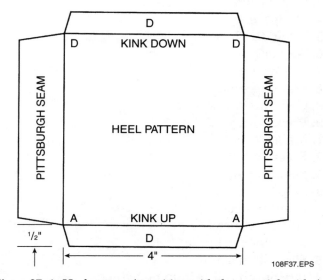

Figure 37 ◆ Heel pattern (transition with three straight sides).

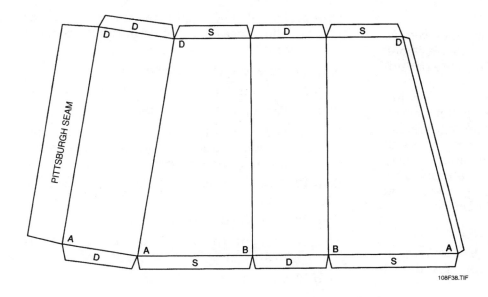

Figure 38 ◆ One-piece pattern (transition with three straight sides).

16.0.0 ◆ TASK 14: TRANSITION WITH TWO STRAIGHT SIDES

In this task you will learn how to lay out and fabricate a transition with two straight sides. This type of trunk line fitting may also be called a change joint transition, because the size changes at each end. This fitting is designed to pass over or under beams, pipes, or other obstructions. However, although the fitting must change in width and height, it must retain its original area so that the airflow volume remains constant throughout the ductrun.

16.1.0 Tools and Materials

1. Appropriate personal protective equipment
2. Two or three pieces of 26-gauge galvanized sheet metal, measured as indicated in the figures or according to your instructor's specifications
3. Scratch awl
4. Straightedge
5. Wing dividers
6. Scriber
7. Felt-tipped marker
8. Framing square
9. Combination square
10. Prick punch
11. Mallet
12. Riveting hammer
13. Hand seamer
14. Snips
15. Hand notcher
16. Squaring shear
17. Bar folder or brake
18. Slip-roll machine
19. Pittsburgh roll-forming machine

16.2.0 Procedure

Because this fitting is to be **FOB** or *flat on bottom*, the bottom and one side pattern are made as one piece. You can make the top and other side pattern either in one piece or separately.

Notice that in this task you will be working with both a *bottom* cheek and heel pattern and a *developed* cheek and heel pattern. You will first lay out the bottom cheek and heel patterns. You will then use measurements from those patterns to lay out the developed cheek and heel patterns. This can be a little confusing at first, but you will soon see how these patterns work together.

Step 1 Study the plan view (see *Figure 39*).

Step 2 Lay out the *bottom cheek and heel* pattern (see *Figure 40*). Establish points A, B, and C on line AC.

Step 3 Square a line upward from point B on line ABC to establish point D.

Step 4 Scribe a horizontal line (squared from line BD) at point D to establish points E and F.

Step 5 Scribe straight lines to connect points A and E and to connect points C and F.

Study the *developed cheek and heel* patterns (see *Figure 41*). You will next lay out the *developed heel* pattern (on the right side of the figure).

Step 6 Establish line PA. Distance PA should equal distance BC on the *bottom heel* pattern.

Step 7 Scribe a perpendicular line upward from point A on line PA to establish point E. Distance AE should equal distance EA on the *bottom cheek* pattern.

Step 8 Square a horizontal line left from point E, perpendicular to line AE, to establish point O. Distance EO should equal distance DF on the *bottom heel* pattern.

Step 9 Scribe a straight line connecting points O and P.

Next, you will lay out the *developed cheek* pattern (on the left side of the figure).

Step 10 Establish line CP on a horizontal line. Line CP should equal distance AB on the *bottom cheek* pattern.

Step 11 Square a perpendicular line upward from line CP at point C to establish point F. Line CF should equal distance FC on the *bottom heel* pattern.

Step 12 Square a horizontal line to the right from point F, perpendicular to line CF, to establish point O. Line FO should equal distance ED on the *bottom cheek* pattern.

Step 13 Scribe a straight line to connect points O and P.

Step 14 Double-check all dimensions as well as allowances for the Pittsburgh locks and S and D edges.

Step 15 Prick-punch all the bend lines.

Step 16 Cut out and notch the patterns.

Step 17 Form the Pittsburgh locks.

Step 18 Form all of the cheek and heel patterns. Double-check all bend directions before forming these pieces.

Step 19 Assemble the components and lock the seams.

Step 20 Turn the drive edges.

Step 21 Present the finished fitting to your instructor.

Step 22 Clean up your work area.

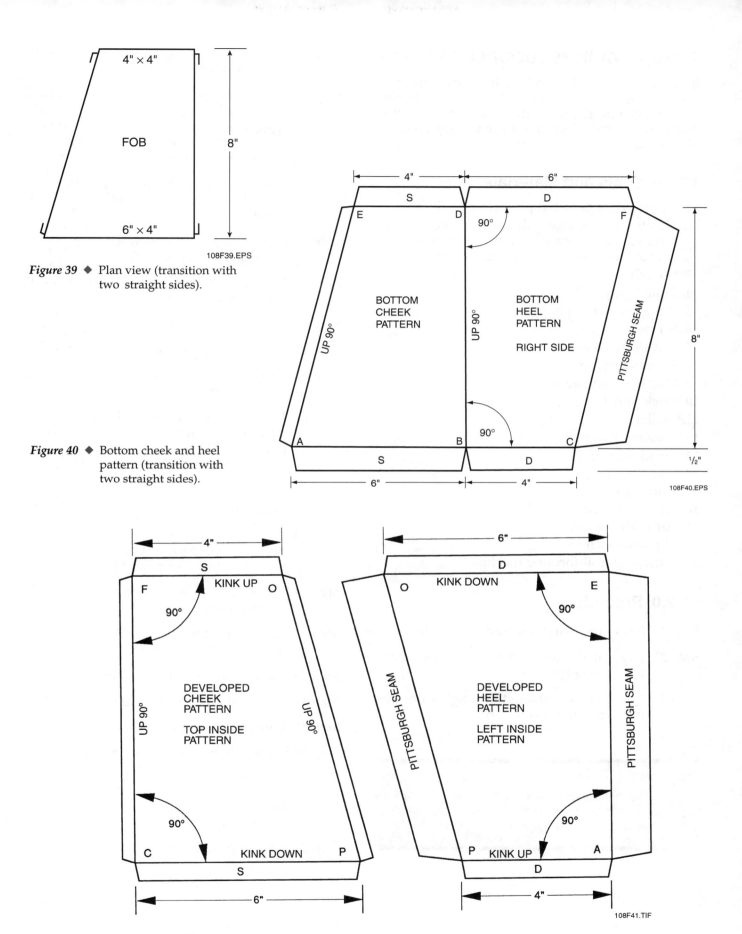

Figure 39 ◆ Plan view (transition with two straight sides).

Figure 40 ◆ Bottom cheek and heel pattern (transition with two straight sides).

Figure 41 ◆ Developed cheek and heel patterns (transition with two straight sides).

17.0.0 ◆ TASK 15: DOUBLE OFFSET

In this task you will learn how to lay out and fabricate a double offset with flat cheeks and heels. This trunk line fitting is designed to move the ductrun around obstacles to maintain airflow efficiency.

17.1.0 Tools and Materials

1. Appropriate personal protective equipment
2. Sheets of 26-gauge galvanized sheet metal, measured as indicated in the figures or according to your instructor's specifications
3. Scratch awl
4. Straightedge
5. Wing dividers
6. Scriber
7. Felt-tipped marker
8. Framing square
9. Combination square
10. Prick punch
11. Mallet
12. Riveting hammer
13. Hand seamer
14. Snips
15. Hand notcher
16. Squaring shear
17. Bar folder or brake
18. Slip-roll machine
19. Pittsburgh roll-forming machine

17.2.0 Procedure

Step 1 Study the plan view (see *Figure 42*).

Step 2 Lay out the top and bottom cheek patterns (see *Figure 43*).

Step 3 Construct a true-length triangle from the plan view (see *Figure 44*).

NOTE

Any lines perpendicular to your line of vision are true lengths. Any lines at an angle to your line of vision are not true lengths.

Step 4 Locate points A, B, and C on the bottom and top cheek pattern.

Step 5 Square a perpendicular line upward from line AC at point C to locate point D. The distance CD should be equal to the distance designated by the letters OM on the true-length triangle.

Step 6 Square a horizontal line, perpendicular to line CD, to the right at point D to locate point E.

Step 7 Draw straight lines between points B and D and between points A and E.

Step 8 Lay out distances for the Pittsburgh lock and the S and D edge allowances.

Step 9 Lay out the side pattern (see *Figure 45*).

Step 10 Locate both points B and point C.

Step 11 Square a horizontal line upward from point C, perpendicular to line BBC.

Step 12 Look back at the top and bottom cheek patterns. Set your dividers equal to the distance BD shown there. Come back to the heel pattern. With your dividers set on point B (the one nearest point C), scribe an arc onto your perpendicular line upward from point C to locate point D.

Step 13 Square a horizontal line to the right at point D, perpendicular to line CD, to establish the other point D.

Step 14 Scribe straight lines connecting both sets of DB points.

Step 15 Make allowances for the Pittsburgh locks and the S and drive edges.

Step 16 Cut out and notch the patterns.

Step 17 Form the Pittsburgh locks.

Step 18 Form up the pattern pieces.

Step 19 Assemble the fitting and lock the seams.

Step 20 Turn the drive edges.

Step 21 Present the finished fitting to your instructor.

Step 22 Clean up your work area.

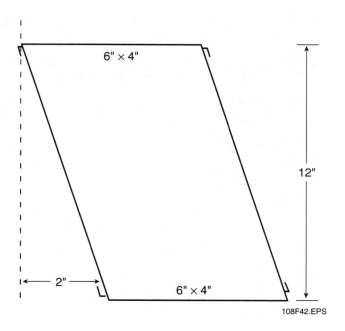

Figure 42 ◆ Plan view (double offset).

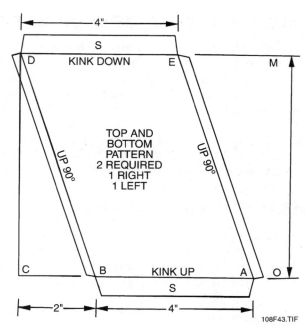

Figure 43 ◆ Top and bottom cheek patterns (double offset).

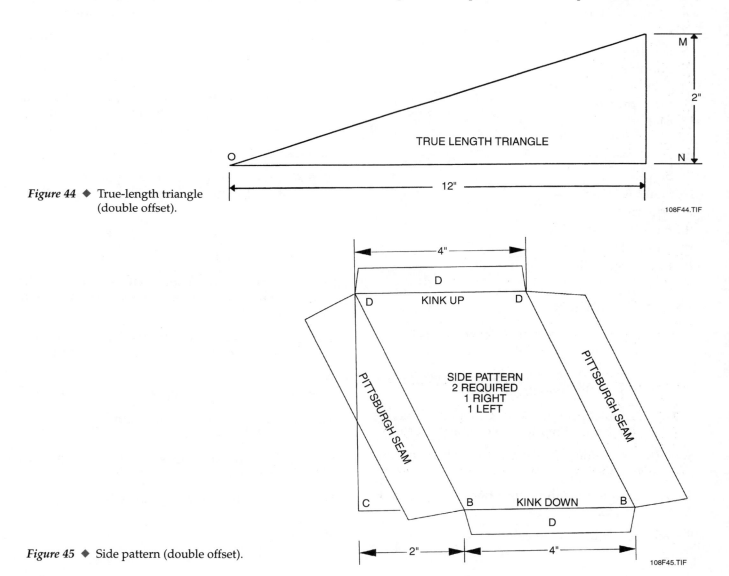

Figure 44 ◆ True-length triangle (double offset).

Figure 45 ◆ Side pattern (double offset).

18.0.0 ◆ TASK 16: OGEE OFFSET

In this task you will learn how to lay out and fabricate an **ogee** offset with radius heels. An ogee offset resembles the letter S. This trunk line fitting is designed to move the duct around obstacles without disturbing the efficiency of the airflow. The length of this fitting must be more than twice the distance of its offset. This design keeps the turn from being too sharp, which would create back pressure in the system.

18.1.0 Tools and Materials

1. Appropriate personal protective equipment
2. Sheets of 26-gauge galvanized sheet metal, measured as indicated in the figures or according to your instructor's specifications
3. Scratch awl
4. Straightedge
5. Flexible steel rule
6. Wing dividers
7. Scriber
8. Felt-tipped marker
9. Framing square
10. Combination square
11. Prick punch
12. Mallet
13. Riveting hammer
14. Hand seamer
15. Snips
16. Hand notcher
17. Squaring shear
18. Bar folder or brake
19. Slip-roll machine
20. Pittsburgh roll-forming machine

18.2.0 Procedure

Step 1 Study the isometric drawing and plan view (see *Figure 46*).

Step 2 Lay out the cheek pattern (see *Figure 47*). Notice that two are required.

Step 3 Establish points A, B, C, D, and E using the dimensions shown on the pattern.

Step 4 Bisect lines AE and CD to establish points G and F.

Step 5 Scribe a straight line between points F and G.

Step 6 Bisect line FG to establish point H.

Step 7 Bisect line FH, scribing the line down across line BC to establish point I.

Step 8 With point I as the center and distance IC as the radius, scribe the throat curve.

Step 9 With point I as the center and distance ID as the radius, scribe the heel curve.

Step 10 With your dividers set at distance IF and using point G (on line AE) as the center, establish point J.

Step 11 With distance EJ as the radius and point J as the center, scribe the top throat/heel curve until it touches the heel radius (HR) curve.

Step 12 With point J as the center and distance AJ as the radius, scribe the bottom heel/throat curve until it touches the throat radius (TR) curve.

Step 13 Lay out the heel/throat pattern (see *Figure 48*). Notice that two are required.

Step 14 Determine the length of the heel pattern with your flexible steel rule. As an alternative, you could step off the lengths from the cheek pattern with your dividers. To do this, measure the length of curve AC on the cheek pattern and transfer this length to the heel pattern.

Step 15 Lay out both heel patterns.

Step 16 Make allowance on the patterns for the Pittsburgh locks and the S and drive edges.

Step 17 Cut out and notch the patterns.

Step 18 Form the Pittsburgh locks.

Step 19 Form up the cheek patterns, noting the bend directions for the Pittsburgh single lock.

Step 20 Form the heel patterns. Use the slip-roll machine, if necessary, to produce the correct curves.

Step 21 Assemble the pieces and lock the seams.

Step 22 Turn the drive edges (on both ends of both heels).

Step 23 Present the finished fitting to your instructor.

Step 24 Clean up your work area.

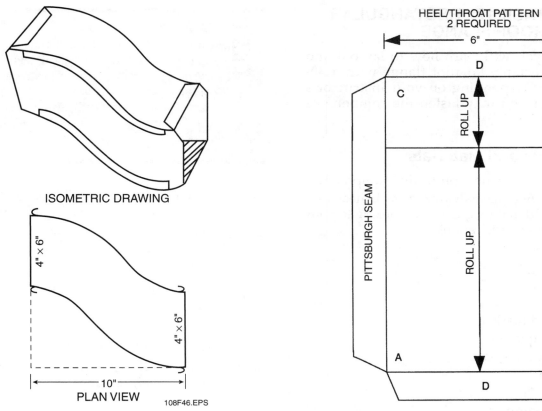

ISOMETRIC DRAWING

PLAN VIEW

108F46.EPS

Figure 46 ◆ Isometric drawing and plan view (ogee offset).

HEEL/THROAT PATTERN
2 REQUIRED

108F48.TIF

Figure 48 ◆ Heel/throat pattern (ogee offset).

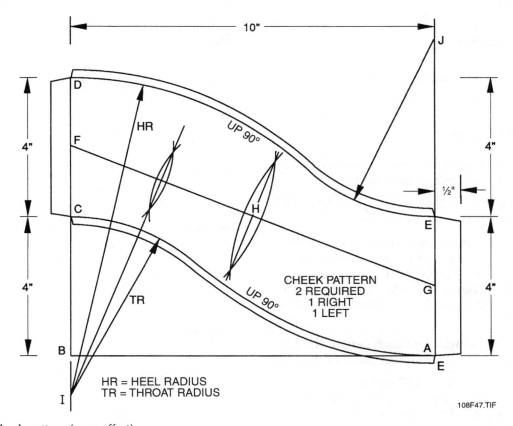

HR = HEEL RADIUS
TR = THROAT RADIUS

108F47.TIF

Figure 47 ◆ Cheek pattern (ogee offset).

19.0.0 ◆ TASK 17: RECTANGULAR ROOF FLANGE

In this task you will learn how to lay out and fabricate a rectangular roof flange with a 30-degree pitch. Depending on your instructor's requirements, you may fasten the components by soldering.

19.1.0 Tools and Materials

1. Appropriate personal protective equipment
2. Sheets of 26-gauge galvanized steel, measured as indicated in the figures or according to your instructor's specifications
3. Scratch awl
4. Straightedge
5. Wing dividers
6. Scriber
7. Felt-tipped marker
8. Framing square
9. Combination square
10. Prick punch
11. Mallet
12. Riveting hammer
13. Hand seamer
14. Snips
15. Hand notcher
16. Squaring shear
17. Bar folder or brake
18. Slip-roll machine
19. Pittsburgh roll-forming machine
20. Soldering equipment (optional)

19.2.0 Procedure

Step 1 Lay out the cheek pattern (see *Figure 49*). Notice that two are required.

Step 2 Scribe the 30-degree roof pitch line (DE) and establish the centerline.

Step 3 Measure up 3 inches from the intersection of the 30-degree line and centerline O. Locate and mark point P, and from this point scribe a horizontal line perpendicular to and extending on both sides of the centerline.

Step 4 Measure 3 inches on each side of the centerline at P and establish points F and G.

Step 5 From points F and G scribe perpendicular lines downward to intersect the 30-degree pitch line. Mark these line lengths A and B.

> **CAUTION**
>
> It is important to make the bends in the right sequence. If you don't, you could wind up with a workpiece that is impossible to assemble. So both your time and the materials will be wasted. Practice making Pittsburgh bends without a machine to get a better feel for how the bend sequence should work.

Step 6 From points D and E measure down 1 inch to allow for the flange on the cheek.

Step 7 Allow for the Pittsburgh single lock on both sides of the cheek as indicated on the pattern.

Step 8 Lay out the pattern for the heel (see *Figure 50*).

Step 9 Draw a horizontal line at the base to allow for the roof flange.

Step 10 Allow for Pittsburgh locks on both sides of the heel, leaving 2½ inches between them.

Step 11 Using your dividers or flexible steel rule, transfer length B above points J and K.

Step 12 Lay out the pattern for the throat (see *Figure 51*).

Step 13 Draw a horizontal line at the base to allow for the roof flange.

Step 14 Allow for Pittsburgh locks on both sides of the throat, leaving 2½ inches between them.

Step 15 Using your dividers or flexible rule, transfer length A above points H and I.

Step 16 Prick-mark the pattern for fabrication. Establish the bending and forming sequence.

Step 17 Cut out and notch the patterns.

Step 18 Form the Pittsburgh locks.

Step 19 Form up the throat, heel, and two cheek patterns, using the bar folder or brake.

Step 20 Assemble the pieces and lock the seams.

Step 21 Solder or otherwise fasten as specified by your instructor.

Step 22 Present the finished fitting to your instructor.

Step 23 Clean up your work area.

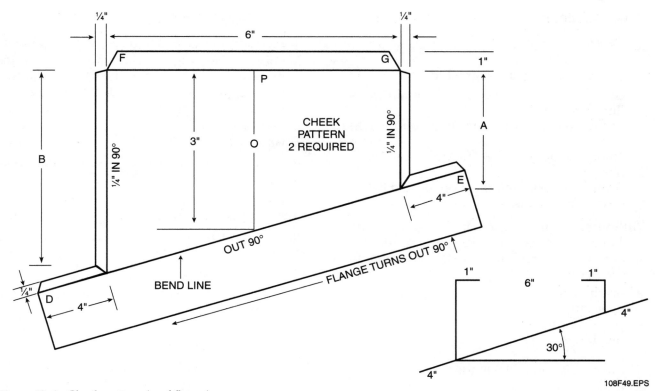

Figure 49 ◆ Cheek pattern (roof flange).

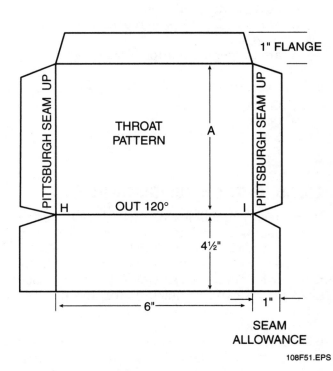

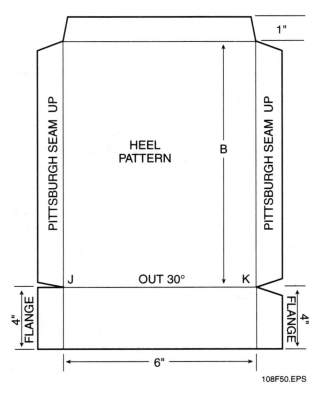

Figure 50 ◆ Heel pattern (roof flange).

Figure 51 ◆ Throat pattern (roof flange).

Review Questions

Sections 13.0.0–19.0.0

1. A transition fitting is designed to _____.
   a. connect a branch takeoff to the main trunk line
   b. change the ductrun from one volume size to another
   c. change from rigid to flexible duct near obstructions
   d. connect a flexible connection located near a blower to a trunk line

2. Although a transition must change in width and height, it must retain its _____ so that the airflow volume remains constant throughout the ductrun.
   a. original area
   b. ogee curve
   c. pressure drop ratio
   d. flexibility

3. The abbreviation FOB stands for _____.
   a. finished on bottom
   b. flared on bottom
   c. flat on bottom
   d. fitted on bottom

4. True lengths are lines that _____.
   a. are perspective lines on a plan view
   b. curve away from your line of vision
   c. are at a 45- or 90-degree angle to your line of vision
   d. are perpendicular to your line of vision

5. An ogee offset resembles the letter _____.
   a. G
   b. O
   c. S
   d. E

20.0.0 ◆ TASK 18: SMOKESTACK

In this task you will learn how to lay out and fabricate a smokestack base to be mounted at the top of a roof with a 30-degree pitch. This fitting is also called a *base over peak* because its use is not limited to that of a smokestack. This fitting may also be used for an exhaust stack or for an outside air intake.

Notice that in this task you will be working back and forth from the *top view* to the *front view*. Because the same letter is used in both drawings to identify some of the points and lines, you must pay careful attention to ensure that you are looking at the correct view.

20.1.0 Tools and Materials

1. Appropriate personal protective equipment
2. Sheets of 26-gauge or heavier galvanized steel, measured as indicated in the figures or according to your instructor's specifications
3. Scratch awl
4. Straightedge
5. Wing dividers
6. Scriber
7. Felt-tipped marker
8. Framing square
9. Combination square
10. Prick punch
11. Mallet
12. Riveting hammer
13. Hand seamer
14. Snips
15. Hand notcher
16. Squaring shear
17. Bar folder or brake
18. Slip-roll machine
19. Pittsburgh roll-forming machine

20.2.0 Procedure

Step 1 Study the isometric drawing and plan view (see *Figure 52*).

Step 2 Construct triangles as illustrated in the top view. Then draw the front view using the following steps (see *Figure 53*). Note that you will take some lengths from the top view.

Step 3 Draw the centerline AE to any length.

Step 4 Draw the top and baselines to the given lengths. Set one-half of the width of the base on each side of the centerline from point E, and one-half of the width of the top on each side of the centerline to establish point D. (Note that this is the top of the fitting, not the apex of the drawing.)

Step 5 Draw a slant line from point F in the front view, crossing point D and intersecting the centerline to establish point A.

Step 6 Draw the 30-degree angle upward from point F on the baseline of the front view to establish point G on the centerline.

Step 7 Transfer the slant length AB from the top view to the baseline points EB on the front view. Draw the slant line AB in the front view crossing lines C and D. This line represents the true length of the corner on the taper pattern.

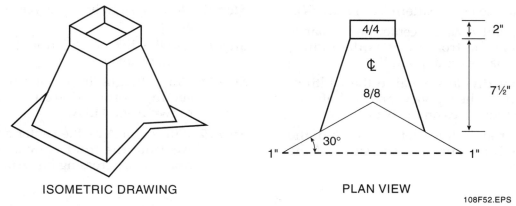

ISOMETRIC DRAWING   PLAN VIEW

108F52.EPS

Figure 52 ◆ Isometric drawing and plan view (smokestack).

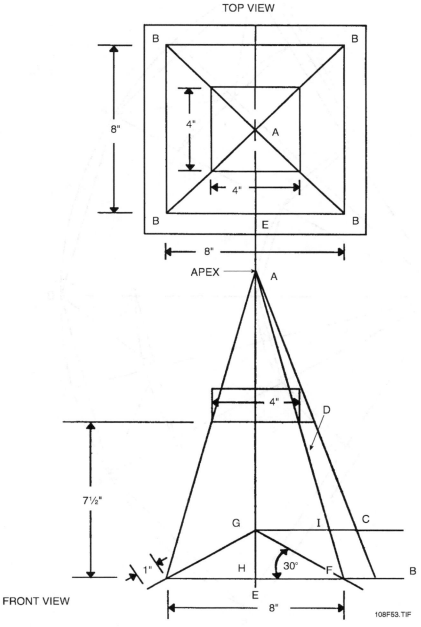

TOP VIEW

FRONT VIEW

108F53.TIF

Figure 53 ◆ Top and front views (smokestack).

Step 8 Lay out the taper pattern (see *Figure 54*).

Step 9 With point A as the center and distance AB from the front view as the radius, scribe a large arc at point B.

Step 10 Set your dividers equal to the width of any side in the top view and step off that width four times on the B arc.

Step 11 Draw straight lines between each of the points B to represent the sides of the pattern.

Step 12 Draw straight lines between each point B and point A.

Step 13 Use the distance AD from the front view to draw arc D.

Step 14 Draw straight lines connecting the intersecting points of arc D and the lines drawn from B to A.

Step 15 With point A as the center and distance AC from the front view as the radius, draw an arc crossing line AB.

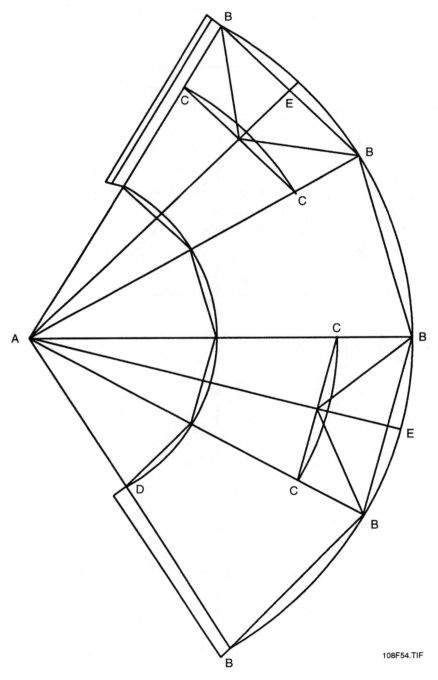

108F54.TIF

Figure 54 ◆ Taper pattern (smokestack).

Draw a straight line from C to C crossing centerline E. Notice that you will do this in two places on the taper pattern.

Step 16 Draw a slant line from B to C at each point crossing the centerline E. This represents the cutout for the 30-degree pitch. Notice that you will do this in two places on the taper pattern.

Step 17 Lay out the roof flange (see *Figure 55*).

Step 18 Transfer the slant length GF from the front view to each side of point G on the centerline.

Step 19 Transfer the distance GI from the front view to each side of point G on the roof flange view.

Step 20 Lay out the stack collar (see *Figure 56*).

Step 21 Transfer the collar dimensions to the stretchout baseline and construct the fitting.

Step 22 Make allowances for the locks and attaching flanges.

Step 23 Cut out and notch the patterns.

Step 24 Form the pieces and assemble the fitting.

Step 25 Lock the seams using the fastening technique specified by your instructor.

Step 26 Present the finished fitting to your instructor.

Step 27 Clean up your work area.

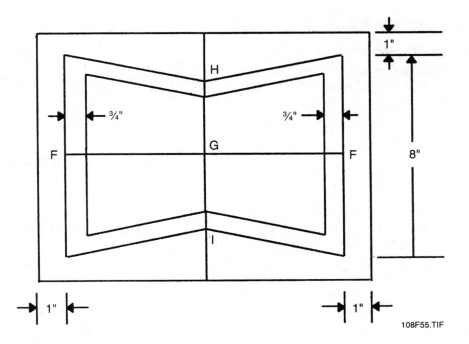

Figure 55 ◆ Roof flange (smokestack).

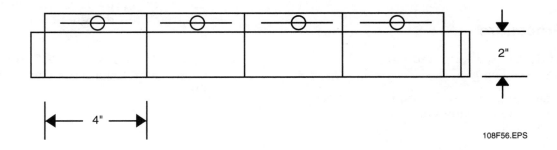

Figure 56 ◆ Stack collar (smokestack).

21.0.0 ◆ TASK 19: GORED ELBOW

In this task you will learn how to lay out and fabricate a round four-piece (gored) elbow. *Note:* Because there are many different methods of fabricating this fitting, the patterns included in this module do not show any allowances for seams or edges.

DID YOU KNOW?
The word *gore* originally described the triangular shape at the top of a spear. It was also used in ancient times to describe a small triangular piece of land. In later use, it also came to mean a tapering or triangular piece of cloth.

21.1.0 TOOLS AND MATERIALS

1. Appropriate personal protective equipment
2. Sheets of 26-gauge galvanized sheet metal, measured as indicated in the figures or according to your instructor's specifications
3. Scratch awl
4. Straightedge
5. Wing dividers
6. Scriber
7. Felt-tipped marker
8. Framing square
9. Combination square
10. Prick punch
11. Mallet
12. Riveting hammer
13. Hand seamer
14. Snips
15. Hand notcher
16. Squaring shear
17. Bar folder or brake
18. Slip-roll machine
19. Pittsburgh roll-forming machine

21.2.0 Procedure

Step 1 Study the working and isometric drawings (see *Figure 57*).

Step 2 Establish points A, B, and C on the baseline of the working view (see *Figure 58*).

Step 3 Square a line upward from baseline AC at point C to establish points A and B.

Step 4 Use point C as the center and line CB as the radius to make the throat curve.

Step 5 Use point C as the center and line AC as the radius to make the heel curve.

Step 6 Divide the heel curve into equal spaces. Use the following formula to determine how many equal spaces are required (G stands for the number of gores required for the elbow):

$$(G \times 2) - 2$$

For a four-piece elbow, the calculation is as follows:

$$(4 \times 2) - 2$$
$$8 - 2 = 6$$

Notice that each middle section is two times as large as each end section. If you count each end section as one and each middle section as two, you will get the same answer.

Step 7 Square a line upward from line AB at point A.

Step 8 Make a straight line from C through the first dividing line on the heel curve to establish point D.

Step 9 Square a line upward from line AB at point B to establish point E on line CD.

Step 10 Make a half circle directly below this pattern. The radius of the circle is half of line AB on the working view.

Step 11 Divide the half circle into eight equal parts. To do this, first bisect the half circle to establish point 5. Then bisect each half to establish points 3 and 7. Bisect the remaining sections to establish points 2, 4, 6, and 8. The number of equal parts is determined by the diameter of the fitting. The working rule is as follows: the larger the diameter, the greater the number of equal parts.

Step 12 Square a line from line AB to each numbered point. Extend these lines upward to DE.

Step 13 Establish points AB equal to the circumference of AB on the working view (3.14 × AB dimension).

Step 14 Divide line AB into 16 equal parts (two times as many parts as are in the half circle). Label each point on line AB as shown (see *Figure 59*).

Step 15 Square lines upward from line AB at each point.

Step 16 Set the dividers from point 5 on line AB to point 5 on the miter line (DE).

Step 17 Set the dividers on each point 5 on the single gore pattern and scribe an arc to locate point 5 on the squared line.

Step 18 Continue in the same manner for each number. Draw a freehand curve connecting these points.

Step 19 To lay out the double gore pattern, trace the single gore pattern above and below line AB.

Your instructor will provide the steps to fabricate this fitting. Remember to clean up your work area after completing the fitting to your instructor's satisfaction.

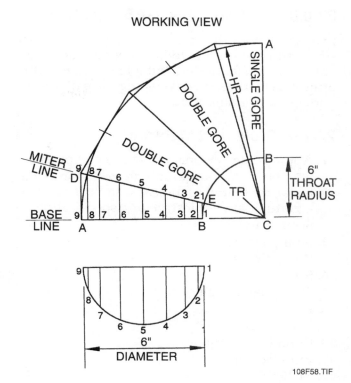

Figure 58 ◆ Working view (gored elbow).

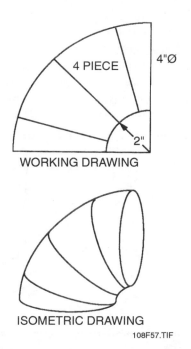

Figure 57 ◆ Working and isometric drawings (gored elbow).

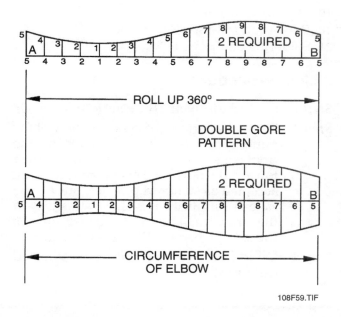

Figure 59 ◆ Single gore pattern (gored elbow).

22.0.0 ◆ TASK 20: OGEE GUTTER

In this task you will learn how to lay out and construct an ogee gutter. Today, most cornices and gutters are prefabricated, but a knowledge of the principles involved in developing the patterns for gutter miters is still useful.

22.1.0 Tools and Materials

1. Appropriate personal protective equipment
2. Sheets of 26-gauge galvanized iron sheet metal, measured as indicated in the figures or according to your instructor's specifications
3. Scratch awl
4. Straightedge
5. Wing dividers
6. Scriber
7. 45-degree triangle
8. Felt-tipped marker
9. Framing square
10. Combination square
11. Prick punch
12. Mallet
13. Riveting hammer
14. Hand seamer
15. Snips
16. Hand notcher
17. Squaring shear
18. Bar folder or brake
19. Slip-roll machine
20. Pittsburgh roll-forming machine
21. Soldering equipment

22.2.0 Procedure

Step 1 Study the isometric drawing (see *Figure 60*).

Step 2 Study the pattern for the front view of the gutter section (see *Figure 61*). Note that the front edge or stiffener illustrated is turned toward the outside. This procedure is not accepted as standard practice, but for the sake of simplicity, it is shown this way in the drawing. The front edge should be turned in when the fitting is formed.

Step 3 Divide the top view into the indicated distances.

Step 4 Develop the radius for the ogee curve either by the radius indicated in the working drawing or by the method shown in *Figure 62*. Note that the ogee curve in this figure is made up of two quarter reverse circles tangent at *m*. To find the center points, G and E, bisect the lines AB and CD, as illustrated.

Step 5 Divide the curve 5-14 (in the lower left area of the top view) into equal spaces.

Step 6 Draw the vertical and horizontal outlines of the top view of the gutter section. Using a 45-degree triangle, establish miter line AB.

Step 7 Number each bend and draw a line from each numbered point, 1 to 18, to intersect the miter line AB.

Step 8 Transfer the spaces 1 to 18 from the top view to lay out the stretchout pattern.

Step 9 Transfer the lengths of the vertical lines 1 to 18 to miter line AB from the top view to the stretchout pattern.

Step 10 Complete the stretchout pattern by drawing horizontal and curved lines to connect each point from A to B.

Step 11 Form the pattern.

Step 12 Add allowances for seams and joints.

Step 13 Mark the patterns for forming and indicate the number required for each.

Step 14 Make patterns for the end pieces and cut and bend them, if required.

Step 15 Assemble the gutter section, solder the required joints, and present the finished workpiece to your instructor.

Step 16 Clean up your work area.

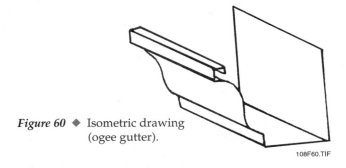

Figure 60 ◆ Isometric drawing (ogee gutter).

108F60.TIF

Ogee Gutter Design

Gutters take water away from a building. The design of the gutter plays an important role in that task. Generally, the gutter's ratio of depth to width is 3:4. The front edge of the gutter should be lower than the back edge so that any overflow will go over the front edge. The elevation difference should be about ½ of the gutter girth with a 1-inch minimum.

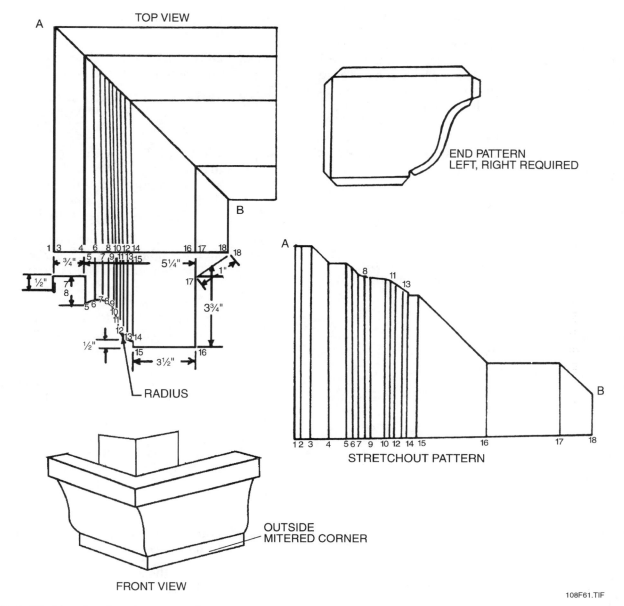

Figure 61 ◆ Working drawings (ogee gutter).

TOP VIEW

END PATTERN
LEFT, RIGHT REQUIRED

RADIUS

STRETCHOUT PATTERN

OUTSIDE
MITERED CORNER

FRONT VIEW

108F61.TIF

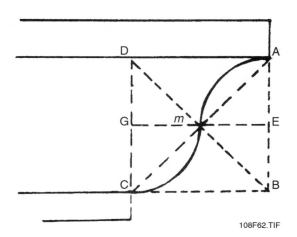

Figure 62 ◆ Ogee curve (ogee gutter).

108F62.TIF

DID YOU KNOW?

A Brief History of Gutters

The cornice shapes used in gutters reflect the styles of classic Greek and Roman architecture. Roman moldings are usually formed from the arcs of one or more circles and are chiefly used in sheet metal cornice work.

During the 19th century and the early part of the 20th century, sheet metal was commonly used to fabricate building cornices. Over time, wood moldings became more popular. Today, wood moldings are more costly while copper and zinc sheet metal are easier to maintain, so the use of sheet metal to fabricate cornices is becoming popular once again.

23.0.0 ◆ TASK 21: BELT GUARD

In this task you will learn how to lay out and construct a belt guard of selected dimensions for unequal-size pulleys. Belt guards cover exposed pulleys and belts so that limbs or clothing can't accidentally be pulled into them. The Occupational Safety and Health Administration (OSHA) requires that belt guards be used wherever workers or building occupants may come into contact with exposed belts or pulleys.

23.1.0 Tools and Materials

1. Appropriate personal protective equipment
2. Sheets of 26-gauge galvanized iron sheet metal, measured as indicated in the figures or according to your instructor's specifications
3. Scratch awl
4. Straightedge
5. Wing dividers
6. Scriber
7. Felt-tipped marker
8. Framing square
9. Combination square
10. Prick punch
11. Mallet
12. Riveting hammer
13. Hand seamer
14. Snips
15. Hand notcher
16. Squaring shear
17. Bar folder or brake
18. Slip-roll machine
19. Pittsburgh roll-forming machine
20. Welding equipment

23.2.0 Procedure

Step 1   Study the working drawing before laying out the belt guard for unequal pulley sizes (see *Figure 63*). The small drawing in the lower right-hand corner shows what the assembled piece will look like.

Step 2   Lay out the front and back patterns (both halves).

Step 3   Draw the two 18-inch (1 ft. 6 in.) horizontal baselines marked AB.

Step 4   Measure 4 inches to the right of point A and establish point R. Measure 2 inches to the left from point B and establish point R1.

Step 5   With point R as the center, set your dividers at 4 inches and scribe the long arcs. With point R1 as the center, set your dividers at 2 inches and scribe the short arcs. Draw lines tangent to the arcs.

Step 6   With point R as the center, set your dividers at a 1-inch radius and scribe the 180-degree arcs for the large pulley ends. With point R1 as the center and ½ inch as the radius, scribe the 180-degree arcs for the small pulley ends. All arcs should intersect the horizontal baselines marked AB.

Step 7   Lay out the rim pattern.

Step 8   Draw a 2-inch horizontal baseline and mark the points as C and D.

Step 9   Square lines upward from CD and, working from the front view, transfer the dimensions 7¼ inches, 11¹¹⁄₁₆ inches, and 2¾ inches to the rim pattern.

Step 10 Draw the working lines and the pattern outline.

Step 11 Add seam allowances and mark the patterns for forming.

Step 12 Lay out the patterns on the metal and cut and notch the shapes in the numbers required.

Step 13 Form the pattern, spot weld the flanges, and set and lock the seams.

Step 14 Present the finished workpiece to your instructor.

Step 15 Clean up your work area.

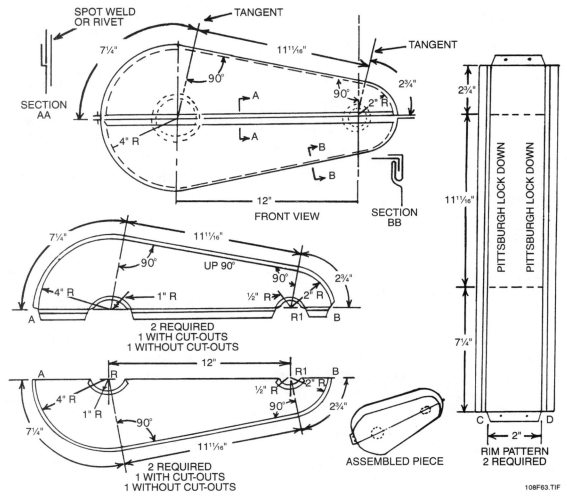

Figure 63 ◆ Working drawing (belt guard).

24.0.0 ◆ TASK 22: 90-DEGREE TEE

In this task you will learn how to lay out a 90-degree tee intersecting a pipe. This type of fitting is used whenever a round branch line intersects a pipe. Your instructor will provide the steps to fabricate this fitting if appropriate. Remember to clean up your work area after completing the fitting to your instructor's satisfaction. The following notes apply to making the working views for this fitting:

• Making half of the front view and side view is sufficient.

• If the diameter of the tee is smaller than the diameter of the pipe, the half circles will not be the same as the full circle, but you will follow the same steps as for this fitting.

• It is not necessary to lay out the full length of the pipe on the front view as long as you make the additional reference line on the pipe pattern.

• Because of the many different methods for fabricating this fitting, the patterns do not show any allowances for seams or edges.

24.1.0 Tools and Materials

1. Appropriate personal protective equipment
2. Sheets of 26-gauge galvanized iron sheet metal, measured as indicated in the figures or according to your instructor's specifications
3. Scratch awl
4. Straightedge
5. Wing dividers
6. Scriber
7. Felt-tipped marker
8. Framing square
9. Combination square
10. Prick punch
11. Mallet
12. Riveting hammer
13. Hand seamer
14. Snips
15. Hand notcher
16. Squaring shear
17. Bar folder or brake
18. Slip-roll machine
19. Pittsburgh roll-forming machine

24.2.0 Procedure

Step 1 Study the working drawing and the isometric drawing (see *Figure 64*).

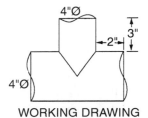 

WORKING DRAWING ISOMETRIC DRAWING

108F64.TIF

Figure 64 ◆ Working and isometric drawings (90-degree tee).

Step 2 Lay out the working views (see *Figure 65*). Establish points A, B, C, and D on the front view.

Step 3 Establish points E and F so that lines CE and FD are equal. (The tee is in the center of the pipe.)

Step 4 Square lines upward from line CD at both points E and F to establish the length of the tee.

Step 5 Draw a half circle above points E and F to establish the diameter of the tee.

Step 6 Divide the half circle into eight equal parts. To do this, bisect the half circle to obtain point 5; then bisect each quarter circle to obtain points 3 and 7. Bisect each remaining section to obtain points 2, 4, 6, and 8. The number of equal parts is determined by the diameter of the fitting. The working rule is as follows: for greatest accuracy, the larger the diameter, the greater the number of equal parts.

Step 7 Square a line downward from line EF at each numbered point. Extend these lines beyond the center of BC.

Step 8 Establish point G at the center of line AD.

Step 9 Square a line outward from line AD at point G.

Step 10 Establish points E and F on the extended line for the side view.

Step 11 Draw a half circle above points E and F to establish the diameter of the tee.

Step 12 Divide the half circle in half to establish point 9-1.

Step 13 Square a line downward from line EF at point 9-1 to establish point H.

Step 14 Use point H as the center and a radius equal to GD to draw the circle on the side view.

Step 15 Transfer the distances from the half circle on the front view to the half circle on the side view.

Step 16 Square lines downward from line EF at each numbered point to establish the points on the circle.

Step 17 Square a line from line AD extending from each numbered point on the circle toward line BC to establish the mitered lines E5 and F5 (the points where the lines intersect).

Step 18 Lay out the tee pattern. Establish points E and F equal to the circumference of EF on the side view (3.14 × dimension EF).

Step 19 Divide line EF into 16 equal parts (twice as many as the half circle). Label each point on line EF as shown.

Step 20 Square lines upward from line EF at each point.

Step 21 Set the dividers from point 1 on line EF below the half circle of the front view to point 1 on line E5 (the miter line).

Step 22 Set the dividers on each point 1 on the tee pattern and scribe an arc to locate point 1 on the squared line.

Step 23 Continue in the same manner for each number.

Step 24 Draw a freehand curve to connect these points.

Step 25 Lay out the pipe pattern. Establish points A, B, C, and D. Line AB on the pipe pattern should be equal to line AB on the front view. Line BC on the pipe pattern is the circumference of line BC on the front view (3.14 × BC dimension).

Step 26 Establish point P as the center of line AD.

Step 27 Square a line downward from line AD at point P.

Step 28 Set the dividers from point 1 to point 2 on the full circle of the side view. Use P (1–9) as the center and mark this distance on line BC on both sides of the pipe pattern.

Step 29 Transfer each distance from the full circle on the side view to the pipe pattern in this manner.

Step 30 Square lines upward from line BC at each numbered point to line AD.

Step 31 Set the dividers from point 1 on line AD of the front view to point 9 of line F5 (the miter line). Use point 1 on line BC of the pipe pattern as the center and mark this distance on the squared line.

Step 32 Set the dividers from point 9 on line F5 of the front view to point 1 on line E5. Use the point just established as the center to mark this distance on the line.

Step 33 Continue in the same manner to establish each point. Draw a freehand curve connecting these points.

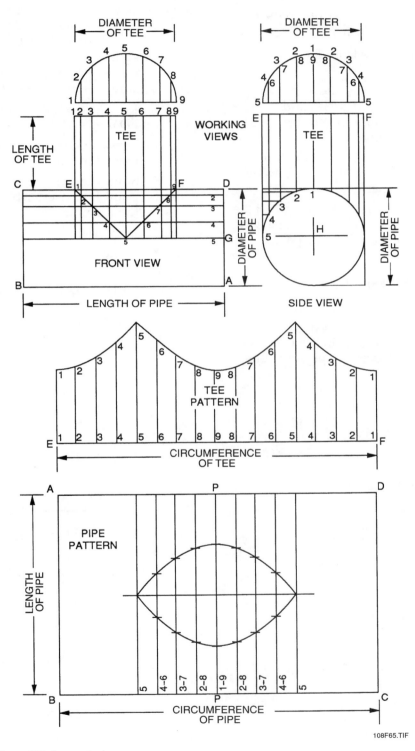

Figure 65 ◆ Working views (90-degree tee).

108F65.TIF

25.0.0 ◆ TASK 23: 45-DEGREE TEE

In this task you will learn how to lay out a 45-degree tee intersecting a pipe. This type of fitting is used to connect a round branch line that enters a pipe at a 45-degree angle. Your instructor will provide the steps to fabricate this fitting, if appropriate. Remember to clean up your work area after completing the fitting to your instructor's satisfaction. The following notes apply to making the working views for this fitting:

• You will need the complete front view but only half of the side view.

• If the diameter of the tee is the same as the diameter of the pipe, the half circles and full circle will be the same size; you will follow the same steps as in this fitting.

• Because of the many methods of fabricating this type of fitting, the patterns do not show any allowances for seams or edges.

• It is not necessary to lay out the full length of the pipe on the front view as long as you make the additional reference line on the pipe pattern.

25.1.0 Tools and Materials

1. Appropriate personal protective equipment
2. Sheets of 26-gauge galvanized iron sheet metal, measured as indicated in the figures or according to your instructor's specifications
3. Scratch awl
4. Straightedge
5. Wing dividers
6. Scriber
7. Felt-tipped marker
8. Framing square
9. Combination square
10. Prick punch
11. Mallet
12. Riveting hammer
13. Hand seamer
14. Snips
15. Hand notcher
16. Squaring shear
17. Bar folder or brake
18. Slip-roll machine
19. Pittsburgh roll-forming machine

25.2.0 Procedure

Step 1 Study the working and isometric drawings (see *Figure 66*). You will use the working views for the layout steps in this task (see *Figure 67*).

Step 2 Lay out the front view. Establish points A, B, C, and D on the front view.

Step 3 To determine the dimension EF, lay out a baseline equal to the diameter of the tee, then square a line upward and measure it so that it's equal to the diameter of the tee. Connect these two points and measure this distance for dimension EF.

Step 4 Establish points E and F so that CE and FD are equal.

Step 5 Draw a 45-degree angle at point F. Establish point 9 so that F–9 is the length of the tee.

Step 6 Square a line outward from line FG at point 9 to establish point H. Line GH is the diameter of the tee.

Step 7 Draw a straight line from point H to point E.

Step 8 Make a half circle directly above the tee.

Step 9 Divide the half circle into eight equal parts. Bisect the half circle to get point 5, then bisect each quarter circle to get points 3 and 7. Bisect the remaining sections to get points 2, 4, 6, and 8.

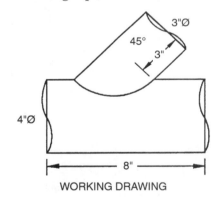

WORKING DRAWING

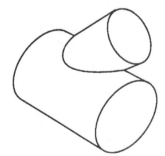

ISOMETRIC DRAWING

108F66.TIF

Figure 66 ◆ Working and isometric drawings (45-degree tee).

Step 10 Square a line downward from line 1–9 at each numbered point. Extend these lines below line EF.

Step 11 Establish point I at the center of AD.

Step 12 Square a line outward from line AD at point I.

Step 13 With a radius equal to ID and the center J on the extended line, draw the full circle on the side view.

Step 14 Square a line upward from line IJ at point J on the side view.

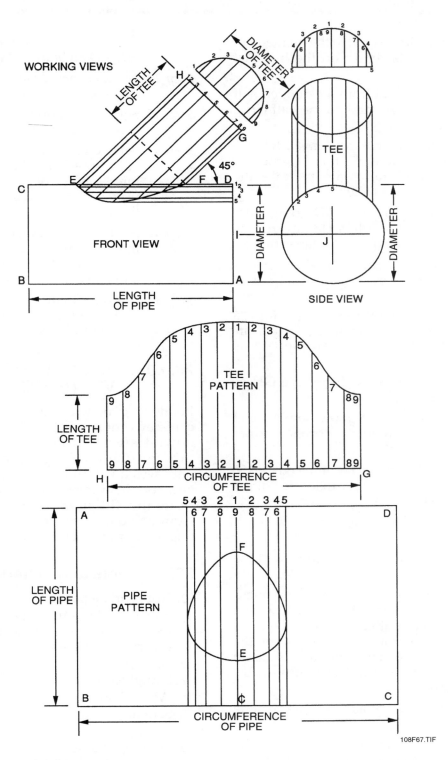

Figure 67 ◆ Working views (45-degree tee).

Riveting Ideas

A Tee Opening Shortcut

Depending on the method of fabrication and the size and degree of accuracy required, it is not always necessary to develop the tee opening on the pipe. Simply form the tee and pipe, place the tee on the pipe, trace along the outside of the tee on the pipe, and cut. You can use this shortcut on 90-degree tees and 45-degree tees that intersect a pipe.

Step 15 Make a half circle equal to the diameter of the tee with its center on the line just drawn.

Step 16 Transfer each point from the divided half circle on the front view to the half circle on the side view.

Step 17 Square a line downward from each numbered point, extending them to the full circle. (It is not necessary to make the ellipse on the side view.)

Step 18 Square a line from line AD going from each point on the full circle toward line BC. Connect the points of intersection.

Step 19 Lay out the tee pattern. Establish points GH equal to the circumference of line GH on the front view (3.14 × GH dimension).

Step 20 Divide line GH on the tee pattern into 16 equal parts (twice as many as the half circle). Label each point on line GH as shown.

Step 21 Square lines upward from line GH at each point.

Step 22 Set the dividers from point 9 on line GH of the front view to the corresponding point of intersection.

Step 23 Set the dividers on each point 9 on the tee pattern and scribe an arc to locate point 9 on the squared line.

Step 24 Continue in the same manner for each point.

Step 25 Draw a freehand curve to connect these points.

Step 26 Lay out the pipe pattern (the tee opening). Establish points A, B, C, and D. Line AB on the pipe pattern should be equal to line AB on the front view. Line BC on the pipe pattern is equal to the circumference of line BC on the front view (3.14 × BC dimension).

Step 27 Establish point 1–9 as the center of line AD.

Step 28 Set the dividers from point 1 to 2 on the full circle of the side view. Use point 1–9 as the center and mark this distance on line AD on both sides of point 1–9.

Step 29 Transfer each distance from the full circle in the same manner.

Step 30 Square lines downward from line AD at each numbered point to line BC.

Step 31 Set the dividers from point 1–9 on line AD of the front view to the first point of intersection. Use point 1 on line AD of the pipe pattern and mark this distance on the squared line.

Step 32 Set the dividers from the first point of intersection to its corresponding point of intersection. Use this point as the center and mark this distance on the line.

Step 33 Continue in the same manner to establish each point. Draw a freehand curve connecting these points.

26.0.0 ◆ TASK 24: TYPE A VENTILATOR

In this task you will learn how to lay out a type A chimney ventilator. This fitting is used to correct a downdraft condition. Air moving across or through the openings creates a suction that improves the draft or vent power within a chimney. Your instructor will provide the steps to fabricate this fitting if appropriate. Remember to clean up your work area after completing the fitting to your instructor's satisfaction.

26.1.0 Tools and Materials

1. Appropriate personal protective equipment
2. Sheets of 26-gauge galvanized iron sheet metal, measured as indicated in the figures or according to your instructor's specifications
3. Scratch awl
4. Straightedge
5. Wing dividers
6. Scriber
7. Felt-tipped marker
8. Framing square
9. Combination square

10. Prick punch
11. Mallet
12. Riveting hammer
13. Hand seamer
14. Snips
15. Hand notcher
16. Squaring shear
17. Bar folder or brake
18. Slip-roll machine
19. Pittsburgh roll-forming machine
20. Soldering equipment

26.2.0 Procedure

This fitting requires three different patterns. You should position the seams so that they do not have to be cut to complete the assembly of the fitting. You can lay out the vertical risers so that the fitting is shaped like an H, but the A shape is considered more pleasing to the eye.

Step 1 Study the isometric drawing (see *Figure 68*).

Step 2 Construct the elevation view first, as indicated in the working drawing (see *Figure 69*).

Step 3 Project the necessary elements at right angles from the baselines, established reference lines, or centerlines.

Step 4 Transfer the lengths of the elements to the stretchout pattern from the elevation view. Be sure to multiply the diameter of the pipe components by 3.14 (pi) to find the length of the stretchout for each component. Two pieces are required for the vertical riser members.

Step 5 Make allowances for the seams and riveting tabs (if required).

Step 6 Cut and form the patterns.

Step 7 Assemble the fitting and secure by soldering.

Step 8 Present the fitting to your instructor.

Step 9 Clean up your work area.

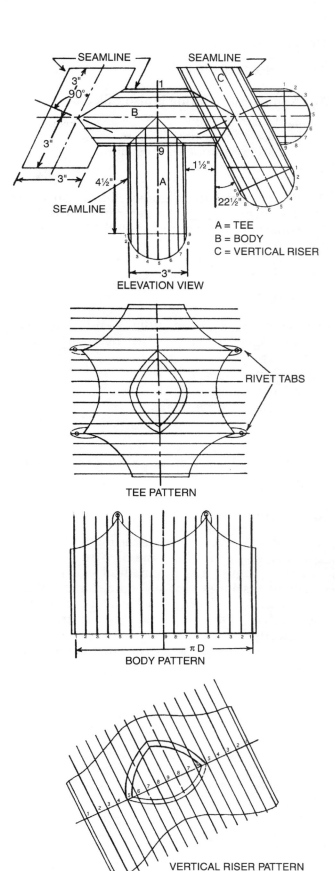

Figure 69 ◆ Working drawing (type A ventilator).

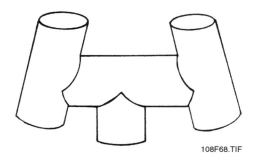

Figure 68 ◆ Isometric drawing (type A ventilator).

Review Questions

Sections 20.0.0–26.0.0

1. A smokestack fitting is also called a _____.
   a. base over ridge
   b. base over peak
   c. base to chimney connection
   d. base over gable

2. When fabricating a gored elbow, you would use formula _____ to determine how many equal spaces are required on the heel curve.
   a. $(G \times 2) - 2$
   b. $G + (2 \times 3.14)$
   c. $G \times 2 \times 3.14$
   d. $(G \times 2) + 2$

3. Wherever exposed pulleys and belts could endanger people, _____ are necessary.
   a. belt cases
   b. pulley boxes
   c. belt guards
   d. belt and pulley caps

4. When a round branch line intersects a pipe, a _____ fitting is used.
   a. flexible
   b. Y-branch
   c. tee
   d. notched V

5. A(n) _____ is used to correct a downdraft situation.
   a. type K ventilator
   b. type A ventilator
   c. inverted V ventilator
   d. type D ventilator

Summary

Parallel line development is the method most frequently used for sheet metal fittings used in HVAC systems. It is the method you will most likely use as a first-year sheet metal apprentice to lay out patterns for fittings. Developing your layout skills is very important. A pattern that is incorrectly laid out will never fit together properly. You will also rely on your math and geometry skills to develop the working drawings and patterns. But perhaps the most important skill is your ability to visualize from the pattern how the finished fitting will look. The tasks in this module were designed to give you practice in honing all of these skills so that you will be able to lay out and fabricate fittings that reflect your pride of craftsmanship.

Ricky Sonnier

Shop Manager and Training Coordinator
Gulfside Mechanical/Comfort Systems USA
Pensacola, Florida

Ricky Sonnier attended high school in Crowley, Louisiana. He was lured into the sheet metal trade by the shop located next door to his boyhood home. Ricky spent his summers and after-school hours working there. As a part-time helper to the sheet metal workers, he did whatever was asked of him. His youthful interest evolved into a professional career in the trade, and Ricky is now a shop manager and training coordinator.

How did you become interested in this industry?

My father was an HVAC tech, and I grew up around the construction industry, so it was a natural choice. After high school, I completed my four-year apprenticeship in Crowley with a sheet metal contractor, while taking classes two nights a week in Baton Rouge to receive my sheet metal journeyman certification.

What path did you take to your current position?

When you become an apprentice, you work with journeymen and you learn from them. When I became a journeyman, I was able to supervise a few jobs and worked in the shop doing layout and fabrication. I got experience. In 1989, I moved to Pensacola, where I worked for a sheet metal contractor as an assistant manager for four years, and for a fabrication company as a supervisor for six years. Then I was hired as a journeyman at Gulfside, where I was named shop manager in mid-1998.

As you become a journeyman—and if you're a good journeyman—you develop the skills to teach new people how to do things. We needed a training program here at Gulfside, and I was asked whether I'd be willing to take on the responsibility. I decided I wanted to do it, so I contacted NCCER, obtained Master Trainer Certification, and went from there.

What do you think it takes to be a success in your trade?

Patience. It takes a lot of patience and dedication. You have to be willing to learn from the journeymen, be patient, and know that you can get there from being an apprentice. People want to be boss after two weeks. You can get there, but it just takes time.

What are some things you do on the job?

My job includes coordinating different types of installation schedules to meet deadlines and to have the product at the job site when it needs to be there. We're a commercial mechanical contractor, and we do a lot of big jobs. Additionally, I coordinate the training schedules for the apprentices and for the instructors.

What do you like most about your job?

I like being the leader, and helping people set and meet their goals. I like being able to meet deadlines, and doing the scheduling to meet those deadlines. I enjoy the construction industry and the different types of challenges we face in the work we do.

What would you say to someone entering the trade today?

When you choose your career, be patient and be willing to learn. Be proud of your career. You have to take pride in what you do. The construction industry has a stigma attached to it—we need to change the way the people look at the industry. We've chosen a career and need to be proud of what we do.

Trade Terms Introduced in This Module

Detail drawings: On plans, a section or sections that enlarge a detail so that it may be more clearly understood.

FOB: An abbreviation that stands for *flat on bottom*. It describes a fitting in which the bottom and one side pattern can be made as one piece.

Oblique drawing: In a mechanical drawing, a view of an object at an angle (other than 90 degrees) to its longest axis.

Ogee: A double curve formed by the union of a convex and a concave line and resembling the letter S.

Pressure drop: The decrease in airflow pressure between two ends of a duct or pipeline, between two points in an air distribution system, or across fittings as a result of friction.

Standard 90A: A standard of the National Fire Protection Association, an organization that sets standards for fire ratings for construction materials.

Trunk line: The main line in a ductrun from which branch lines connect to other areas.

Additional Resources

This module is intended to present thorough resources for task training. The following reference works are suggested for further study. These are optional materials for continued education rather than for task training.

Metal Fabricator's Handbook, 1990. Ron Fournier. New York, NY: H.P. Books.

Ultimate Sheet Metal Fabrication, 1999. Tim Remus. Stillwater, MN: Wolfgang Publications, Inc.

Figure Credits

Parrott Mechanical, Inc.   108F06, 108F07

NCCER CRAFT TRAINING USER UPDATES

The NCCER makes every effort to keep these textbooks up-to-date and free of technical errors. We appreciate your help in this process. If you have an idea for improving this textbook, or if you find an error, a typographical mistake, or an inaccuracy in the NCCER's Craft Training textbooks, please write us, using this form or a photocopy. Be sure to include the exact module number, page number, a detailed description, and the correction, if applicable. Your input will be brought to the attention of the Technical Review Committee. Thank you for your assistance.

Instructors – If you found that additional materials were necessary in order to teach this module effectively, please let us know so that we may include them in the Equipment and Materials list in the Instructor's Guide.

Write: Curriculum Revision and Development Department
National Center for Construction Education and Research
P.O. Box 141104, Gainesville, FL 32614-1104

Fax: 352-334-0932

E-mail: curriculum@nccer.org

Craft _____ Module Name _____

Copyright Date _____ Module Number _____ Page Number(s) _____

Description _____

_____

_____

_____

(Optional) Correction _____

_____

_____

(Optional) Your Name and Address _____

_____

_____

Index

Index